THE NATURE
AND GROWTH OF
MODERN MATHEMATICS

Volume 2

by Edna E. Kramer

A FAWCETT PREMIER BOOK

Fawcett Publications, Inc., Greenwich, Connecticut

To

My husband,

Benedict Taxier Lassar

THE NATURE AND GROWTH OF MODERN MATHE-MATICS, Volume 2

THIS BOOK CONTAINS THE COMPLETE TEXT OF THE SECOND HALF OF THE ORIGINAL HARDCOVER EDITION.

A Fawcett Premier Book reprinted by arrangement with Hawthorn Books, Inc.

Thanks are due to the Oxford University Press of New York for permission to reprint, in revised and updated form, the following pages from the 1951 edition of THE MAIN STREAM OF MATHEMATICS by Edna E. Kramer, on which Oxford University Press holds the copyright: 16, 17(1.1–21), 99(1.13–26), 215–239, 240(1.1–5), 259, 260, 264–284, 293(1.17–40), 297–301, 302(1.1–15).

Library of Congress Catalog Card Number: 73–91317.

Printed in the United States of America
June 1974

CONTENTS for Volume 2

least resistance / Masses in rapid motion / Nuclear energy / General frames of reference

Lie groups and Lie algebras / Linking geometric ideas of Lie, Levi-Civita, and Cartan / Chern, Chevalley, and Whitehead on Cartan / Fiber bundles

21

East Meets West in the Higher Arithmetic 191

The "queen of mathematics" / Primes / Eratosthenes' sieve / One of Euclid's theorems / Pseudo-primes / Formulas for primes / Tabulations / Tchebycheff and Sylvester / Prime number theorem / Perfect numbers / Mersenne primes / Fermat's Last Theorem / Congruences / Fermat's "little theorem" / Quadratic reciprocity / Analytic number theory / Riemann zeta-function / Riemann hypothesis / Additive number theory / Goldbach's conjecture / Elements of complex analysis: Geometric interpretations, Cauchy-Riemann equations, Cauchy integral theorem, analytic functions/ Hardy and Ramanujan / Titchmarsh on Hardy / The most romantic mathematical personality

22

The Reformation of Analysis 232

Paradoxes resulting from intuitive interpretation of pure mathematical concepts / Peano curve / Pierpont produces "monsters" to motivate Cauchy-Weierstrass rigor / Reform through "arithmetization" / Approximative sequences / Standards of approximation / Limit of a sequence / The natural logarithmic base / Infinite series / Convergence and divergence / Limit of a function with a continuous domain / Continuity, epsilon-delta style / Cauchy / Weierstrass and Kovalevsky

23

Royal Roads to Functional Analysis 261

Functions and the functionals of Volterra, Hadamard, Lévy / Dido's problem / Isoperimetric problems / Heron and the reflection of light / Natural and mathematical parsimony / Calculus of variations / Bernoulli and the brachistochrone problem / Euler-Lagrange methodology / Functionals in integral equations / Whittaker on Volterra / Integral equations: simplest types / Systems of linear equations / Infinite Systems of Hill, Poincaré, von Koch / Eigenvalues and eigenvectors / Infinite linear systems and their corresponding integral equations / Linear operators and spectral theory / Laplace and Fourier transforms / Hilbert space /

output / International viewpoint / For "the man in the street" / German contemporary / Shaping the future of mathematics / Weyl's tribute / Number theory, mathematical physics, Dirichlet principle, unsolved problems, invariants, foundations and axiomatics, differential equations, integral equations, Hilbert space, logical formalism / Hermann Weyl, major contributor to function theory, topology, analytic number theory, group theory, differential equations, eigenvalues and eigenfunctions, relativity, differential geometry, quantum mechanics, logic and foundations, philosophy of science / "Those were the happiest months of my life" / Zurich and Göttingen / Protest against Nazi removal of his colleagues / Change to United States mathematical environment / Details of Weyl's discoveries / His "intuitionism"

27

Twentieth-Century Vistas—Analysis 382

Calculus and the measurement of (abstract) lengths, areas, volumes, masses, pressures, etc. / Borel, Lebesgue, and the problem of measure for general point sets / Association with theory of integration / Mengoli-Cauchy integral once more / Riemann integral / Lebesgue-Young integral / Average temperature as a Riemann integral / As a Lebesgue integral / Where Riemann fails but Lebesgue succeeds / Lebesgue measure / Measure as a function / All Borel sets as domain / Lebesgue's enlargement of the domain / He illustrates *non*measurable sets / Placid existence of a revolutionary / Denjoy, Perron, and Stieltjes integrals / Colorful biography of a co-inventor

28

Twentieth-Century Vistas—Algebra 406

Emmy Noether, a major influence on recent developments / Early years at Erlangen / Later work at Göttingen / The "Noether boys" / Her last years in the United States / Her ability at abstract formulation / A disciple of Dedekind / Her personality / Ideals as special subrings / The ring of integers and its modulo 3 image / Homomorphism of rings / Kernel of a homomorphism / Principal ideals / Analogy between inclusion and divisibility / Factorization of ideals / Failure of uniqueness / Integral domains and fields reexamined / Homomorphisms of the ring of integers / Noether and hypercomplex systems / Brauer on Artin / Artin on Wedderburn / Climactic memoir on hypercomplex numbers /

Linear associative algebras / Discovery by Grassmann and Hamilton / Nilpotency / Division algebras / General structure theorems / Peirce-Frobenius theorem / The Adams-Bott-Kervaire-Milnor generalization / Manipulations with quaternions / Applications to physics / Limited scope of Grassmann algebras / Grassmann, the man / Wedderburn's structure theorems and his *curriculum vitae*

29

Twentieth-Century Vistas—Logic and Foundations   444

Axiomatics as a partial cure for paradoxes / Gödel's incompleteness theorem / Metamathematics / Absolute consistency / Gödel's proof / Richard paradox / Arithmetization / An undecidable proposition / Side effects / Essential incompleteness / Impossibility of internal consistency / The need for "finitistic" methods / Wavre on Brouwer / Taboos on law of excluded middle, existence proofs, use of defining properties / Rejection of Cantor's continuum / Summary of intuitionist dogma

30

Retrospect and Prospect   463

Mathematicians and the shape of things to come / If history repeats itself, then— / The content of mathematics, past and present / *Mathematical Reviews* as a guide / Will pure mathematics be predominant? / Bourbaki / Freedom or exile for mathematicians? / The fertile soil of American science / Women in the past, present, and future of mathematics / Applied mathematics and the future / Better communication as a guarantee of healthy survival / New worlds for mathematical exploration and development / Pessimism / Will future mathematics follow the example of Hilbert and Weil? / "Great mathematicians will solve the great problems we shall bequeath to them" / The honor of the human spirit

Preface

The Nature and Growth of Modern Mathematics traces the development of the most important mathematical concepts from their inception to their present formulation. Although chief emphasis is placed on the explanation of mathematical ideas, nevertheless mathematical content, history, lore, and biography are integrated in order to offer an overall, unified picture of the mother science. The work presents a discussion of major notions and the general settings in which they were conceived, with particular attention to the lives and thoughts of some of the most creative mathematical innovators. It provides a guide to what is still important in classical mathematics, as well as an introduction to many significant recent developments.

Answers to questions like the following are simple and will be found in this book:

Why should Pythagoras and his followers be credited with (or blamed for) some of the methodology of the "new" mathematics?

How do modern algebras (plural) generalize the "common garden variety"?

What single modern concept makes it possible to conceive in a nutshell of *all* geometries plain and fancy—Euclidean, non-Euclidean, affine, projective, inversive, etc.?

What is the nature of the universal language initiated by a thirteenth-century Catalan mystic, actually formulated by Leibniz, and improved by Boole and De Morgan?

How did Omar Khayyám solve certain cubic equations?

What are the common features of any boy's "engagement problem," the geishas' pantomime of baseball, and modern engineering decisions?

11

Who are the "Leonardos" of modern mathematics?

How did Queen Dido set a precedent for mathematicians and physicists?

Why should isomorphism, homomorphism, and homeomorphism be an intrinsic part of the vocabulary of every mathophile?

How did Maxwell's "demon" make the irreversible reversible?

Why did the mere matter of counting socks lead a millionaire mathematical genius to renounce mathematics in favor of finance?

What are the beautiful "ideals" formulated by Richard Dedekind and advanced by Emmy Noether?

Proceeding from illustrative instances to general purposes, let us state that the author's objectives are:

1. To survey the entire field of mathematics, with emphasis on twentieth-century ideas.

2. To furnish the type of exposition that should make it possible for a layman who is educated but not a specialist in mathematics to gain insight into the manifold aspects of modern mathematics, including its essential relationship to all areas of scientific thought. This objective was formulated because the "new" mathematics which has become the vogue in our schools is not really new, and those who seek popular treatment of contemporary mathematics can find only occasional superficial articles in periodicals. Books offering fuller exposition, including the author's *Main Stream of Mathematics*, have generally terminated with material from the early decades of the present century. In the potentially democratic world which men of good will envision, the man in the street must be entitled to more mathematical stimulation than the puzzle column in a Sunday newspaper, an occasional profile of a Nobel prize winner, an enigmatic summary of some recent discovery in applied mathematics—whether that man is an engineer in a remote village in India who is seeking to fill loopholes in his mathematical knowledge, a retired physician anxious to convince himself he is a mathematician *manqué*, a high school senior in quest of a research topic for a science talent contest, a nun whose objective is to inspire her students with an account of the accomplishment of women mathematicians, or a stockbroker eager to indulge in some pure mathematics.

(Such are some of the individuals who have corresponded with the author *in re* mathematical information.)

3. To stress "human interest" and thereby to reveal mathematics as a living, growing endeavor, holding a strong place in man's culture. This aim was conceived because there is danger to the humanities in the present educational crash programs designed to produce a large number of mathematicians, physical scientists, engineers, and technical workers. Our times make such programs a necessity, and the leaders who suggest the concentrated curricula or write the texts are rendering an inestimable service. Although these men understand the value of the pure mathematical content of the courses of study they prescribe, can the same be said of the students or of the teachers in elementary and secondary schools, or of the general public? They must have the opportunity to realize that there is more purpose to the "new" mathematics than recounting the tale of Little Red Riding Hood in terms of set theory or computer language. Thus, part of the third objective of the present work is to supply material which can serve as a cultural background or supplement for all those who are receiving rapid, concentrated exposure to recent advanced mathematical concepts, without any opportunity to examine the origins or gradual historical development of such ideas. Hence, although designed for the layman, this book would be helpful in courses in the history, philosophy, or fundamental concepts of mathematics.

At this point I should like to express my indebtedness to a number of persons. First and foremost, there is my husband, Dr. Benedict T. Lassar, through whose advice and assistance the manuscript has received a "fondest father's fondest care." I appreciate the many valuable suggestions made by Linda Allegri, who served as mathematics editor, as well as those of C. B. Boyer. The author is especially grateful to the mathematicians who gave their kind permission to quote from important articles they have written. Exact references to those mathematicians and the particular papers are provided at appropriate points in the body of the work. Thanks for the special permission must also be extended to the organizations sponsoring the publications in which the articles appeared, namely, the Royal Society of London, the Université de Paris, the American Mathematical Society, the Mathematics Association of America, and to the editors of *Biometrika*, *Econometrica*, the *Annals of Mathematical Statistics*, the *Journal of the American Oriental Society*, *Scripta Mathematica*. Oxford University Press graciously gave permission to quote from the author's previous book, *The Main Stream of Mathematics*. A most valuable form of assistance was rendered by those who encouraged the author to initiate or to continue (through long years) the writing of this book. They are Hanna Neumann, Bernhard H. Neumann, Peter M. Neumann, Jean Leray, Christie J. Eliezer, Sigekatu Kuroda, John M. Danskin, Stanislaw Ulam, Wilhelm Magnus, Fred Kerner, the late E. B. Wilson. Finally, thanks are due to William Taylor for the careful preparation of the diagrams, and to Beth Goldberg for the translation of barely decipherable scribbling into neat, accurate typescript, for noting errors, and for making suggestions.

New York   E. E. K.
January, 1970

Introduction

The era in which we live has variously been described as the age of the common man, the age of anxiety, the nuclear age, the space age, and so on. To this list of appellations one might well add the *age of mathematics*. At no other time in history has the man in the street been informed emphatically and repeatedly that the further progress of mathematics concerns him vitally because it is sure to have effects, direct or indirect, on his material comforts, his mode of thought, and his very survival. The nonspecialist cannot help wondering at this sudden prominence of a subject whose higher branches have always seemed to belong to a world apart, a sphere where physical scientists find advanced mathematics a useful tool, while philosophers and numerical geniuses indulge in it as an art or as an intellectual hobby. The present phenomenon may have been precipitated by the political and economic circumstances of our day, but the major role of the new mathematics is no fortuitous overnight occurrence. It represents the cumulative effect of some four thousand years of scientific thought.

Circles of Thought

Most interest must center on the outcome of this long period of fruition, and therefore emphasis must be placed on mathematical activity as it exists today. However, since many classic aspects of mathematics have stood the test of time, they are actually part of the present and must be considered in relation to it. Some of the older notions pave the path for recent developments, and others clarify the new

15

replacements or generalizations. In order to integrate the traditional with the modern in mathematics, a "spiral" organization is used by the author in tracing the progress of concepts from their origins in antiquity or some period prior to the twentieth century up to their ultimate formulation. In some instances the first presentation of a topic may be compared to a trip around one of the small inner whirls of a spiral. After this initial full circle, the subject may be dropped until later chapters where new convolutions are examined and the original journey continues through one or more additional broader circles of thought.

Something Old, Something New

The use of the spiral sequence necessitates the juxtaposition of "something old, something new" in a number of chapters. For example, since certain Pythagorean problems are similar to issues handled by Dedekind and Cantor in the late nineteenth century, it seems logical to discuss some aspects of the earlier and later viewpoints side by side. If Euclid's discoveries in the higher arithmetic were first generalized by the great Russian mathematician Tchebycheff, there seems no reason to defer all mention of the nineteenth-century analytical number-theorist simply because he lived much later. If Euler, the most prolific of mathematicians, was "analysis incarnate" but nevertheless employed intuitive methods with grave logical defects, why not reveal at once just how these faults were remedied a couple of centuries later, after they had produced a veritable crisis in mathematics? In the same way, the games of chance played by primitive man and his more civilized successors are linked with the more sophisticated games of military, industrial, or economic strategy, whose theory has been studied by Borel, Wald, and above all, by von Neumann, heroic figures in recent mathematical history.

Thus the mode of organization makes it impossible to adhere to strict chronological order. Continuity of subject matter seems a more important criterion than sequence in time. When, for example, Newtonian mathematical physics is specified as a set of "deterministic" laws, an obvious way to secure emphasis and clarification is to proceed to the "indeterminacy" in a vast major modern area. Therefore a treatment of probabilistic or statistical thought follows the discussion of the deterministic "differential equation type" of mechanics produced by Newton, Euler, Lagrange, Laplace, and Hamilton. Thus, relatively early in the book there appear the names and discoveries of some recent probabilists, statisticians, and researchers in statistical mechanics, whereas mathematical ideas which developed earlier are deferred for later presentation.

Treatment of Biography and Mathematical Lore

As for the biographical material, it is not necessary, in a layman's cyclopedia, to present details of the lives of all the mathematicians in history, and a few of the more usual favorites are given only brief mention in order to give more space to the newer names. It is inevitable, moreover, for an author to have individual enthusiasms and personal preferences. Again, history has left more detailed information about the lives of some mathematicians, or else they were particularly fortunate in having had friends or contemporary biographers to record facts before they were lost forever. In a few instances where the biographical material on record may be apocryphal or, on the other hand, has been repeated again and again as part of the anecdotal stock-in-trade of mathematical writers, the present author has employed an imaginative narrative instead of a biography. For example, there is the story of Hypatia, influenced inevitably by Charles Kingsley's Victorian version.

Integration of Exposition with Source Material

Popularization need not, and should not, be vulgarization, and the quotation of original sources is one method that is often used to maintain a scholarly level of exposition. But since recent mathematical research is exceedingly advanced and abstract in nature, the actual symbolic or technical format in which the creators clothe their ideas might baffle a general reader. If first formulations cannot be used on account of their difficulty, it is sometimes possible to examine how the foremost mathematicians of our era present popularization of ideas related to their own. Some of their narrative or expository writings, quoted occasionally in the present work, were not originally directed to the man in the street. Nevertheless they constitute popularizations in the sense that they were prepared for an audience of biologists, psychologists, economists, engineers, philosophers, chemists, physicists or for mathematical readers who were not specialists in the field under discussion. This sort of secondary source serves the dual purpose of indicating the clarity of such exposition and bringing recent mathematical leaders into the story by having them speak for themselves as well as for those whose research they are evaluating or eulogizing.

In making use of such source material, it is not feasible, in most cases, to quote material *in toto*, with assistance merely from prefatory or supplementary notes. Instead, one may need to combine statements by a number of mathematicians or else interrupt the course of a discussion in order to provide clarification or amplification at the exact points where difficulties may arise. What is done resembles the plotting of a detective story. When a Scotland Yard sleuth is congratulated on his solution of a case, he will respond modestly: "Oh, but if not for your questions, I should never have been able to find the answers, for you have a perfect talent for failing to understand at the very instant when clarification is most needed."

Special Features

As in the matter of biographies, so in the question of topics to be discussed, it is necessary to make some choice. The writer of a popular work on mathematics must select subjects at varied levels of difficulty and present these with varying degree of completeness in order to appeal to a wide audience. That is why, in a few instances, the life and times of a creative thinker are given more space than the advanced mathematical theories to which he gave birth. Again, an informal, anecdotal, even discursive introduction may be the best approach to certain topics. As for variety in exposition, a general work can enjoy a freedom which mathematical textbooks have never had. It seems to the author that even in books for students at school much would be gained by banishing a pattern that makes each chapter a "pedagogic" stereotype. *The Nature and Growth of Modern Mathematics* avoids such a pattern, and hence a discussion is sometimes initiated with a biography or a narrative while at other times the story of the discoverers is told last, not first. Or if mathematicians have worked in the same or related fields, it may be interesting to consider their biographies simultaneously. Where ideas are particularly dramatic, one should plunge into them without preliminaries. The flashback technique, used so frequently in nonmathematical literature, is employed occasionally in the present work in order to emphasize the culminating result of decades, even centuries, of preliminary theorizing, or to give the most general concepts priority over the special cases from which they evolved, or to reveal the goal of a particular chapter or portion of the book.

An Overall Picture

It is the author's opinion that one can provide an appreciation of the development of mathematics and its position in our present culture without according full technical treatment to every mathematical specialty in existence at the present time. To attempt more than brief reference to certain areas would be impracticable and might, moreover, have the effect of confusing or overpowering a general reader. Nevertheless, the origins and elementary aspects of the most important subjects are presented in broad outline. Also there is explanation of why the "multivalence" of modern pure or completely abstract theories makes them all-encompassing so that, in actuality, consideration of a single theory implies a vast content in the specific models to which it applies. This is one reason why the mathematical present can be properly termed the age of abstractness. But the author does not limit the material or adjust the style in accordance with the current emphasis on pure mathematics, and the book deals with much that can be described as "applied mathematics." Although the present abstract trend may have potent effects on the future of mathematics, we are where we are just now because "applied" problems, especially in astronomy and mechanics, are part of our cultural heritage and were, in the past, the motivating factors which stimulated the growth of mathematics toward its present magnitude and condition.

In any comprehensive presentation of mathematics as it exists today, it is inevitable that certain phases of "higher" mathematics must be treated. A reader need not be fearful on this account, however, since part of the present picture is the fact that some of the new advanced mathematical ideas are easier to comprehend as well as far more stimulating than many technical fine points of traditional elementary mathematics.

THE NATURE
AND GROWTH
OF MODERN
MATHEMATICS

Chapter 16

Sweet Manuscript of Youth

> Yet ah that Spring should vanish with the Rose
> That Youth's sweet-scented manuscript should close!
> *Omar Khayyám*

In Galois' mind the fever of life that he had lived recently became a present spectacle; the prison walls seemed once more about him. He stood up. The few moments of liberty he had had were only those after his release from the hospital, where he had spent the last month of his prison term. Even those few had been cut short by the two strangers who had met him on the street corner that very morning and forced him to accept their challenge to a duel scheduled for the next day.

This was how everything was ending. He could have died happily side by side with the engineers during the glorious July days in 1830. He could have died happily in another revolution to wipe out the reactionary Louis Philippe. And now he might die over some wretched girl completely unworthy of the sacrifice of his life. But he must not reason himself out of the duel like a coward. If he had not the courage to face the consequences of his own stupidity, he had no place among the brave friends in the revolution to come. And he realized, with a smile of misery, the irony of the situation, for if he did have the courage to go through with the duel, it might end fatally, and there would still be no place for him in the revolution.

And what of his plans to complete what so many other mathematicians had left undone? Like his plans for revolution these would die with him—except for the little that he

23

had already accomplished, and what he could do during this night.

In prison the nights had been long; so long that he sometimes felt that a man could live a whole life in a single night. And now he was beginning a night in which he must accomplish what others had had generations to work out; already the night seemed waning, it seemed to be the moment before dawn.

He must waste no more time in revery. On the table were blank sheets he had made ready for the night's labor. He sat down to the table, took up the pen, and in a moment was lost in a fever of mathematical theory.

Galois pressed a hand to his aching forehead. Two pages gone, two hours, and all the field of thought lay untouched before him. He laid his head on his arms and wept. "I have no time," "I have no time," he scrawled in the margins. Galois glanced over the pages. What he was writing would keep the Academicians busy for years to come—just this bit! —and how much more could he have accomplished with a lifetime before him! He clenched his fists in an agony of hatred and despair at the thought of how Cauchy had lost his memoir—if it had been seen by the Academy, he might never have come to this death. How fate—or man—had conspired to break him! Fourier was to present another paper of Galois' to the Academy—and had died. The manuscript was lost. Only a few months ago Poisson had promised to read still another paper of his to the Academy, and because the fool could not understand it, he had returned it unread.

Fate was in league with a kingdom of fools to destroy him, as they had driven his father to suicide two years ago. What else could have kept him out of the École Polytechnique? He recalled the second time he had gone to take the entrance examinations. It was a bitter memory. Why were all the things he wanted in the hands of fools? He would have been among people like himself at the Polytechnique; but he had been forced to return to Louis-le-Grand, and after plaguing that faculty with his outspoken radicalism he had been expelled even from there.

The night was wearing on. He looked up wearily from his work. It was useless to go on. He could never do in this brief space the many things he had left to do; the pages he had written were his scientific will and he knew that what he was leaving as a boy was far more than most men leave in their old age; but the tragic waste was there and ate into his heart; when a bullet found its mark in the morning, a machine would run down almost before it had really begun to operate. Hastily he gathered together the papers and letters written all during the night and stuffed them into his pockets. He went up to the window for his coat. A chill moist draft of air fell upon him from the window. Very shortly he was due at the field.

On the field it was cold, with a thin morning mist. Dimly Galois saw, as though from a great distance, the figure of his opponent. Galois sucked in the cold air, trying to bring a feeling of reality into his consciousness, but the dizzying dream sensation persisted; he saw the raised arm of Dubois, the referee, and heard the voice cutting the air. "Ready" and "Aim"; then it was the dream and a sudden stab and burning in the abdomen and . . .

Was it the dream? The hospital walls again and the stiff white linen; the hard cot and the loneliness—it could not be —the door was opening softly and a figure from the past slipped in and was by his side— why should he not weep if all this was true?

"You will be well, Évariste," the boy said—it was his brother—"you will be well," and he wept and took Évariste's hand.

This was not the way, Galois thought, and he whispered "Don't cry, I need all my courage to die at twenty."

If there is anything to tell of the brief tragic life of Évariste Galois (1811–1832), we have touched on it in our vignette. Let us not dwell on the sordid details of the wretchedly unhappy existence of our "Keats," but study instead the facts contained in the mathematical testament which the twenty-year-old youth wrote on the eve of the fatal duel.

Galois' will and the research papers he had prepared earlier in his life (starting at the age of sixteen) were eventually published and recognized as the work of one of the greatest geniuses of all time. Fourteen years after the boy's death, his testament and early memoirs were placed in the hands of the great French analyst Joseph Liouville, whom we have mentioned in connection with Gibbs's statistical mechanics.

The Galois papers were then published in the *Journal de Mathématiques pures et appliquées,* of which Liouville was the editor. In his introduction, Liouville implied that Galois' material and style were beyond the capabilities of the "referees" of the Academy of Sciences, who had rejected or lost the youth's writings.

Posterity credits Galois perhaps even more than Hamilton with the founding of modern "abstract algebra." Whereas Hamilton's quaternions, designed with physics in mind, led him to break ground for modern axiomatics, Galois' point of view emphasized far-reaching general theorems associated with abstract structures like groups and fields. He gave tremendous impetus to the development of the theory of abstract groups, a subject which has a unifying effect within mathematics itself and also has important applications in modern physics. We shall consider Galois' contribution in the present chapter and provide examples of unification and physical application in the two chapters that follow.

Earlier in this book (Chapter 4) we alluded to *Galois fields* and told how Galois' great theorem spelled the end of classical algebra. Although the statement of the epochal proposition has already been given (Volume 1, page 150), details of the proof and the related concepts created by Galois were postponed, lest our readers, like the Academy's "referees," find Galois' notions incomprehensible. But now that we have gradually built up some background in modern advanced mathematical ideas, we feel that we can safely wind around a wider loop of the original "spiral" of thought. This will require that we emphasize once again just what Galois meant by the term *group.*

In playing "Hamilton's game" of gradual removal of the postulates for a field, we finally arrived at the simplest of all structures, a *groupoid,* which is a system, $\{S, \circ\}$, where S is a set of elements and $\circ$ symbolizes a binary operation on S. Of course, the structureless system consisting of the set S alone, with no operations or relations whatsoever, is even simpler.

From now on we shall consider "operation on a set S" to signify that the result of the operation is a unique member within S. In other words, the term "operation" will hereafter imply *uniqueness* and *closure.* Therefore, "square root" will *not* be considered a unary operation on the set of real numbers since, for example, the square root of 4 is *not* unique. The result is either $+2$ or -2. Again, subtraction will *not* be considered a binary operation on the set of natural numbers, because closure is lacking, since $2 - 5$, for example, is not defined within the natural number aggregate. In summary, we shall hereafter say that o is a binary operation on S if and only if $a \circ b$ is a unique member of S, when a and b are any elements of S.

We shall, in the spirit of Galois, now consider *abstract* groupoids in which the members of the fundamental set S are *undefined* elements which need not be numbers but may be capable of varied interpretations in particular situations. We must try to think of the binary operation o as an abstraction, too, and not as a sort of addition or multiplication, but merely as a way of combining pairs of elements in S. For this purpose, we review the comments at the end of Chapter 7, where it was stated that any *binary operation* on S can be expressed as a *ternary relation* on S, that is, as a subset of S^3. Suppose then that we consider a groupoid $\{S, \circ\}$ where $S = \{a, b\}$ and $a \ne b$. To define a specific *binary* operation of S there must be a unique answer within S for $a \circ a$, $a \circ b$, $b \circ a$, $b \circ b$. There are two possible choices for the answer in each of the four cases, since that answer must be either a or b. Hence, applying the fundamental combinatorial principle of Chapter 13, there are $2 \cdot 2 \cdot 2 \cdot 2 = 16$ permissible ways of assigning a set of answers to the four combinations and hence 16 potential binary operations on S. By making any one of these choices, we define a specific binary operation on S. From the abstract point of view, we are free to postulate that, for example, $a \circ a = b$, $a \circ b = b$, $b \circ a = a$, $b \circ b = a$. This is equivalent to the following ternary relation or subset of S^3:

$$\{(a, a, b), (a, b, b), (b, a, a), (b, b, a)\}$$

The reader can, if he wishes, list some of the other fifteen ternary relations that define binary operations. Thus, from the combinatorial point of view, there are 16 possibilities for groupoids when the fundamental set contains 2 elements. (Some of these, however, are isomorphic, that is, abstractly identical, as we shall see.) If we rewrite the example above as

$$((a, a), b), ((a, b), b), ((b, a), a), ((b, b), a)$$

it will illustrate that a binary operation is a *special type* of ternary relation on S, namely, a *function* whose domain is

S^2 and whose range is a subset (proper or improper) of S. So much for the purely logical meaning of binary operations on a set.

Let us now reverse Hamilton's game by *adding* postulates instead of deleting them. In other words, instead of starting with a field and proceding to more general structures, let us start with a groupoid and advance in the direction of specialization. Thus a *special* groupoid in which the binary operation is *associative* is called a *semigroup*. For purposes of illustration, let us choose $S = \{a, b\}$. Then we shall be able to see that not all sixteen groupoids $\{S, \circ\}$ are semigroups. Let us show that the groupoid of our previous example is *not* a semigroup. For convenience in the present instance, we shall rewrite our previous definition of the particular binary operation in the form of a "multiplication table," a format introduced by Cayley, and used by us on page 125 in Volume One to define multiplication of quaternions. Thus we say that we have the groupoid, $\{S, \circ\}$, where $S = \{a, b\}$ and $\circ$ is defined by

$\circ$	a	b
a	b	b
b	a	a

One uses this table by reading $a \circ b$, for example, as the entry in "Row a" and "Column b." Thus $a \circ b = b$. To show that $\circ$ is *not* an associative binary operation on S, we need only a single counterexample. Hence we now indicate that

$$(a \circ b) \circ a \neq a \circ (b \circ a)$$

For, using our "multiplication table," we obtain

$$(a \circ b) \circ a = b \circ a = a$$

and

$$a \circ (b \circ a) = a \circ a = b$$

But some of the other fifteen possibilities for groupoids with $S = \{a, b\}$ as fundamental set are semigroups. For example, if $\circ$ is the binary operation with "multiplication table"

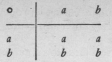

it is not difficult to prove that ∘ is associative. The proof would involve demonstrating the truth of eight statements like

$$(a \circ a) \circ a = a \circ (a \circ a)$$
$$(a \circ b) \circ a = a \circ (b \circ a)$$
$$(a \circ b) \circ b = a \circ (b \circ b)$$

etc. We shall leave the task to the reader but, as a sample, we shall show that

$$(b \circ a) \circ b = b \circ (a \circ b)$$

This is true because, consulting the above table, we have

$$(b \circ a) \circ b = b \circ b = b$$

and

$$b \circ (a \circ b) = b \circ a = b$$

When all eight statements are proved to be true, it is established that ∘, as defined by the above table, is associative, and {S, ∘} is a semigroup.

The reader will see that the semigroup illustrated is not a structure permitting interpretation in terms of ordinary addition or multiplication of numbers. For, if a and b are numbers and if ∘ is interpreted as $+$, the table says that $a + a = a$ which would mean that $a = 0$. But the table tells us that $a + b = a$ and hence, if $a = 0$, $0 + b = 0$ or $b = 0$, which is impossible, since a and b are distinct elements. If we interpret ∘ as multiplication, the table says that $a \circ a = a$, which now means $a^2 = a$ or $a^2 - a = 0$, $a(a - 1) = 0$ so that $a = 0$ or $a = 1$. Suppose that we choose $a = 0$. The table says $b \circ a = b$, which now means $ba = b$ and $b \circ 0 = b$, or $b = 0$, which is impossible since a and b are distinct elements. Suppose that $a = 1$. The table says that $ab = a$, which would mean $b = 1$, which is once again impossible since a and b are distinct elements.

Since there is apparently no concrete interpretation of the semigroup in terms of ordinary addition or multiplication of numbers, perhaps we can suggest a hypothetical application and the reader can then find other interpretations of his own. Suppose that a psychologist experiments with the sensation of taste by having subjects taste things that are either markedly "sweet" or "salty." He claims (hypothetically) that the subjects have an extreme prejudice in favor of the first sensation experienced, whether "sweet" or "salty." If we interpret a as "sweet," b as "salty," and $\circ$ as "is followed by," then $a \circ a = a$ and $a \circ b = a$ signify that tasting a sweet thing followed by tasting something salty produces a sweet sensation just as much as the succession of two "sweets." Similarly, $b \circ a = b$ and $b \circ b = b$ signify that "salty followed by sweet" produces a salty sensation just as much as tasting two salty things in a row. The reader will observe that associativity permits us to carry out extended products like $a \circ b \circ b \circ a \circ a \circ b$, etc., and since in the present instance the first "factor" determines the binary "product," it also determines the extended product. Decidedly hypothetically, the sweet or salty sensation continues no matter how many successive things are tasted.

The reader can establish that the system $\{S, \circ\}$ is a semigroup if $S = \{a, b\}$ and $\circ$ is defined by the "multiplication table"

$\circ$	a	b
a	b	b
b	b	b

All he needs to do is to prove that $\circ$ is associative, a fact that is practically obvious since all binary "products" yield the same result. Perhaps one might provide an interpretation of the semigroup in terms of a paranoid personality who makes a distinction between $a =$ "good" and $b =$ "bad" if only a single event of any importance occurs in a particular period. If one event is followed by another (or still others), he pronounces every composite *bad*. In this interpretation, $\circ =$ "is followed by."

Next, if $\circ$ is a binary operation defined by the table

$\circ$	a	b
a	a	a
b	a	a

one obviously obtains a semigroup. If *a* and *b* are interpreted as "good" and "bad," one might consider the semigroup a model for the behavior of the super-optimist who can distinguish between good and bad for single events but pronounces all composites *good*.

The reader can see that there is similarity in the hypothetical patterns of behavior of the paranoid and the optimist. In other words, although the multiplication tables apparently define different binary operations, the two semigroups are *isomorphic* (Chapter 1) or structurally identical. To make this exact, one should show that in the two semigroups there is matching of elements, operations, and the results of operations. This is evident since the correspondence is:

Semigroup I	Semigroup II

$$a \longleftrightarrow b$$
$$b \longleftrightarrow a$$
$$o \longleftrightarrow o$$

and also

$$a \circ a \longleftrightarrow b \circ b$$
$$a \circ b \longleftrightarrow b \circ a$$
$$b \circ a \longleftrightarrow a \circ b$$
$$b \circ b \longleftrightarrow a \circ a$$

The reader can give still other definitions (among the sixteen possible) for the binary operation $\circ$ on the set $S = \{a, b\}$ and test for associativity, that is, see whether or not the groupoid defined is a semigroup. He can show, for example, that multiplication is *not* associative for the first table below and hence that the groupoid it defines is not a semigroup. Thus the table indicates that $(ba)b$ is *not* equal to $b(ab)$. Next he can demonstrate that the groupoid defined by the second table is isomorphic to the groupoid of the first. It follows that associativity of multiplication and the property of being a semigroup are lacking in the second groupoid as well as in the first.

$\circ$	a	b
a	a	b
b	a	a

$\circ$	a	b
a	b	b
b	a	b

Our interpretations suggest that if we are to obtain nontrivial applications, we may have to consider a larger fundamental set or else continue the reversal of Hamilton's game in order to obtain specialization of a semigroup.

A special semigroup such that S contains an *identity* or *unit element* and also an *inverse* for every element is called a *group*. A special group in which the binary operation is *commutative* is called an *abelian group* (Chapter 4). We shall not continue the process of specialization any further, but before proceeding we shall summarize by means of the definition: A *group* is a system, $\{S, \circ\}$, that is, a *set S* and a *binary operation* $\circ$ on S such that the following three postulates are satisfied.

(1) *Associativity:* If a, b, and c are any elements in S, then

$$(a \circ b) \circ c = a \circ (b \circ c)$$

(2) *Identity:* There is in S a unique element I (called the *identity* or *unit element*) such that, for any element a in S,

$$a \circ I = I \circ a = a$$

(3) *Inverses:* For any element a of S, there exists a unique element a^{-1}, called the *inverse* of a, such that

$$a \circ a^{-1} = a^{-1} \circ a = I$$

If, once more, our universe is the set $S = \{a, b\}$ and we wish to define a binary operation $\circ$ so that $\{S, \circ\}$ will be a group, it can be shown that of the sixteen multiplication tables possible for a groupoid, only two will define a *group* and the two groups so defined are isomorphic or structurally identical. In other words, there is essentially only one group of *order* 2, that is, for a system of two elements. The two group multiplication tables are

$\circ$	a	b		$\circ$	a	b
a	a	b	and	a	b	a
b	b	a		b	a	b

In the first case, a is the *identity* or *unit element*, and in the second case, b is this element. This is so because the first table indicates that the "product" of a with any element of

S leaves the element unchanged, for example, $a \circ a = a$, $b \circ a = b$, $a \circ b = b$. The second table indicates that when any element is combined with b that element is unchanged. In both tables each element of S is its own inverse since $a \circ a$ and $b \circ b$ are both equal to the unit element (a in the first table, b in the second). We observe also that, in either table, the group defined is commutative or abelian, since $a \circ b = b \circ a$. The reader can prove that the groups defined are isomorphic or abstractly identical by matching $a \leftrightarrow b$, $b \leftrightarrow a$, and using the tables to see that $a \circ a \leftrightarrow b \circ b$, $a \circ b \leftrightarrow b \circ a$, etc. Or one can say that both tables refer to an identity element, which can be labeled I ($a = I$ in the first table, $b = I$ in the second table), and another element, called X ($b = X$ in the first table, $a = X$ in the second table). With this replacement, the tables become

$\circ$	I	X		$\circ$	X	I
I	I	X		X	I	X
X	X	I		I	X	I

These "multiplication tables" are identical and differ only in the order of the rows and columns labeled I and X.

What are some of the concrete interpretations that can be given to the single abstract group of order 2? One example is furnished by taking $\circ$ to be ordinary multiplication and $I = +1$, $X = -1$. Then the above tables become

$\times$	$+1$	-1
$+1$	$+1$	-1
-1	-1	$+1$

which, obviously, gives the correct products for the numbers listed.

Another interpretation of the same abstract group is provided by taking $I =$ "even," $X =$ "odd," that is,

$$I = \{ \ldots, -2, 0, +2, +4, \ldots \}$$
$$X = \{ \ldots, -1, +1, +3, \ldots \}$$

If we take $\circ = \oplus$, where $\oplus$ is the kind of "addition" in which each number in one set is added (in the ordinary sense) to every number of the other, then it can be seen that $\{S, \oplus\}$ is a group. To show that "even" $\oplus$ "odd" = "odd," that is, that $I \oplus X = X$, we form

$$I \oplus X = \{ \ldots, -2-1, -2+1, -2+3, \ldots, 0-1,$$
$$0+1, 0+3, \ldots, +2-1, \ldots \}$$
$$= \{ \ldots, -3, -1, +1, +3, \ldots \} = X$$

(where we list the odd integers that occur repeatedly only once). The illustration we are considering is a concrete interpretation of the one and only *finite* abstract group with two elements, but it will be observed that each of the two elements is an *infinite set*.

There is another way of describing the interpretation just given. The alternative description will now be revealed because it avoids the necessity of alluding to "infinite" sets before we discuss them (Chapter 24); also it may seem simpler to the reader; furthermore it will be helpful in later applications. To begin, we recall that in previous chapters we stated repeatedly that a single idea may have many different names. Thus "cardinal 3" may be named *drei* or III or $2+1$ or $8-5$, etc. and all such names are considered equivalent. Again, the ratio $1:2$ or the fraction $1/2$ has many equivalent names like $4/8$ or 0.5, etc. Then, in the present instance, we might consider all even numbers as "congruent" or equivalent (in the sense of "evenness" or exact divisibility by 2) and take a single even integer 0 as the representative of I, the class of even numbers. We could then say that the symbol 0 represents the idea of evenness, and -2 or $+2$ or $+4$, etc. are just other names for the same idea. In the same way, the integer 1 can be taken as the representative of the set of odd numbers, all of which are equivalent in the sense of leaving the *remainder* or "residue" 1 when divided by 2. Then we can say that the symbol 1 represents "oddness," that is, the property described, and -1, $+3$, $+5$, etc. are just other names for the same idea. Then instead of saying "odd" $\oplus$ "even" $= X \oplus I = X$, we shall say $1 \oplus 0 = 1$, which will seem satisfactory to the reader, as will $0 \oplus 0 = 0$, and $0 \oplus 1 = 1$. Instead of saying "odd" $\oplus$ "odd" $=$ "even," we now say $1 \oplus 1 = 0$, which may trouble the reader unless he realizes that it merely means that the ordinary sum of *any pair* of odd integers is even (or that in true statements like $3+5=8$, $7+9=16$, etc., each number on the left side of the equations is equivalent to 1 and the numbers on the right are equivalent to 0 in the sense just indicated). In the present instance, $\oplus$ is called *addition modulo* 2, and the symbols 0, 1 are often said to represent the *residue classes I* and X (whose members leave "residues" 0 and 1 when divided by 2, the "modulus"). Then $\{S, \circ\}$ is a group in which S consists of the residue classes 0 and 1, $\circ = \oplus$, which is *addition modulo* 2 as defined by the table

$\oplus$	0	1
0	0	1
1	1	0

Since the "new" school mathematics includes *addition modulo* 2 in its courses of study, that type of addition (with modulus 2 and other moduli) is often called "clock addition." Thus, in an ordinary clock the *modulus* would be 12, and the "residues" after division by 12 would be 0, 1, 2, ..., 11. If it is now 9 o'clock and we ask what time it will be in 5 hours, the answer is 2 o'clock. If $\oplus$ is addition modulo 12, $9 \oplus 5 = 2$, and similarly $8 \oplus 7 = 3$. If it is now 9 o'clock and we ask what time it will be 29 hours from now, then starting at 9, we have to go around the clock twice and then 5 hours more. This shows that 29 is just another name for 5 in the modulo 12 system, that is, in the sense that it leaves a "residue" 5 when divided by 12. Hence $9 \oplus 5 = 2$ o'clock gives the answer to the question raised. If we take a clock which (Figure 16.1) has just two markings, 0 and 1, we can use it to picture the binary operation of our previous illustration, namely, *addition modulo* 2. In particular, if the clock of Figure 16.1 now reads 1 o'clock and we

Figure   16.1 The time is "half past zero" on a modulo 2 clock.

ask what time it will be one "interval" from now, the answer is 0 o'clock, so that we have a picture of $1 \oplus 1 = 0$ in the modulo 2 system.

An interpretation similar to modulo 2 addition can be obtained if in the multiplication table for the abstract group of order 2 we consider I and X as two positions of a wheel, I as its original position and X its position after rotation through 180°. But the wheel would also be in the original position I after rotation (in either direction) through 360° or 720°, etc. and would be in position X after rotation (in either direction) through 540° or 900°, etc. Thus there is an "equivalence class" of rotations for each of the two positions, and we have a group of order 2 in which the elements are the two sets of rotations

$$I = \{0°, \pm 360°, \pm 720°, \ldots, \pm 360n°, \ldots \}$$

$$X = \{\pm 180°, \pm 540°, \pm 900°, \ldots, \pm (180 + 360n)°, \ldots \}$$

and here $\circ =$ "is followed by," an operation signifying that one rotation is to be succeeded by another rotation.

We could give still other interpretations of the single abstract group of order 2, but the whole point is that all such concrete groups are isomorphic and thus abstractly identical. If we increase the number of elements in the fundamental set S, there is a special theorem of group theory establishing the fact that there is one and only one abstract group for the orders $n = 2$, 3, 5, 7, 11, 13, 17, 19, . . . or any *prime number*. A prime number is a natural number whose only exact divisors are itself and 1. The theorem states that there is one and only one abstract group for any prime number. Then if we take $n = 3$, or $S = \{a, b, c\}$ where a, b, and c are distinct elements, there is one abstract group $\{S, \circ\}$. The reader can establish this fact by bearing the group postulates in mind and then deriving the multiplication table by a process of trial with groupoids as we did in the case of the groupoid of order 2.

But let us accept the fact that all groups of order 3 are isomorphic. Then we can derive the general multiplication table from a specific instance. Let us show that if $\circ = \oplus =$ *addition modulo* 3, and $S = \{0, 1, 2\}$ where 0, 1, and 2 are the "residues" or "residue classes" modulo 3, then $\{S, \circ\} = \{S, \oplus\}$ is a group. The reader will have no trouble with addition modulo 3 except possibly with the combinations, $1 \oplus 2 = 2 \oplus 1 = 0$, $2 \oplus 2 = 1$. He can carry this out on a clock with only 3 "hours" labeled 0, 1, 2 by means of questions like: If it is 1 o'clock now, what time will it be 2 "hours" from now? Or he can carry out the ordinary additions $1 + 2 = 3$, $2 + 2 = 4$ and say that 3 and 4 are equivalent (modulo 3) to 0 and 1, respectively. The modulo 3 addition table is

$\oplus$	0	1	2
0	0	1	2
1	1	2	0
2	2	0	1

Here 0 is obviously the identity element and is its own inverse. Also 1 and 2 are inverse elements since $1 \oplus 2 = 2 \oplus 1 = 0$. It is easy to show that $\oplus$ is associative, and this would complete the proof that the system $\{S - \{0, 1, 2\}, \oplus \}$ is a group.

Since there is only one abstract group of order 3, we can represent it by replacing $S = \{0, 1, 2\}$ in the above table by $S = \{I, a, b\}$. Then $\{S, \circ \}$ is a group in which $\circ$ is defined by

$\circ$	I	a	b
I	I	a	b
a	a	b	I
b	b	I	a

An interpretation of the group of order 3 in terms of rotations of a wheel would take I as the original position of the wheel, a and b as positions after rotations through 120° and 240°, respectively. Here $\circ =$ "is followed by" and rotations of 0°, ±360°, ±720°, . . . , ±360n°, where n is any integer, are equivalent, as are rotations through 120°, 480°, −240°, . . . , 120° ± 360n°, etc.

The table defining a binary operation on a set is customarily called the "multiplication table," and results of operations are usually called products. The reader will therefore understand such terminology when we use it. Also, instead of $a \circ b$, $a \circ b \circ c$, etc., it is customary to employ the usual product symbolism of elementary algebra and write ab, abc, etc. In fact, $a \circ a \circ a \circ a$ would not be written $aaaa$ but more compactly as a^4.

The use of such symbolism will indicate a special property of the abstract group of order 3. Consulting the multiplication table, we see that $aa = b$, that is, $a^2 = b$. From the same table, $ba = I$. Substituting a^2 for b in this last statement, we have $a^2a = I$ or $a^3 = I$. Thus the three group elements, a, b, I, can be symbolized as a, a^2, a^3, that is, as "powers" of one of them.

If all the elements of a group can be expressed as powers of one of them, the group is described as *cyclic*. Thus the group of order 3 is cyclic. If we examine the multiplication table of the abstract group of order 2 (page 32), we see that $X \circ X = XX = X^2 = I$. Hence the two group elements are X and X^2. Therefore the group of order 2 is cyclic. In group theory it is proved that *all groups of prime order are cyclic*. Thus if the order of a group is 7, its elements are a, a^2, . . . , a^6, $a^7 = I$ and it is easy to "multiply" any pair of elements.

Since the group of order 2 is cyclic, we can represent its elements by a, $a^2 = I$. This explains one of the interpretations we have already given. If $\circ$ = multiplication of *numbers* and I is a *multiplicative* identity, then $I = 1$. Hence $a^2 = 1$ and $a = +1$ or $a = -1$. Since a must differ from I, $a = -1$. Therefore our group is $\{S = \{+1, -1\}, \times\}$, as defined by the table on page 33.

The abstract group of order 3 is cyclic, and its elements are a, a^2, $a^3 = I$. Once again if we interpret $\circ$ as multiplication of numbers and I as the multiplicative identity 1, $a^3 = 1$. We cannot have $a = 1$ since a and I are distinct elements. We can solve $a^3 = 1$ by writing it as $a^3 - 1 = 0$ or

$$(a - 1)(a^2 + a + 1) = 0$$

The first factor gives $a = 1$ and application of the quadratic formula (Vol. I, page 139) gives $a = -1/2 + i/2\sqrt{3}$, $a = -1/2 - i/2\sqrt{3}$. Since these answers satisfy the equation $a^3 = 1$, they are called *cube roots* of 1. Thus 1 has the real cube root 1, and two complex cube roots. A little manipulative algebra shows that either complex root is the square of the other. The first complex root above is often symbolized by the Greek letter omega, ω, and hence the three cube roots of 1 are ω, ω^2, $\omega^3 = 1$. Therefore an interpretation of the abstract group of order 3 is given by

$$\{S = \{\omega, \omega^2, \omega^3 = 1\}, \times\}$$

Thus far our study of finite groups has led only to abelian groups. To obtain a noncommutative group, we refer to the multiplication table for quaternions in Chapter 4. If the quaternion multiplication is to define a binary operation on a finite set, the table will have to be enlarged so as to provide *closure*. For example, in quaternion multiplication, $i^2 = -1$ and $kj = -i$. Hence -1 and $-i$ will have to be included in S. If $S = \{1, i, j, k, -1, -i, -j, -k\}$ and $\circ$ = quaternion multiplication, $\{S, \circ\}$ is the *quaternion group* of order 8, which is not commutative. By using Hamilton's assumption (Chapter 4) that $q_1 q_2 = -q_2 q_1$ where q_1 and q_2 are any two quaternions, the reader will be able to state that $ij = -ji$ and hence, from the table in Chapter 4, $-ji = -k$. From such considerations he can construct the multiplication table (with 8 rows and 8 columns) corresponding to the set S, and then show that $\{S, \circ\}$ is a group.

One can obtain a finite *abstract* group of any order merely by deciding to postulate a cyclic group. Thus, although the quaternion group is one abstract group of order 8, there is also the abstract cyclic group of order 8 whose elements are $\{a, a^2, \ldots, a^7, a^8 = I\}$. This is a commutative (abelian) group and hence certainly *not* isomorphic to the quaternion group. As a numerical interpretation there is the multiplicative group whose elements are the 8 solutions (in the complex domain) of the polynomial equation, $x^8 = 1$, that is, the eight eighth-roots of 1, two of which are the real numbers $+1$ and -1, the other six being complex. There are three more abstract groups of order 8, but we shall not discuss them here. Instead, we shall summarize the situation by saying that there are 5 nonisomorphic abstract groups of order 8, of which 3 are abelian and 2 nonabelian.

The reader may think that mathematicians are able to make statements like those in the preceding paragraph about finite groups of any given order, however large. But that is not the case. There is at least one abstract group for every finite order, namely, the cyclic group. If the order is prime, the cyclic group is the only one. But there is as yet no universal formula that will tell the number and nature of abstract groups for all composite (nonprime) orders. The way this unsolved problem is being tackled today derives directly from the thought of the boy Galois.

All the groups discussed in the present chapter have been of *finite* order. But we have illustrated infinite groups earlier in this book. Thus if S is the set of integers and $\circ$ is ordinary addition, $\{S, \circ\}$ is an abelian group. Its identity element is 0, and there is an inverse, $-a$, for every element a. We observe that the set of natural numbers, $S = \{1, 2, 3, \ldots\}$ is *not* a group with respect to addition because there is no identity element (and this also makes it impossible to define additive inverses). If S is the set of rational numbers (or the set of real numbers) with zero excluded and $\circ$ is ordinary multiplication, then $\{S, \circ\}$ is an abelian group. The unit element is 1 and inverses are reciprocals. If $\circ$ is multiplication and S is the set of natural numbers, $\{S, \circ\}$ is not a group because inverses are lacking. In our next chapter we shall illustrate infinite groups whose elements are not numbers.

Cauchy and Galois considered finite groups in which the elements were *not* points or numbers (complex or hypercomplex) or qualities but *mappings* (functions) of a certain kind. In Chapter 7 a mapping (function) was defined as a binary relation or set of ordered pairs in which every element of the domain is matched with a unique element of the range. We gave as an example (Vol. I, page 205) the mapping of a set of three cities *into* a set of points, and *onto* a proper subset of that set. Thus, as another example, if $S = \{a, b, c, d\}$ and $T = \{e, f, g\}$, then (using the format we shall employ in the present chapter)

$$\begin{pmatrix} a & b & c & d \\ f & g & f & f \end{pmatrix}$$

represents a mapping whose domain is S and whose range is $\{f, g\}$. It is a mapping of S *into* T, or *onto* $\{f, g\}$, a proper subset of T.

The ordered pairs in the mapping illustrated are (a, f), (b, g), (c, f), and (d, f). If we reverse the order of elements in each pair, we obtain the *inverse relation*, $\{(f, a)$, $(g, b), (f, c), (f, d)\}$. This inverse relation is *not a mapping* (*function*) because there are three pairs containing the same first element, f. Corresponding to f, an element of the domain, there are *three* elements of the range. Another way of pointing up the same fact is to state that, in general, a mapping may be a "many-to-one correspondence." In the original mapping, for example, the "many" elements, a, c, and d, all correspond to f. Then the inverse of such a mapping will be a "one-to-many correspondence" and is therefore, in general, *not* a mapping.

By contrast, there are special cases like the mapping

$$\begin{pmatrix} a & b & c \\ d & e & f \end{pmatrix}$$

which is a *one-to-one correspondence* and has an inverse that is a mapping, namely

$$\begin{pmatrix} d & e & f \\ a & b & c \end{pmatrix}$$

Cauchy and Galois considered a still further specialization—a function that is not only a *one-to-one* correspondence, but also maps the fundamental set *onto itself*. For example, if $S = \{a, b, c, d\}$, then

$$\begin{pmatrix} a & b & c & d \\ d & a & c & b \end{pmatrix}$$

is a *one-to-one mapping* of S onto itself. Here S is both domain and range. The effect of the mapping is merely to rearrange or *permute* the elements of the set. Hence today we call it a *permutation*, a usage akin to that in the combinatorial algebra of Chapter 13.

We shall now be considering *groups* of permutations not only because they are applied in Galois' theory but also because such groups can be used to represent *all finite groups*, since it can be proved that *every finite group is isomorphic to some group of permutations*.

In the case of a *finite* set, it is tautological to refer to a *one-to-one* mapping of the set *onto* itself, since any mapping onto itself must be one-to-one. For if it were many-to-one, several elements of the domain would be mapped onto a single element of the range. Hence there would be fewer elements in the range than in the domain and therefore the latter could not be mapped *onto* the former, as required. However, in the case of an infinite set, as the next chapter will show, a mapping of such a set *onto* itself need *not* necessarily be one-to-one (and a one-to-one mapping can be *into* instead of *onto* itself).

But we are now discussing finite sets and finite groups. Hence we can state that a *permutation is a mapping of a finite set onto itself*. As an example, from everyday life, suppose that three objects, a paperweight, a pencil, and an eraser, are located in certain positions on top of a desk. For convenience, let us attach the labels 1, 2, 3, respectively, to these objects. Then, the symbolism

$$\begin{pmatrix} 1 & 2 & 3 \\ 3 & 1 & 2 \end{pmatrix}$$

will be used to signify that objects are to be shifted so that those named on the lower line replace or are *substituted* for the corresponding ones on the upper line. This suggests why Cayley and Galois called permutations *substitutions*. In the present example, eraser is *substituted* for paperweight, paperweight replaces pencil, pencil replaces eraser. The following array of numbers represents the very same permutation or substitution of objects (except that the original location of objects on the desk is different, being pencil, paperweight, and eraser, in that order):

$$\begin{pmatrix} 2 & 1 & 3 \\ 1 & 3 & 2 \end{pmatrix}$$

Likewise, there are four other formats for this same permutation, namely,

$$\begin{pmatrix} 1 & 3 & 2 \\ 3 & 2 & 1 \end{pmatrix}, \quad \begin{pmatrix} 2 & 3 & 1 \\ 1 & 2 & 3 \end{pmatrix}, \quad \begin{pmatrix} 3 & 1 & 2 \\ 2 & 3 & 1 \end{pmatrix}, \quad \begin{pmatrix} 3 & 2 & 1 \\ 2 & 1 & 3 \end{pmatrix}$$

Again, the rearrangement keeping the paperweight wherever it happens to be, but interchanging positions of pencil and eraser is a *single* permutation or substitution with any one of the six formats:

$$\begin{pmatrix} 1 & 2 & 3 \\ 1 & 3 & 2 \end{pmatrix}, \quad \begin{pmatrix} 1 & 3 & 2 \\ 1 & 2 & 3 \end{pmatrix}, \quad \begin{pmatrix} 2 & 1 & 3 \\ 3 & 1 & 2 \end{pmatrix}, \quad \begin{pmatrix} 2 & 3 & 1 \\ 3 & 2 & 1 \end{pmatrix},$$

$$\begin{pmatrix} 3 & 1 & 2 \\ 2 & 1 & 3 \end{pmatrix}, \quad \begin{pmatrix} 3 & 2 & 1 \\ 2 & 3 & 1 \end{pmatrix}$$

Presently we shall want to show that certain sets of permutations constitute groups with respect to ∘ = "is followed by" or "succession." Just what will happen, then, if one permutation follows another? If we label the two illustrative permutations above A and B respectively, what is the meaning of $A \circ B = AB = $ "A followed by B"? Picturing AB in terms of the objects involved, we have

First, $A =$ $\begin{pmatrix} 1 & 2 & 3 \\ 3 & 1 & 2 \end{pmatrix}$

Then, $B =$ $\begin{pmatrix} 3 & 1 & 2 \\ 2 & 1 & 3 \end{pmatrix}$

The net result is that the eraser is in its original position on the desk, but the pencil and paperweight have been interchanged, that is,

$$AB = \begin{pmatrix} 1 & 2 & 3 \\ 2 & 1 & 3 \end{pmatrix}$$

an array which could have been obtained merely by deleting the common row (or intermediate arrangement of objects), 3 1 2, in the above arrays for A and B.

Let us reverse the order of succession, and find the meaning of BA. If we express B in the form

$$B = \begin{pmatrix} 1 & 2 & 3 \\ 1 & 3 & 2 \end{pmatrix}$$

then we shall want to use that one of the six forms for A that has 1 3 2 as the top row (so that B and A will have a common row that can be deleted). Hence we have

$$BA = \begin{pmatrix} 1 & 2 & 3 \\ -1-\!-3-\!-2- \end{pmatrix} \begin{pmatrix} -1-\!-3-\!-2- \\ 3 & 2 & 1 \end{pmatrix} = \begin{pmatrix} 1 & 2 & 3 \\ 3 & 2 & 1 \end{pmatrix}$$

which is *not* the same permutation as AB. In the case of BA, the pencil is in its original position whereas the other two objects are interchanged. Thus the "multiplication" of A and B is *not* commutative.

Our examples illustrate that the succession of two permutations of certain objects, that is, the succession of two mappings of a finite set onto itself, results in some permutation (rearrangement) of the objects (some mapping of the set onto itself). Then if we are given an aggregate or class whose elements are *all* possible permutations of a particular finite set (that is, all possible mappings of that set onto itself), it will be *closed* under the operation of succession. In other words, "is followed by" or "succession" will truly be a *binary operation* on the class of *all* possible permutations of a particular finite set.

If we consider the same example of three objects on a desk (or any three distinguishable objects), we know (from Chapter 13) that 3! or 6 different arrangements are possible. Hence we can define 6 distinct permutations or substitutions involving any three objects. We shall now label these substitutions $S_1, S_2, \ldots, S_6$ and show that, given the class, $C = \{I = S_1, S_2, \ldots, S_6\}$, and $\circ = $ "succession," the system $\{C, \circ\}$ is a *group*. As we have just explained, $\circ$ will truly be a binary operation on C because C includes *all* possible permutations of the particular set of objects. Now the six permutations or substitutions that are members of C are

$$I = S_1 = \begin{pmatrix} 1 & 2 & 3 \\ 1 & 2 & 3 \end{pmatrix} \quad \text{(the } identity\text{)}$$

$$S_2 = \begin{pmatrix} 1 & 2 & 3 \\ 2 & 3 & 1 \end{pmatrix}$$

$$S_3 = \begin{pmatrix} 1 & 2 & 3 \\ 3 & 1 & 2 \end{pmatrix}$$

$$S_4 = \begin{pmatrix} 1 & 2 & 3 \\ 1 & 3 & 2 \end{pmatrix} \quad \text{(1 is left fixed)}$$

$$S_5 = \begin{pmatrix} 1 & 2 & 3 \\ 3 & 2 & 1 \end{pmatrix} \quad \text{(2 is left fixed)}$$

$$S_6 = \begin{pmatrix} 1 & 2 & 3 \\ 2 & 1 & 3 \end{pmatrix} \quad \text{(3 is left fixed)}$$

To prove that $\{C, \circ\}$ is a group, one must show (1) that $\circ$ is *associative*, (2) that there is a unit or identity element in C, and (3) that each one of the six elements of C has an inverse in C.

Although the operation $\circ = $ "succession" need not be commutative, it is always *associative* for a class of permutations, as we shall indicate by a general argument below. But if the reader wishes to do so, he can establish associativity in the present instance for all triples of permutations formed from substitutions in C; that is, he can find the result, $(S_2 S_3) S_4$, for example, and show that it is the same as $S_2 (S_3 S_4)$.

We have already labeled S_1 as I, the identity element, but we should show that it really is a unit element, by proving $IS_2 = S_2 I = S_2$, $IS_3 = S_3 I = S_3$, etc. This presents no problem, since, for example,

$$IS_4 = \begin{pmatrix} 1 & 2 & 3 \\ -1- & -2- & -3- \end{pmatrix} \begin{pmatrix} -1- & -2- & -3- \\ 1 & 3 & 2 \end{pmatrix} = \begin{pmatrix} 1 & 2 & 3 \\ 1 & 3 & 2 \end{pmatrix} = S_4$$

$$S_4 I = \begin{pmatrix} 1 & 2 & 3 \\ -1- & -3- & -2- \end{pmatrix} \begin{pmatrix} -1- & -3- & -2- \\ 1 & 3 & 2 \end{pmatrix} = \begin{pmatrix} 1 & 2 & 3 \\ 1 & 3 & 2 \end{pmatrix} = S_4$$

As for inverses, the reader can show that each of the permutations S_1, S_4, S_5, and S_6 is its own inverse. The argument in the case of S_6, that is, the proof that $S_6 S_6 = S_6{}^2 = I$ is as follows:

$$S_6 S_6 = \begin{pmatrix} 1 & 2 & 3 \\ -2- & -1- & -3- \end{pmatrix} \begin{pmatrix} -2- & -1- & -3- \\ 1 & 2 & 3 \end{pmatrix} = \begin{pmatrix} 1 & 2 & 3 \\ 1 & 2 & 3 \end{pmatrix} = I$$

It is also easy to show that S_2 and S_3 are inverse elements. The argument proving that $S_2 S_3 = S_3 S_2 = I$ is as follows:

$$S_2 S_3 = \begin{pmatrix} 1 & 2 & 3 \\ -2- & -3- & -1- \end{pmatrix} \begin{pmatrix} -2- & -3- & -1- \\ 1 & 2 & 3 \end{pmatrix} = \begin{pmatrix} 1 & 2 & 3 \\ 1 & 2 & 3 \end{pmatrix} = I$$

$$S_3 S_2 = \begin{pmatrix} 1 & 2 & 3 \\ -3- & -1- & -2- \end{pmatrix} \begin{pmatrix} -3- & -1- & -2- \\ 1 & 2 & 3 \end{pmatrix} = \begin{pmatrix} 1 & 2 & 3 \\ 1 & 2 & 3 \end{pmatrix} = I$$

Since all three requirements of the definition of a group are met, the class of 6 permutations of 3 objects constitutes a group with respect to "succession." The same is true for the 2! or 2 permutations of 2 objects, the 4! or 24 permutations of 4 objects, the 5! or 120 permutations of 5 objects, etc. Hence if $\circ$ = succession, the $n!$ permutation of n objects constitute a group, called the *symmetric group* of *degree n*. The nature of the symmetry will appear presently. In Galois theory, the 2, 3, 4, 5, . . . , n objects that are permuted are not pencils or paperweights but the 2, 3, 4, 5, . . . , n roots of a quadratic, cubic, quartic, quintic, . . . , nth degree polynomial equation.

Let us now show, as we promised to do, that $\circ$ = "succession of permutations" is an associative operation. If P_1, P_2, and P_3 are *any three* permutations of n objects, we must now indicate that

$$(P_1, P_2) P_3 = P_1 (P_2 P_3)$$

The reader will see why this statement is true if he considers P_1, P_2, and P_3 as shuffles of a single suit of cards. Let him concentrate on what happens to the top card in each shuffle. A similar chain of reasoning will then apply to the bottom card or to a card in any position. Let us suppose that the top card is the ace and that shuffles have the following effect:

$$P_1 = \begin{pmatrix} \text{ace} --- \\ \text{queen} --- \end{pmatrix}, \quad P_2 = \begin{pmatrix} \text{queen} --- \\ \text{king} --- \end{pmatrix}, \quad P_3 = \begin{pmatrix} \text{king} --- \\ \text{deuce} --- \end{pmatrix}$$

Then the effect of P_1 followed by P_2 would be to replace ace by king. Thus

$$P_1 P_2 = \begin{pmatrix} \text{ace} --- \\ \text{king} --- \end{pmatrix} \quad \text{and} \quad P_3 = \begin{pmatrix} \text{king} --- \\ \text{deuce} --- \end{pmatrix}$$

Hence $(P_1 P_2) P_3$ would replace ace by deuce.

Let us now consider $P_1(P_2 P_3)$, the right member of the above equation. We see from the effects stated above that since P_2 replaces queen by king, and P_3 replaces king by deuce, P_2 followed by P_3 would have the effect of replacing queen by deuce, that is,

$$P_2 P_3 = \begin{pmatrix} \text{queen} --- \\ \text{deuce} --- \end{pmatrix}$$

Then $P_1(P_2 P_3)$ means

$$P_1 = \begin{pmatrix} \text{ace} --- \\ \text{queen} --- \end{pmatrix} \quad \text{followed by} \quad P_2 P_3 = \begin{pmatrix} \text{queen} --- \\ \text{deuce} --- \end{pmatrix}$$

and $P_1(P_2 P_3)$ replaces ace by deuce, which is the same as the effect of $(P_1 P_2)P_3$.

In summary, succession of permutations (or, in general, of *mappings of any set onto itself*) is associative because three shuffles in succession have the same effect whether you are like the "player on the right" who examines the effect on a typical position in the deck after the first shuffle (and the last) or like the "player on the left" who makes his examinations after the second and third shuffles.

If all the elements of one group are also elements of another group, then the former is called a *subgroup* of the latter. We note that any group is thus a subgroup of itself. If we refer to this special case as an "improper subgroup," all subgroups of a group except the group itself can be termed *proper*. For example, in the illustration considered on page 44, namely, the group of six permutations of three objects (the symmetric group of "degree" 3), it can be proved that the group has subgroups with the following rosters:

$$A = \{S_1, S_2, S_3\}$$
$$G_1 = \{S_1, S_4\}$$
$$G_2 = \{S_1, S_5\}$$
$$G_3 = \{S_1, S_5\}$$
$$J = \{S_1\}$$

The reader will find it easy to prove that each one of these aggregates qualifies as a group under the operation of "succession," but we shall nevertheless give him some help by indicating how to prove that the system $\{A, \circ \}$ is a group. In the first place, we must be sure that $\circ = $ "succession" is truly a binary operation on the set of elements in A. We cannot use our previous general argument concerning closure because the class A does *not* include *all* permutations of three objects. If we are to show that $\circ$ is a binary operation on A, that is, possesses closure on A, we must show that we can construct a "multiplication table" giving S_1 or S_2 or S_3 as the answer to any of the nine products S_1S_1, S_1S_2, . . . , S_2S_1, S_2S_2, etc. Since S_1 is the element we previously labeled I, we know that $S_1S_2 = IS_2 = S_2$, etc., and the entries in the first row (and first column) of the multiplication table will therefore be S_1, S_2, S_3, respectively. We also showed previously that $S_2S_3 = S_3S_2 = I$, and this will provide for two more entries. Hence we need only find the meaning of S_2S_2 and S_3S_3. We see that

$$S_2S_2 = \begin{pmatrix} 1 & 2 & 3 \\ -2--3--1- \end{pmatrix} \begin{pmatrix} -2--3--1- \\ 3 & 1 & 2 \end{pmatrix} = \begin{pmatrix} 1 & 2 & 3 \\ 3 & 1 & 2 \end{pmatrix} = S_3$$

$$S_3S_3 = \begin{pmatrix} 1 & 2 & 3 \\ -3--1--2- \end{pmatrix} \begin{pmatrix} -3--1--2- \\ 2 & 3 & 1 \end{pmatrix} = \begin{pmatrix} 1 & 2 & 3 \\ 2 & 3 & 1 \end{pmatrix} = S_2$$

Now we can fill in the multiplication table with entries that are either S_1 or S_2 or S_3. Hence "succession" is truly a binary operation on the class A, and the multiplication table is as follows:

$\circ$	S_1	S_2	S_3
S_1	S_1	S_2	S_3
S_2	S_2	S_3	S_1
S_3	S_3	S_1	S_2

The general argument that "succession" is associative applies in the present case. $S_1 = I$ is obviously an identity or unit element in A. Once again S_1 is its own inverse and S_2 is the inverse of S_3, whereas S_3 is the inverse of S_2, because $S_2S_3 = S_3S_2 = S_1 = I$, and this completes the proof that $\{A, \circ \}$ is a group.

Recalling that the number of elements in a group is called the *order* of the group, we can state that A, G_1, G_2, G_3, J have orders 3, 2, 2, 2, 1, respectively, and the entire symmetric group of third degree has order 6. Note that the orders of the subgroups are exact divisors of the order of the entire group. Lagrange established, in fact, one of the fundamental theorems of finite group theory when he proved that the order of a subgroup of a finite group must be an exact divisor of the order of the entire group.

A consequence of the Lagrange theorem is that the ratio of the order of a group to the order of a subgroup must be an integer. This integer is called the *index* of the subgroup in the larger group. Thus, for the subgroups tabulated above, the index of A in the symmetric group is 2, and the index for G_1 is 3; the indices of G_2, G_3, J in the symmetric group are 3, 3, 6, respectively; the index of J in G_1 is 2.

As has just been indicated, the group A has index 2 in the symmetric group because it contains just half as many elements as the entire symmetric group of degree 3. Now it can be proved that for the symmetric group of *any* degree there is always a unique subgroup containing half as many elements as the entire group. In other words, the symmetric group contains $n!$ permutations, or is of order $n!$, and the subgroup in question has order $n!/2$, with index 2 in the larger group. This special subgroup is called the *alternating* group of degree n. In the case of degrees 4, 5, 6, for example, the symmetric groups have orders 24, 120, 720 and the corresponding alternating groups have orders 12, 60, 360, respectively.

Forming subgroups of a given finite group may be a fruitful way of creating new groups, but Galois' great success came about through specializing the subgroups formed. He created the concept of a *normal subgroup* which he described (for a special reason which will appear shortly) as *invariant* or *self-conjugate*. A normal subgroup may be defined in various ways, but a general reader would probably find the following definition the easiest to understand: Given that K is a subgroup of G, then it is a *normal subgroup* if and only if it *commutes* with every element of G.

The meaning of the definition just stated can best be clarified through an example. Let us then show that in the case of the symmetric group of degree 3, the alternating group is not only a subgroup but is also a *normal* subgroup. Using the notation previously employed, the rosters of the group and subgroup are

$$G = \{I, S_2, S_3, S_4, S_5, S_6\}$$
$$A = \{I, S_2, S_3\}$$

To prove that A is *normal*, we must show that $Ax = xA$ where x is any one of the six members of G. Thus let us choose $x = S_4$, for example, and show that $AS_4 = S_4A$. First, AS_4 signifies that *each element* of A, the alternating group, is to be "multiplied" by S_4 to form the set

$$\{S_4, S_2S_4, S_3S_4\}$$

The reader can use the definitions of S_2, S_3, and S_4 on page 44 to show that $S_2S_4 = S_5$ and $S_3S_4 = S_6$ so that

$$AS_4 = \{S_4, S_5, S_6\}$$

Sometimes AS_4 is described as a *right coset* of the subgroup A. Let us now "multiply" S_4 by each element of A to form the *left coset*,

$$S_4A = \{S_4, S_4S_2, S_4S_3\}$$

The reader can show that $S_4S_2 = S_6$ and $S_4S_3 = S_5$ so that

$$S_4A = \{S_4, S_6, S_5\}$$

which is the *same aggregate* as AS_4 even though the elements are listed in different order. We observe that the commutativity of A with S_4 is a matter of proving that a right coset of A is identical with the corresponding left coset.

The reader can imitate the above example in order to prove that $AS_5 = S_5A$ and $AS_6 = S_6A$. It is obvious that $AI = IA$ for, if each element of A is "multiplied" either on the right or on the left by I, it is unchanged. Hence $AI = A$ and $IA = A$. It is less obvious that AS_2, S_2A, AS_3, S_3A are all identical with A, but if we interpret any one of these symbols, it signifies that the members of A are all "multiplied" by a member of A (S_2 or S_3). Since A is a subgroup, the "products" are all members of A. Because A commutes with all six members of G, A is a *normal* subgroup of G.

Now let us explain Galois' use of the adjectives "invariant" and "self-conjugate" in referring to a normal subgroup. We can continue with the above example, in which the condition for the normality of A was expressed by

$$Ax = xA$$

where x is any element of G. Since G is a group, every element must have an inverse. Let us symbolize the inverse of x in the usual way by x^{-1}, and then "multiply" or follow x^{-1} by either side of the above equation to obtain

$$x^{-1}Ax = x^{-1}xA$$

Since x and x^{-1} are inverse elements, $x^{-1}x = I$, and hence the right member of the equation becomes IA, or A. Therefore

$$x^{-1}Ax = A$$

The last statement indicates that the normal subgroup A (or any normal subgroup) will be *invariant* under a certain procedure, called "conjugation" of its elements. Therefore a normal subgroup is *invariant* or *self-conjugate*. The last equation above can be interpreted to mean that if x is any element whatsoever in G, then

$$\{x^{-1}Ix, \; x^{-1}S_1x, \; x^{-1}S_2x\}$$

is merely a listing of the membership of the normal subgroup A. Here $x^{-1}S_1x$ is called the conjugate of S_1 with respect to x and $x^{-1}S_2x$ is the conjugate of S_2 with respect to x.

Observe that $x^{-1}Ix = I$, and hence I is its own conjugate (is self-conjugate) with respect to any element of G.

To obtain some practice with the concept of normality, the reader can prove that $H = \{I, a^2, a^4\}$ and $K = \{I, a^3\}$ are both normal subgroups of the cyclic group, $G = \{a, a^2, a^3, \ldots, a^6 = I\}$. He can verify that K has *two* right cosets which are the same as the corresponding left cosets, respectively. As an additional exercise, he can prove that all sub-groups of an abelian group must be normal. He can also investigate subgroups of the noncommutative quaternion group and prove that they are all normal. At the other extreme from such groups there are the *simple* groups *none* of whose proper subgroups (except the identity) is normal.

Galois applied not only the concept of *normal* subgroup but that of *maximal* normal subgroup. If G is a given group and G_1 is a proper normal subgroup of G, then G_1 is called a *maximal* normal subgroup of G if no other proper normal subgroup of G contains G_1. This definition permits a group to have more than one maximal normal subgroup, and such subgroups need *not* be of the same order.

Galois' procedure for determining the "algebraic" solvability of a given polynomial equation of degree n starts by associating with the equation a certain permutation group. Today we call that group the *Galois group* of the equation. Galois defined the "group of an equation" in such a way that, for specified polynomial equations of degree n, the group must be either the symmetric group of degree n or a proper subgroup of that group. The first step in the Galois process then is to determine the Galois group of the given equation.

The second step is to choose a maximal normal subgroup of the Galois group. (There may be several such subgroups, and any one of them may be selected.) The next step is to choose a maximal normal subgroup of the maximal normal subgroup chosen in the second step, etc. In successive steps there is a selection of a maximal normal subgroup of the maximal normal subgroup chosen in the previous step. The process will terminate (and this might happen even as early as the second or third step) when the only possible choice for a maximal normal subgroup is $\{I\}$, where I is the identity element of the Galois group. The process must come to an end in a finite number of steps because the Galois group is always of *finite* order and a maximal normal subgroup is *proper* and hence of lower order. Thus the sequence of choices must lead to smaller and smaller subgroups, inevitably terminating with $\{I\}$.

If G is the Galois group, then the sequence

$$G, G_1, G_2, \ldots, G_r, \{I\}$$

where each $G_1, G_2, \ldots, \{I\}$ is a maximal normal subgroup of the preceding one, is called a *composition series*. If the orders of the groups in the composition series are respectively,

$$g, g_1, g_2, \ldots, g_r, 1$$

we can compute the *index* of each normal subgroup in its predecessor as

$$\frac{g}{g_1}, \frac{g_1}{g_2}, \ldots, \frac{g_r}{1}$$

We shall shortly see that these *composition indices* are of the utmost importance.

As we have already stated, the Galois group for the *general* polynomial equation of degree n is always the symmetric group of degree n. It can be proved that the symmetric group has *only one* maximal normal subgroup, namely, the *alternating* group of degree n. Therefore, in the general case, the first of the composition indices is always 2 because the order of the symmetric group is $n!$ and that of the alternating group is $\frac{1}{2}n!$. The composition indices for various composition series starting with the symmetric group for $n = 2, 3, 4, 5, 6, 7$ are listed below:

n	Composition Indices
2	2
3	2, 3
4	2, 3, 2, 2
5	2, 60
6	2, 360
7	2, 2520

The composition indices listed for $n = 4$ were obtained from choices of maximal normal subgroups as follows:

	Order	Index
S: Symmetric group	24	
		$\frac{24}{12} = 2$
A: Alternating group	12	
		$\frac{12}{4} = 3$
H: Maximal normal subgroup of alternating group	4	
		$\frac{4}{2} = 2$
K: Maximal normal subgroup of H	2	
		$\frac{2}{1} = 2$
J. {Identity permutation} = maximal normal subgroup of K	1	

We have indicated that when a maximal normal subgroup is to be selected, there may possibly be more than one maximal normal subgroup from which to choose. If the possible choices are subgroups of different orders, different indices will result. Then the continuation of the procedure thereafter will vary with the selection made, since the membership—and hence the order and the index—of the next maximal normal subgroup selected depends on the previous choice. Long after Galois, the group-theorists Camille Jordan (1838–1922) and Otto Hölder (1859–1937) proved that the very same set of composition indices will result, no matter what choice of maximal normal subgroup is made at any point of the process. The index numbers may appear in different orders, however, depending on the normal subgroup selection at each step.

And now it is possible to explain how Galois defined a *solvable group*. Such a group is one in which the composition indices are all *prime* numbers. The above tabulations indicate, therefore, that the symmetric groups for $n = 2$, 3, and 4 are solvable; the others are *not* solvable. Galois proved that if $n > 4$, the sequence of maximal normal subgroups is: Symmetric group, alternating group, identity, and hence that the composition indices are 2, $n!/2$. Since $n!/2$ is not a prime number (but is composite) for $n > 4$, the symmetric groups of degree higher than 4 are *not* solvable groups.

Galois' criterion for solvability is: *A polynomial equation is algebraically solvable if and only if its group is solvable.* Since the symmetric group is the "group of the equation" if the equation is perfectly general, and since the symmetric group is *not* a solvable group for $n > 4$, it follows that it is impossible to solve "algebraically" the general polynomial equation of degree greater than four. This is the theorem to which we alluded in Chapter 5, where we explained why Galois' discovery provided a terminus for traditional algebra.

Several points must be emphasized in connection with this great theorem. The first is the significance of the words "to solve algebraically." By an "algebraic solution" of the general polynomial equation of the nth degree,

$$a_0x^n + a_1x^{n-1} + a_2x^{n-2} + \cdots + a_n = 0$$

is meant a formula expressed in terms of the coefficients a_0, $a_1, a_2, \ldots, a_n$, and using only a *finite* number of additions, subtractions, multiplications, divisions, and root extractions. Because the root extractions are expressed by radical signs, algebraic solution is often called *solution by radicals*.

The impossibility of solution by radicals of polynomial equations of degree higher than 4 applies only to general polynomial equations. Many special equations of higher degree, that is, equations in which the literal coefficients are not arbitrary but are related in some way, or else have particular numerical values, can be solved by radicals, and the Galois criterion indicates that this is so. In applying the Galois theory in such cases, it turns out that the group of the particular equation is *not* the symmetric group, but some *proper subgroup* of the symmetric group. Then the search for maximal normal subgroups starts with the group of the equation, which is a smaller group than the symmetric group. Since the starting point is different, so are the possibilities for maximal normal subgroups at each step, and if $n > 4$, the set of index numbers may, in special cases, consist only of *primes*, thereby indicating that the particular equation has a solvable group, and hence that this equation is algebraically solvable.

Another point to be emphasized is that "algebraic" solution requires expression in a *finite* number of arithmetic steps. Solution of general equations of degree higher than 4 is possible if an *infinite* number of steps is permitted. But such solutions are nonalgebraic, and are sometimes expressed in terms of special nonalgebraic (*transcendental*) functions. The reader may think of such functions as formulated by the *infinite series* so important in analysis, and in this way realize that an infinite number of arithmetic steps is involved. Now trigonometric functions (which are nonalgebraic or transcendental functions) are effective in obtaining solutions when the cubic formula yields irreducible results (Vol. I, page 147). Therefore, mathematicians after Galois' day conceived the idea that the *elliptic functions*, which generalize ordinary trigonometric functions, might offer a means of expressing solutions of some higher-degree equations that are not solvable algebraically. Thus, Charles Hermite (1822–1905) succeeded in solving the general quintic equation ($n = 5$) in terms of *elliptic modular functions*. Felix Klein (1849–1925) was also interested in the general quintic, and geometrized the problem of its solution by relating it to rotations of the regular icosahedron, a polyhedron whose surface is made up of 20 equilateral triangles (Chapter 25). He suggested similar geometrizations for equations of still higher degrees. Hilbert indicated the types of transcendental function required for expressing the solutions of ninth-degree equations, and Poincaré discussed the application of his *automorphic functions* (generalizations of elliptic functions) to equations that are not solvable algebraically.

To round out the discussion of Galois' theory, one should explain exactly what is meant by the "group of an equation," provide some instances where it is not the symmetric group but a subgroup of the latter, and examine how this may affect the possibility of algebraic solvability or the nature of the solutions. A problem of Galois' theory then begins *not* with a general equation whose coefficients are completely arbitrary, but with an equation where there is some restriction on the nature of the coefficients. If these coefficients are given specific numerical values, the equation is a particular one. Even when the coefficients are literal, they are considered to be *rationally known*, or "known," in the following sense. The values they may assume are limited to a number *field F*. In Chapter 4 we listed the postulates for a *field*. Among them were two requiring closure with respect to addition and multiplication. But the existence of additive and multiplicative inverses provides closure also with respect to subtraction and division (except by zero). Hence a field is closed under all four "rational" operations.

A problem of Galois theory always begins with a given polynomial equation and a given field of numbers F, to which the coefficients of the given equation are required to belong. For example, the given equation might be

$$x^7 - a = 0$$

and the given field F might be the set of rational numbers. This means that a must be a rational number; it cannot have the value $\sqrt{3}$, for example.

Given an equation and a number field F, the first question asked is: Are the solutions of the equation "known," that is, are they numbers in the field F? For example, given the equation

$$x^2 - 2 = 0$$

with F, the field of rational numbers. The coefficient, -2, belongs to this field, as required. The theory of equations indicates that if this equation has rational solutions, they must be exact divisors of -2. Then $+1, -1, +2, -2$ are the only rational numbers that could possibly be solutions. Substitution in the equation shows that they are *not* solutions. Therefore the answer to the question raised above is no. The solutions do *not* belong to F, the rational field. Given the same equation with F specified as the field of numbers, $a + b\sqrt{2}$, where a and b are any rational numbers (Vol. I, page 128), one has an entirely different problem. Here the answer to the crucial question is yes, since $+\sqrt{2}$ and $-\sqrt{2}$ check in the equation and are members of the specified field.

As one more example, let F be the field of real numbers and let the given equation be

$$x^2 + 1 = 0$$

The solutions cannot be real numbers because $x^2 = -1$ and there is no real number whose square is -1. Therefore the solutions are *not* "known," that is, are not quantities in the given field. If, however, the given field had been the set of complex numbers, the equation would have been solvable in that field, since $x = +i$ and $x = -i$ are solutions.

The equations $x^2 - 2 = 0$ and $x^2 + 1 = 0$ illustrate a special point, namely, that if an equation is not solvable for a particular field, it may become solvable when the field is embedded in a larger field. Thus, in the first case there was "extension" from the field of numbers a, where a is rational, to the field $a + b\sqrt{2}$ (a and b rational). The second equation above is not solvable in the field of numbers a, where a is real, but is solvable in the field $a + b\sqrt{-1}$, (a and b real), an "extension" of the original field.

Presented with F, the field of rational numbers, and a quintic equation like

$$x^5 + 6x^4 - x^3 - 19x^2 + 103x - 1 = 0$$

with coefficients in F, what sort of information will help in the determination of its Galois group (and thus ultimately make it possible to decide on its solvability by radicals)? An elementary fact of the theory of equations indicates that the only possible solutions in the rational field F must be exact divisors of the constant term, -1, of this equation. Therefore the only rational possibilities are $+1$ or -1. Substitution of these values indicates that they do not satisfy the equation. Although this equation has no rational solutions, certain functions of the solutions are rationally "known," that is, are numbers in F, as we shall now indicate. We know that the polynomial in the left member can be factored as follows (Chapter 5):

$$(x - x_1)(x - x_2) \ldots (x - x_5)$$

to indicate solutions $x_1, x_2, \ldots, x_5$, real or complex. Now the sum and product of the solutions are "known." Specifically,

$$x_1 + x_2 + x_3 + x_4 + x_5 = -6$$
$$x_1 x_2 x_3 x_4 x_5 = 1$$

To see how the numerical values -6 and 1 are obtained, let us state that it is merely a case of generalizing certain elementary facts of school algebra. Thus the general quadratic equation

$$x^2 + bx + c = 0$$

(whose coefficients are arbitrary) can be expressed as

$$(x - x_1)(x - x_2) = 0$$

where x_1 and x_2 are the solutions (distinct or identical). Since the two forms of the quadratic must be identical,

$$(x - x_1)(x - x_2) = x^2 + bx + c$$

and expanding the left member,

$$x^2 - (x_1 + x_2)x + x_1x_2 = x^2 + bx + c$$

Therefore

$$x_1 + x_2 = -b$$

and

$$x_1x_2 = c$$

The reader may recall the derivation of these formulas from school algebra, or their statement as a theorem: In a quadratic equation, if the coefficient of x^2 is 1, then the sum of the solutions is equal to the negative of the coefficient of x, and the product of the roots is equal to the constant term.

From the more advanced point of view of the present chapter, interest in the formulas lies in the fact that they express the functions $x_1 + x_2$ and x_1x_2 in terms of the coefficients of the quadratic equation, so that these functions are "known," that is, belong to any field F prescribed for the coefficients b and c. In passing, it should be mentioned that the *symmetric group* of degree 2 contains only the permutations $I = \begin{pmatrix} 1 & 2 \\ 1 & 2 \end{pmatrix}$, the identity, and $P = \begin{pmatrix} 1 & 2 \\ 2 & 1 \end{pmatrix}$, the interchange of the two roots. Therefore, $x_1 + x_2$ and x_1x_2 are described as *symmetric functions* because they are unaltered by I and changed to the equivalent forms, $x_2 + x_1$ and x_2x_1, by P; that is, they are *invariant* under all permutations of the symmetric group of degree 2.

In the case of a particular quadratic like

$$x^2 + 2x - 4 = 0$$
$$b = 2, \quad c = -4$$

and the formulas reveal that

$$x_1 + x_2 = -2$$
$$x_1x_2 = -4$$

The solutions of the particular quadratic were found (Chapter 5) to be

$$x_1 = -1 + \sqrt{5}, \quad x_2 = -1 - \sqrt{5}$$

If the given field F is that of the rational numbers, one observes that while the sum and product of the solutions are in F, the solutions themselves do not belong to this field, and the equation is not solvable within F.

Returning to the general quadratic,

$$x^2 + bx + c = 0$$

it will now be indicated that symmetric functions other than $x_1 + x_2$ and $x_1 x_2$ can be expressed in terms of these two elementary functions, and therefore in terms of b and c, the coefficients of the quadratic. Thus

$$x_1^5 x_2^5 = (x_1 x_2)^5 = c^5$$
$$x_1^2 + x_2^2 = (x_1 + x_2)^2 - 2x_1 x_2 = b^2 - 2c$$
$$x_1^3 - 6x_1 x_2 + x_2^3 = x_1^3 - 6c + x_2^3$$
$$= -6c + (x_1 + x_2)^3 - 3x_1^2 x_2 - 3x_1 x_2^2$$
$$= -6c - b^3 - 3x_1 x_2 (x_1 + x_2)$$
$$= -6c - b^3 + 3bc$$
$$\frac{x_1^2 + x_2^2}{3x_1^2 x_2^2} = \frac{b^2 - 2c}{3c^2}$$

Since the expressions in terms of the coefficients involve only the rational operations—addition, subtraction, multiplication, and division— on these coefficients, the symmetric functions are "known," that is, are equal to quantities in the field of the coefficients. For the particular quadratic above, where $b = 2$, $c = -4$, the four functions have the rational numerical values -1024, 12, -8, and $1/4$, respectively

The facts illustrated for the quadratic equation generalize to equations of higher degree. For the general cubic

$$x^3 + ax^2 + bx + c = 0$$

with roots x_1, x_2, x_3, the expression of the elementary symmetric functions (those *invariant* under the *symmetric group* of degree 3) in terms of the coefficients is

$$x_1 + x_2 + x_3 = -a$$
$$x_1 x_2 + x_2 x_3 + x_3 x_1 = b$$
$$x_1 x_2 x_3 = -c$$

For the general equation of nth degree,

$$x^n + a_1 x^{n-1} + a_2 x^{n-2} + a_3 x^{n-3} + \cdots + a_{n-1} x + a_n = 0$$

with roots x_1, x_2, x_3, . . . , x_n,

$$x_1 + x_2 + x_3 + \cdots + x_n = -a_1$$
$$x_1 x_2 + x_2 x_3 + \cdots + x_{n-1} x_n = a_2$$
$$x_1 x_2 x_3 + x_2 x_3 x_4 + \cdots + x_{n-2} x_{n-1} x_n = -a_3$$
$$\cdots \quad \cdots \quad \cdots \quad \cdots \quad \cdots \quad \cdots \quad \cdots \quad \cdots$$
$$x_1 x_2 x_3 \cdots x_{n-1} x_n = a_n \quad \text{or} \quad -a_n$$

according to whether n is even or odd.

In equations of higher degree, just as in the case of the quadratic, more complicated symmetric functions are expressed in terms of the above elementary symmetric polynomials and ultimately in terms of the coefficients. In fact, not only can symmetric *polynomials* be so expressed, but also *rational* symmetric functions, which are defined as quotients of symmetric polynomials, for example,

$$\frac{4x_1^3 x_2^3 x_3^3 - 3x_1 x_2 - 3x_2 x_3 - 3x_3 x_1}{x_1^2 + x_2^2 + x_3^2} = \frac{-4c^3 - 3b}{a^2 - 2b}$$

where x_1, x_2, x_3 are the solutions of the general cubic equation. There is a fundamental theorem of great importance: Every rational symmetric function (with coefficients in F) of the solutions of an algebraic equation can be expressed rationally in terms of the coefficients, and therefore is "known" or equal to a quantity in F, the field of the coefficients. This fundamental theorem can be reworded as follows: If, for a given algebraic equation and a given field F, a rational function (with coefficients in F) of the solutions is invariant under all permutations of the symmetric group, then this function is "known" or equal to a quantity in the given field F.

If the equation is *general* and the field is that formed by rational operations (addition, multiplication, etc.) on the coefficients, the converse of the above theorem is true. When a proposition and its converse are both true, they provide "necessary and sufficient conditions" that can be used to furnish a *definition* (see Chapter 6). Thus the above theorem and its converse might be worded so as to provide a definition of the symmetric group.

A slight modification of the above conditions leads directly to a definition of the *group of an equation,* that is, its *Galois group:* The group G of a given equation for a given field F is a group possessing the two characteristics:

(1) If a rational function (with coefficients in F) of the solutions of the equation remains numerically unchanged by all the permutations of G, it is equal to a quantity in F.

(2) Conversely, if a rational function (with coefficients in F) of the solutions of the equation is equal to a quantity in F, it remains numerically unchanged by all the permutations of G.

Applying this definition, let us determine the Galois group, or group of the equation,

$$x^3 - 3x + 1 = 0$$

for the field F of all rational numbers. Its group is either the entire *symmetric group* of degree 3 (page 44) or one of the *proper subgroups* of this group (page 47). Now

$$(x_1 - x_2)^2(x_1 - x_3)^2(x_2 - x_3)^2$$

is a symmetric function, since it is unchanged by all permutations of the symmetric group. Therefore, by the fundamental theorem, it can be expressed rationally in terms of the coefficients, or is in the field F. In other words, its numerical value must be a rational number. By the type of manipulation previously used, it can be shown that for the general cubic

$$x^3 + bx + c = 0$$

the above symmetric function of the roots is equal to $-4b^3 - 27c^2$. For the particular case above, $b = -3$, $c = 1$, and the function has the value $(-4)(-27) - 27 = 81$. Since

$$(x_1 - x_2)^2(x_1 - x_3)^2(x_2 - x_3)^2 = 81$$

the rational function $(x_1 - x_2)(x_1 - x_3)(x_2 - x_3)$ must be equal to either $+9$ or -9. The latter function is equal to a rational number, a number of the field F. Therefore this function should be numerically invariant under all permutations of the Galois group for the field F. Then this group cannot be the symmetric group, because the permutation $S_4 = \begin{pmatrix} 1 & 2 & 3 \\ 1 & 3 & 2 \end{pmatrix}$, for example, changes the function into

$$(x_1 - x_3)(x_1 - x_2)(x_3 - x_2)$$

which would have the value -9 if the original function is equal to $+9$, or the value $+9$ if the original function is equal to -9. Only three permutations of the symmetric group leave the rational function invariant, namely, the identity and the permutations $\begin{pmatrix} 1 & 2 & 3 \\ 2 & 3 & 1 \end{pmatrix}$ and $\begin{pmatrix} 1 & 2 & 3 \\ 3 & 1 & 2 \end{pmatrix}$. These form the alternating group A (page 48). Since the Galois group cannot be the symmetric group, it must then be the alternating group, or else a proper subgroup of this group. The only proper subgroup of A is the identity group. Then A or $\{I\}$ are the two possibilities for the Galois group. Now the rational function x_1 (consisting of just one of the solutions) is numerically unaltered by the identity permutation, the only permutation in $\{I\}$. Therefore, if $\{I\}$ should be the Galois group, x_1 would have to be "known," that is, it would have to be a rational number in the field F. But a theorem from the elementary theory of equations indicates that if the equation

$$x^3 - 3x + 1 = 0$$

had a rational solution, it would have to be an exact divisor of the constant term $+1$. Hence it would be $+1$ or -1. When we substitute these values in the equation, it is evident that they do not satisfy it. Therefore it has *no rational root*, and x_1 cannot possibly be a rational number. Thus $\{I\}$ cannot be the Galois group, and therefore the Galois group for the particular equation and the rational field F is

$$A : \left\{ S_1 = \begin{pmatrix} 1 & 2 & 3 \\ 1 & 2 & 3 \end{pmatrix},\ S_2 = \begin{pmatrix} 1 & 2 & 3 \\ 2 & 3 & 1 \end{pmatrix},\ S_3 = \begin{pmatrix} 1 & 2 & 3 \\ 3 & 1 & 2 \end{pmatrix} \right\}$$

It is often exceedingly difficult in practice to determine the Galois group for a given equation and a given field F. Various ways of approaching the problem are based on different (but equivalent) definitions of the group of an equation, or on special theorems. At any rate, when the Galois group for the field F has been found, the Galois criterion will indicate whether or not the group is "solvable." If it is a solvable group, the (theoretical) procedure is as follows: There is an auxiliary or *resolvent* equation (defined in a special way) which *can actually be solved by radicals*. Its degree is the first index number in the series of prime index numbers (page 53). Then the field F is extended to a field F' by "adjunction" of the radicals appearing in the solution of the auxiliary equation. Let us explain what is meant by *adjunction*.

If, for example, $\sqrt{2}$ is to be adjoined to the field of rational numbers, one must form all rational combinations (sums, differences, products, quotients) involving $\sqrt{2}$ and the rational numbers. Thus $5 + \sqrt{2}$, $\frac{1}{2} - \sqrt{2}$, $7\sqrt{2}$, $(2 + 6\sqrt{2}) \div (-1 - 3\sqrt{2})$ would all be numbers in the extension field and, in fact, that field would contain all numbers $a + b\sqrt{2}$ where a and b are rational numbers. The rational field corresponds to $b = 0$ and is a *subfield* of the extension. Again, if $\sqrt[3]{2}$ is adjoined to the rational field, the extension field will have to contain $(\sqrt[3]{2})(\sqrt[3]{2}) = \sqrt[3]{4}$, $(2 - 3\sqrt[3]{4}) \div (5 + 7\sqrt[3]{2})$, etc.

When the field F' has been specified, the Galois process must start anew with the determination of the Galois group G' for the field F', the extension of F. This new Galois group, G', is a maximal normal subgroup of G, the original Galois group. Then a second auxiliary or resolvent equation is solved. Its degree is that of the second index number in the series of composition indices. The field F' is extended to F'' by adjunction of radicals appearing in the solutions of the second auxiliary equation.

The procedure is repeated by finding the Galois group for the field F'', solving a third auxiliary equation, adjoining its radical solutions to F'' to yield the extension F''', etc. Since a composition series is of finite length, iteration of the procedure described will yield, for some extension field $F^{(m)}$, a Galois group equal to $\{I\}$, the group containing only the identity element. Since the solutions $x_1,\ x_2,\ x_3,\ \ldots,\ x_n$, are all functions invariant under the identity permutation, they must (by the definition of the Galois group) be equal to quantities in the final extension field. Since the only adjunctions to the original field are radicals, the equation can thus be solved in terms of radicals. In addition, since the nature of these radicals is known (whether they are square roots or cube roots, etc.) the character of the solution is fully determined by the Galois procedure, even if it is not always the simplest practical way to solve an equation.

In closing the present discussion, we shall give historic bearings for the ideas involved. Lagrange's contributions to the theory of equations were doubtless the most potent anticipations of Galois' own ideas. In a 1770–1771 memoir, Lagrange attempted to find a uniform procedure for solving equations of all degrees. He analyzed the methods that had yielded general solutions for degrees 2, 3, 4, and found that in each case the technique involved the use of a *resolvent* equation. Although the latter was of lower degree than the original for $n = 2$, 3, 4, Lagrange discovered that application of the previously successful pattern to the quintic $(n = 5)$ led to an irreducible sextic $(n = 6)$, and the problem became more difficult instead of being resolved.

He then suggested timidly that perhaps the general quintic cannot be solved by the apparently "universal" method. In other words, he hinted at the impossibility of solution by radicals, and let the matter drop. Perhaps he was discouraged by the reception accorded to his great 1770–1771 memoir. The historian of the French Academy, for example, wrote:

"Monsieur de la Grange (Lagrange) seems convinced that it will be necessary to replace the customary procedure for solving equations, while Monsieur Vandermonde (an algebraist, contemporary with Lagrange) is inclined to believe the latter still may succeed. As for me, I favor Monsieur Vandermonde's opinion because it is less disheartening."

But Paolo Ruffini (1765–1822), an Italian physician who taught mathematics as well as medicine at the University of Modena, continued the thread of Lagrange's thoughts. In 1799 Ruffini wrote a book on the theory of equations, in which he gave a proof that virtually established the unsolvability of the quintic by radicals. Ruffini's demonstration was improved by Abel, and in 1822 the young Norwegian mathematician proved conclusively that the general equation of degree $n > 4$ cannot be solved algebraically. There were some minor flaws in Abel's proof, but it inspired Galois to seek a fundamental reason for unsolvability or, more positively stated, a basic criterion for algebraic solvability.

The present chapter has dealt with Galois' resolution of the deeper issues of solvability. His group-theoretic approach provided a simpler proof of Abel's theorem and, in general, replaced the algebraic theories of Lagrange, Ruffini, and Abel. Concerning the mathematical testament which Galois wrote on the eve of his death and in which he incorporated his theory, Hermann Weyl, a leading twentieth-century mathematician, had this to say: "If judged by the novelty and profundity of ideas it contains, it is perhaps the most substantial piece of writing in the whole literature of mankind."[*]

The effect that this great document had upon modern abstract algebra has been noted and will be emphasized again later. Chapter 17 will indicate how the group concept can be used to unify various types of geometry, and Chapter 18 will illustrate an application to modern mathematical physics. There it will be revealed that the special theory of relativity is, in abstract content, nothing more than the geometry of one special group, and is therefore another important instance of the influence of

> . . . the marvelous boy,
> The sleepless soul that perished in his pride.[†]

* Hermann Weyl, *Symmetry,* Princeton University Press, Princeton, N.J., 1952, p. 138.
† William Wordsworth, "Resolution and Independence," Stanza 7.

Chapter 17

The Unification of Geometry

Yet may we not entirely overlook
The pleasures gathered from . . . geometric science . . .
With . . . awe and wonder,
. . . meditate.
On the relations those abstractions bear
To Nature's laws.

Wordsworth

At Düsseldorf, on the night of April 25th, 1849, there was anxiety in the house of the secretary to the Regierungspräsident. Without, the cannon thundered on the barricades raised by the insurgent Rhinelanders against their hated Prussian rulers. Within, although all had been prepared for flight, there was no thought of departure; on that night was born a son to the stern Prussian secretary. That son was Felix Klein. His birth was marked by the final crushing of the revolution of 1848; his life measured the domination of Prussia over Germany, and typifies all that was best and noblest in that domination; with his last illness came the consummation of its downfall.

Few mathematicians have left such ample material for forming an opinion of their life and work as Felix Klein (1849–1925). We have his life, written by his own hand two years before his death. We have his Collected Mathematical Papers, in three volumes thoroughly revised by himself, and interspersed with supplementary notes and introductory articles of an autobiographical character. We have the greater part of his mathematical lectures in print, lectures which had for many years enjoyed a considerable publicity in lithographed form; we have even a faithful record of lectures given by him in the years just preceding his death, carefully annotated by his colleague and successor, Professor Richard Courant. Klein's personal influence was as great, or greater even outside his own country, than that, perhaps, of any mathematician of modern times. He owed this to his forceful and attractive personality, to his wide mathematical outlook and to his objective openmindedness, only occasionally tinged by the play of personal feeling, for Klein had by no means the cold, calculating nature, supposedly typical of the mathematician. He owed it also partly to that intangible agent, so often and so callously cited "Luck," which afforded him, by a succession of unforeseen external events, the opportunity without which a man of the highest intellectual and moral endowments may remain mute inglorious. He owed it partly to his success in interesting his audiences, even in branches of mathematics of which his own command was comparatively slight. And he owed it to his untiring devotion to the cause of education.

Klein's genius had been precocious. At seventeen he was chosen by Julius Plücker (1801–1868) as his assistant in his physics laboratory at Bonn; that laboratory where Plücker had invented what today we call the Geissler tube. Plücker had reverted in his later years to his early interest in geometry. When he died in 1868, he left an unfinished manuscript, entitled "New Geometry of Space, founded on the straight line as element." The task of completing the work and issuing the second half of the book was entrusted to Plücker's young assistant, Felix Klein.

Shortly after he began his work on the "New Geometry" Klein became affiliated with the University of Göttingen. He was there for a short time in 1869, for a second stay from 1871 to 1876, and his final migration thither was in 1886. Between his first and second periods at Göttingen there were three important events in his life—a sojourn in Berlin, a trip to Paris, and the Franco-German war, in which he took part in the ambulance corps, and from which he was sent home invalided with typhoid fever.

From August 1869 to March 1870 Klein was at the University of Berlin where he hoped to profit from personal contact with Weierstrass (Chapter 22). But in the latter's mind a veritable antagonism to Klein seems to have arisen. When Klein spoke at Weierstrass' Seminar and made the suggestion that there was a connection between non-Euclidean geometry and Cayley's Theory of the Absolute, Weierstrass absolutely rejected the notion. Later Klein developed his idea in a series of papers extending over several years [page 95].

At the early age of twenty-three, Klein obtained the full chair of mathematics at the University of Erlangen. There he met and married the beautiful, cultured Anna Hegel, daughter of an Erlangen professor and granddaughter of the philosopher Hegel. In mathematics he produced what he himself regarded as his most notable achievement, the so-called Erlanger Programme. It would be no exaggeration to say that it has revolutionized the treatment of Geometry. Only in details has exception been taken to any part of it, which is the more remarkable when we consider the age of the author and the state of mathematics at the time when it was composed. The notes which Klein himself has added, and the account which he has given of its production, have greatly increased its interest. The new idea which lies at its basis was that all the various species of Geometries which, during the 19th century in particular, had multiplied exceedingly (metrical geometry, projective geometry, line geometry, etc.) could be regarded from a single standpoint, that of the Theory of Groups, each different geometry being conceived as the theory of the invariants of an appropriate group. This idea, which as then formulated, seemed "very astonishing," was an abiding one in the mind of 'Klein, who thought he foresaw its extension to regions of mathematics other than geometry. In particular, the development by Einstein of the Theory of Relativity revived in his later years Klein's interest in his Erlanger Programme, and it was with some mortification that he found among his physicist friends no interest whatever in the possibility of a physical interpretation of the most general group of conformal transformations of four dimensional space, as leaving invariant the Maxwell-Lorentz equations of relativity.

The above is an excerpt from a biography of Felix Klein by the British mathematician William Henry Young (1863–1942),[*] one of the leading analysts of the twentieth century and a personal friend of the German mathematician. This friendship had come about through Young's wife, Grace Chisholm Young (1868–1944), Klein's "favorite pupil," an excellent mathematician in her own right. She was the first woman to receive a German Ph.D. (1895) based on regular examinations. More will be said later about the Youngs, husband and wife, and their specific discoveries in the field of modern analysis (Chapter 27). We have paused at the above point in Young's biography of Klein in order to examine the background, content, and application of the mathematical contribution which Klein (according to Young) regarded as his greatest achievement, namely, the Erlanger Program.

In the Program, Klein advanced the idea that any species of geometry is simply the study of *invariants* associated with a particular *group of transformations*. If we explain that the term "transformation" (favored in geometry) is merely a synonym for function or mapping and that the Klein transformations are, like the Cauchy-Galois permutations, *one-to-one* mappings of a set *onto* itself, the reader will

* Royal Society of London, *Proceedings*, Series A, Vol. 121 (November–December 1928), pp. 1 ff.

see the kinship of Klein's notions and those of Galois. The great difference arises from the fact that algebra is concerned with *finite* sets like the roots of a polynomial equation, whereas traditional geometries apply to "spaces" like the line or plane or 3-dimensional Euclidean space, etc., and these are the *infinite* continuous sets of "points" we called R, R^2, R^3, etc. in Chapter 7. In the Klein geometries the points of such a space may be shifted to new positions, but the space or set of points as a whole remains intact.

To connect invariance with geometry, one need only return to Euclid. In the physical geometry that predated his *Elements*, it was taken for granted that measuring tools were *rigid bodies*, that is, that they remained *invariant* in size and shape as they were moved about in the course of use. Modern surveyors modify this point of view when they make corrections for temperature, tension, and sag of tape. Nevertheless their work is still based on Euclidean geometry, with the tacit assumption: A figure can be moved about freely in space without changing its size or shape.

In Euclid, congruent figures are defined as those that can be made to coincide. If one figure is already superposed on another, an immediate verdict of congruence can be rendered. But, if figures in coincidence were the customary situation, Euclid would hardly have troubled to define congruence or to prove so many special congruence theorems. In practical affairs, the tool must usually be brought into contact with the object to be measured, whereas the Euclidean congruence proofs generally start by moving a triangle through a sequence of positions. Then deductive reasoning is used to demonstrate that the final position is one of complete coincidence with a second triangle.

Suppose that we are given that triangle $A'B'C'$ of Figure 17.1 agrees with triangle ABC in the sides AB, AC and the angle A, and that we are required to demonstrate the congruence of the two triangles. We must prove that the triangles can be made to coincide. Let us slide triangle ABC so that every point of it moves in the direction AA' until A falls on A' (Figure 17.1). Such a motion is called a *translation*. Next, using A of Figure 17.2 as a pivot, we carry out a counterclockwise *rotation* of ABC through an angle sufficient to bring the triangle into superposition with $A'B'C'$.

We have given the Euclidean picture of translation and rotation of a particular triangle to a new position. Klein ex-

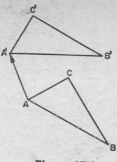

Figure 17.1

tended the motion of the triangle to a *transformation* of the entire plane, a mapping of that set of points onto itself. Thus, not only points of the triangle but all points of the plane slide in the direction of AA' (Figure 17.1) through a distance equal to AA'. Again, all points of the plane describe a circular motion about A as pivot (Figure 17.2).

If the original position of triangle ABC is somewhat different (Figure 17.3), a translation-rotation motion will not suffice to bring about its coincidence with $A'B'C'$. After translation in the direction AA' and rotation through an angle sufficient to accomplish the superposition of AB on $A'B'$ (Figure 17.3), we might use AB as a hinge and revolve ABC as if it were a door, until it returns to the plane of $A'B'C'$, at which point coincidence is achieved. But if we were creatures confined to a plane, that is, if for us a physical third dimension did not exist, the final door-like motion of ABC would be a physical impossibility. We might, instead, think of AB as a mirror with ABC transformed into $A'B'C'$

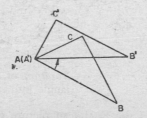

Figure 17.2

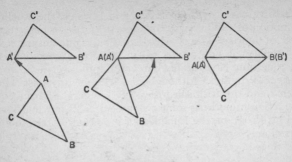

Figure 17.3

by *reflection*. Then the triangles of Figure 17.3 are mirror images of one another, and in this sense identical, even if not physically superposable.

The *proper* congruence motions, that is, the displacements or *rigid motions* that can be carried out within the plane itself, are thus translations, rotations, or combinations of translations and rotations. A *reflection* like the one described above, or the combination of a reflection with a proper displacement, is an *improper* rigid motion, one that would be a physical impossibility within the plane itself. Later we shall show that the set of *all* rigid motions,* proper and improper, is a group which has the set of proper rigid motions as a (proper) subgroup. Klein asserted that plane Euclidean *metric* geometry can be described as the study of properties unchanged by the group of all rigid motions. As illustrations of such metric properties, there are equality of the radii of a circle, equality of sides and angles in regular polygons, equality and parallelism of opposite sides in a parallelogram, perpendicularity of adjacent sides in a rectangle, area formulas. All of these characteristics are dependent on two *fundamental invariants* in terms of which they can be expressed, namely, *distance* and *angle*.

Euclid's pure geometry of measurement assumed that the effects of motion must leave size *invariant*. The issue of whether this is a good assumption for motion in the real world arises in twentieth-century physics. We have all heard of the "Lorentz-Fitzgerald contractions" of early relativity.

---

* These are also called *isometries*, signifying "same measures."

To resolve some of the paradoxes in physics, the Euclidean assumption of rigidity was abandoned in cases where relative speed of motion is very large, that is, commensurate with the velocity of light. Felix Klein was concerned with this very question later in his career and did relate it to the Erlanger Program. Although the Dutch physicist H. A. Lorentz and the Irish scientist G. F. Fitzgerald advanced the contraction hypothesis some twenty years after Klein formulated his Program, the Euclidean assumption of free mobility bears closely on relativity. In fact the postulate that displacement does not affect the geometric properties of a figure is often called the *principle of relativity for Euclidean geometry*. The classic axiom contains implications concerning the kind of space to which Euclidean geometry applies. If free mobility is permissible, no *point* and no *direction* in space are preferable to other points and directions. In relativity language, the fact that all points are on an equal footing becomes: Euclidean space is *homogeneous*. That there is no special significance for measurement of a line segment in whether its direction is north or east or south-southwest, etc. is stated: Euclidean space is *isotropic*.

Our presentation thus far has emphasized *measurement* as the fundamental question of geometry. But draftsmen make scale drawings; architects construct models; photographers prepare enlargements. Hence properties of *similar* figures as well as of congruent ones are the concern of both physical and pure Euclidean geometry. Congruent figures are considered equivalent because they are exact duplicates. But for a draftsman a scale drawing is equivalent to the actuality it represents. Except for aesthetic effect, a colossal statue of a human figure is a work of sculpture geometrically equivalent to a life-size model. We can define this new type of equivalence by means of a generalization of the idea of displacement. In similarity geometry, two figures are "equivalent" if they can be brought into coincidence by means of a rigid motion combined with an enlargement or contraction. Since the scale ratio is permitted to have the special value 1:1, congruent figures are included in the new definition, that is, congruent figures are similar, but not conversely. Similarity geometry is the study of properties unchanged by all possible combinations of rigid motion with change of scale (enlargement or contraction). These properties are fewer in number than in the metric case. Distances are no longer invariant, since enlargement or contraction affects them. Hence metric theorems involving lengths are not part of the new geometry, but angles are still invariant.

We are now fully launched on the Klein technique of classification. His Erlanger Program takes the various types of geometry existing in 1872 and makes each one after the first a generalization of some preceding one. As we have indicated, fewer properties are invariant in a generalization, and for this reason only part of the subject matter of the preceding geometry is pertinent. The rigid motions of Euclidean metric geometry have already been extended so as to include change of scale. Now they can be generalized still further to define figures which, for the purposes of some special geometry, can be considered equivalent. The generalizations are transformations that tend to distort figures, for example, the *affine* transformations. In the corresponding *affine geometry*, circles and ellipses are equivalent. There is a still further generalization to *projective* transformations and *projective geometry*, in which all the conic sections are equivalent. In other words, circles, ellipses, parabolas, and hyperbolas can be transformed into one another by means of projective transformations.

As we have already stated, the Klein transformations are *one-to-one mappings of a set S onto itself.* Now in the previous chapter we indicated that a mapping of a *finite* set onto itself is necessarily one-to-one. But we shall now see that this is no longer true in the case of an infinite set. A mapping of such a set onto itself need *not* be one-to-one and, in reverse, a mapping can be one-to-one *into* a set and need *not* be onto the entire set. For an example of the former situation, consider the following mapping of the set of whole numbers, $S = \{0, 1, 2, 3, \ldots\}$, *onto* itself. Each even number is mapped onto its half and each odd number is mapped onto zero, as suggested below:

$$\begin{pmatrix} 0 & 1 & 2 & 3 & 4 & 5 & 6 & \ldots & 2n & 2n+1 & \ldots \\ 0 & 0 & 1 & 0 & 2 & 0 & 3 & \ldots & n & 0 & \ldots \end{pmatrix}$$

Here *every* whole number will appear in the lower row, so that the mapping is actually *onto* S. But since *many* numbers (zero and all odd numbers) are mapped onto zero, the mapping is *not* one-to-one. Again, let us consider the *one-to-one* mapping where each whole number is mapped onto its double, namely,

$$\begin{pmatrix} 0 & 1 & 2 & 3 & 4 & 5 & \ldots & n & \ldots \\ 0 & 2 & 4 & 6 & 8 & 10 & \ldots & 2n & \ldots \end{pmatrix}$$

Here the lower row contains only the nonnegative *even* integers, a proper *subset* of the whole numbers. Therefore we have a one-to-one mapping of the set S *into* but *not onto* itself.

We see therefore that if a Klein transformation is to permute an infinite set, it must be defined as a mapping that is both one-to-one and onto, since neither condition implies the other. From now on we shall use the term "transformation" only in this specialized sense. Then since we have shown in the previous chapter that "multiplication" or a succession of "one-to-one onto mappings" must be *associative*, we can say that this is true for the Klein transformations, a fact that will be useful when we wish to indicate that a certain set of transformations is a *group* under the operation of succession.

As an example of the sort of transformation which we shall be considering, there is a one-to-one mapping of the set of integers onto itself in which each integer is increased by 2. We can picture the mapping as follows:

$$\begin{pmatrix} \ldots & -4 & -3 & -2 & -1 & 0 & 1 & 2 & 3 & \ldots & n & \ldots \\ \ldots & -2 & -1 & 0 & 1 & 2 & 3 & 4 & 5 & \ldots & n+2 & \ldots \end{pmatrix}$$

One *invariant* under this transformation is the property of being an *even* integer, for the numbers -4, -2, 0, 2, 4, etc. are transformed into -2, 0, 2, 4, 6, etc., respectively. The characteristic of being an *odd* integer is also unchanged by the transformation. The *difference* between any two integers is invariant. Thus $10 - 3 = 7$; 10 is transformed into 12, 3 into 5, and $12 - 5 = 7$. In general, if m and n are any two integers, their transforms are $m + 2$ and $n + 2$, and

$$m + 2 - (n + 2) = m + 2 - n - 2 = m - n$$

As a further illustration, there is the transformation that doubles every real number (a one-to-one mapping of R onto itself). Then 0 is an *invariant number* under this transformation, since it is changed to $2 \cdot 0 = 0$. Also the ratio of any two numbers is invariant, for if x_1 is any real number, and x_2 is any real number except zero, the ratio of their transforms is $2x_1 : 2x_2$, which is equal to $x_1 : x_2$. Since Klein's classification was concerned with geometry, let us give our transformation a geometric interpretation. As explained earlier (Chapter 2), a Cartesian coordinate system can be set up on a straight line by establishing a one-to-one correspondence between its points and the set of real numbers. Then $x' = 2x$ represents the transformation we have been discussing, where x is a real number, namely, the Cartesian coordinate of point P in Figure 17.4, and x' is the coordinate of P', the point into which P is transformed. The origin remains fixed and the distances of all other points from the origin are doubled by the transformation. (It is an example of a one-dimensional *affine* transformation.)

Because a one-to-one mapping has an *inverse* that is a mapping, every Klein transformation has an inverse which can be pictured as the transformation that carries the "points" or elements of a "space" back to their original positions. In the first example above, the *inverse* for an increase of 2 is a decrease of 2, and if the increase were followed by the decrease, the total effect would be nil. In the second illustration, if we transform all real numbers into their

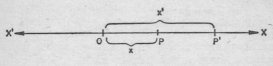

Figure 17.4

doubles and these latter into their halves, each number will be back to its original value. The net result of the succession of a transformation and its inverse is obviously the *identity* transformation which maps each element of the fundamental set onto itself.

We shall now show that the various sets of motions constitute transformation *groups*. Let us first consider the set of all possible translations. It is evident that if we walk, or translate ourselves two miles north, rest briefly, and then translate ourselves another three miles north, we could also have reached our destination by an uninterrupted walk of five miles north. Again, if we translate all points of the plane (Figure 17.5) so as to bring A to A', and then perform a second translation bringing to A' to A'', the succession of the two translations is equivalent in effect to a single translation bringing A to A''. Similarly, the succession of *any* pair of translations is a translation, that is, a *transformation within the specified set*. Hence succession is truly a binary operation on the set of all translations. Moreover, each translation has an *inverse* that is a translation or member of the funda-

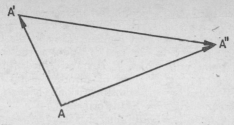

**Figure 17.5   The succession of translations
resembles vector addition.**

mental set, since a trip two miles north can be followed by
an about-face through two miles south, and a translation
from A to A' can be inverted by a *translation* from A' to
A, etc. with "no progress," the *identity* translation, as the
outcome. Since (1) succession is a binary associative operation on the set of all translations and (2) that set includes
an identity translation and (3) all translations have inverses
that are translations, therefore the set of all translations
constitutes a *group* under "succession."

It is readily seen that succession is a binary operation on
the aggregate of all *rotations*, since the succession of any two
rotations is obviously equivalent to a single rotation. For
example, a counterclockwise rotation through 130° followed
by a clockwise rotation through 80° is equivalent to a single
counterclockwise rotation through 50°. Succession of transformations is always associative, as we have said. Each rotation has an inverse that is also a rotation, namely, a rotation
of the same magnitude in the opposite direction. The
identity is the 0° rotation. Thus the set of all rotations is a
group under "succession."

Now we shall indicate that the set of *all* rigid motions or
displacements constitutes a group. That this aggregate is
closed can be deduced from the following form of Euclid's
definition of congruence: If there is a displacement bringing
one figure into coincidence with another, then the two
figures are congruent; conversely, if two figures are congruent, there exists a displacement bringing one into coincidence with the other. Let us imagine a displacement carrying a particular figure F_1 to coincidence with F_2, followed
by a second displacement carrying F_2 (with F_1 superposed
on it) to coincidence with F_3. Then F_1 is congruent to F_3,

since it has been superposed on it. Since this is the case, the second part of Euclid's definition requires the existence of a *single* displacement that will superpose F_1 on F_3, that is, the succession of the two displacements F_1 to F_2, F_2 to F_3 is equivalent to one displacement, and the set of displacements is closed under succession, which is therefore a binary operation on the set. In addition, displacements can always be reversed, and figures can be brought back to the identical original position. For example, a displacement which consists of a three-mile north translation followed by a clockwise rotation through 20° and then a reflection in a line has as its inverse a reflection in the same line followed by a counterclockwise rotation through 20° and a three-mile south translation. Since (1) succession is a binary associative operation on the set of all displacements and (2) the set contains an identity displacement and (3) each motion has an inverse that is a member of the set, the system is a *group* under the operation of "succession." Note that our argument will still hold if we consider only *proper* rigid motions (where no reflections are involved). Hence those motions form a proper subgroup of the group of *all* rigid motions.

But the above discussion can be made more exact and more lucid by *algebraic* arguments. Klein made use of analytic geometry, and since we shall do likewise, we must digress briefly to develop the Cartesian representation for the trans-

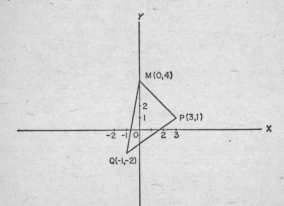

Figure 17.6

formations to be considered. Once again, then, we use a rectangular network of "streets" and "avenues." Suppose that the layout and numbering of streets in Figure 17.6 is merely tentative, pending the sale of lots and the types of buildings constructed on them. Suppose further that as things develop, property around Q $(-1, -2)$ in Figure 17.6 is reserved for building the town hall and the corner at P $(3, 1)$ is to be the site of a major office building. The planners decide on a modification of the layout of Figure 17.6 so that the town hall will be at the center of things. Preserving the directions of the streets and avenues in the figure, they *translate* the entire network diagonally downward to the left in the direction OQ until O occupies the position that was formerly Q. The result is pictured in Figure 17.7. To facilitate

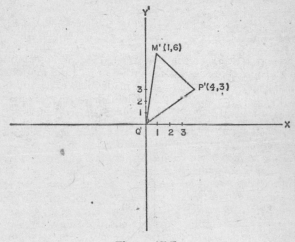

Figure 17.7

visualization of the translation of the meshwork, the triangle PQM has been outlined in Figure 17.6. This triangle is at rest as the rectangular framework slides diagonally beneath it but has been renamed $P'Q'M'$ (in Figure 17.7) in order to indicate that the vertices now have different coordinates. In the case of Q, the desired change has been effected. Now labeled as Q', its new coordinates are $(0, 0)$, that is, it is now at the origin of coordinates, or the center of town. Its coordinates have been increased by 1 and 2, respectively, and the translation of the network would have the same effect on the coordinates of any other point, so that

$$x' = x + 1$$
$$y' = y + 2$$

where (x, y) are the original coordinates and (x', y') the coordinates with respect to the new frame of reference. In this new frame, the coordinates of the original P (3, 1) and M (0, 4) are now P' (4, 3) and M' (1, 6).

Since the offices at P' (4, 3) will be important ones, the planners consider the new layout from the point of view of P'. They notice that P' is not on the main street or main avenue, and hence a further transformation in the layout is considered. None of the residences have been constructed as yet, and thus there is no real restrictions on the directions of streets and avenues. The planners keep $P'Q'M'$ at rest and using Q' (that is, O') as a pivot, they revolve the network beneath the triangle in a counterclockwise direction until P' falls on the main avenue. A rotation of 37° (approximately) accomplishes this. The final result is indicated in Figure 17.8 with $P''Q''M''$ identical with the original PQM except for the coordinates of vertices.

The city planners accomplished the desired transformations by displacement of the street-avenue mesh system, while the building sites P, Q, M stayed according to plans. If one wishes to picture this as the displacement of a *rigid body*, one must see the Cartesian network as the rigid object —a sort of iron grille that one can slide and rotate. Then the displacement will be a mapping of the plane onto itself, a transformation in the spirit of Klein. It is possible to effect the same transformation of the coordinates of P, Q, and M by keeping the framework at rest and displacing the triangle PQM. The mathematician Dirk Struik refers to the alternative points of view as "alias" and "alibi" because the first method merely gives different coordinates (names) to the same points, whereas the other technique shifts the points and geometric figures to other places. The "alibi" procedure is closer to Euclid's handling of congruence, except that in the Erlanger Program, in relativity, and in modern geometries in general, the displacement is not limited to triangle PQM, but extends to *all* points of the space. All points are shifted diagonally upward to the right in the "alibi" picture, and the Cartesian network that remains at rest is pictured as

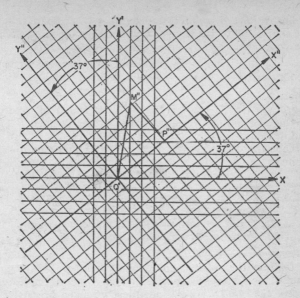

Figure 17.8

a sort of fine web through which one observes the motion and sees that its effect is the one described by the algebraic formulas above, namely, to increase the coordinates of *each* point of the plane by 1 and 2, respectively.

A particular situation might require that the special point Q $(-1, -2)$ be translated to the origin (either by shifting the framework or else by sliding all points of the plane). In a different problem one might desire to have some other point as the new origin. There is infinite variety in the particular point one might want at the center of town, and therefore the original coordinates of Q might be symbolized as $(-a, -b)$ where a and b are *any* real numerical values. Therefore the general formula for a translation is

$$x' = x + a$$
$$y' = y + b$$

where a and b are any real numbers.

If one considers Q as $(-a, -b)$, where a and b are positive real numbers, then Q will occupy a position similar to the one pictured in Figure 17.6. But suppose, for example, that a is negative and $-a$ is positive. We leave to the reader the visualization of the translation of the framework or the points of the plane in such a case, or in the case where a is positive, b negative, or where both coordinates are positive, or one of them is zero, etc. At any rate, the above formulas represent *all* possible translations, as a and b range through all real numbers. *Constants* like a and b which, paradoxically, are *variable* from one particular instance to another (in this case, from translation to translation) are called *parameters*. The set of all translations is thus said to constitute a *two-parameter group*.

Let us prove once again, this time by algebraic methods, that the translations actually do constitute a group. First, to show that "is followed by" is a binary operation on the set of translations, we must show that the succession of any two translations is a translation. Consider then

$$T_1 = \begin{cases} x' = x + a_1 \\ y' = y + b_1 \end{cases} \quad \text{followed by} \quad T_2 = \begin{cases} x'' = x' + a_2 \\ y'' = y' + b_2 \end{cases}$$

The net result, $T_1 T_2$, is obtained by substituting the first pair of equations in the second to obtain

$$T_1 T_2 = \begin{cases} x'' = x + (a_1 + a_2) \\ y'' = y + (b_1 + b_2) \end{cases}$$

which is a *translation*, since it fits the translation formulas with values of the parameters $a_1 + a_2$, $b_1 + b_2$, respectively. If the reader wishes to analyze the composition of translations as carried out above, he can see it as strictly analogous to the method used for combining permutations in the previous chapter. Since it it impossible to list all points, because they form the continuum R^2 (Chapter 7), one follows the changes in position (or coordinates) of a typical point. Thus

$$T_1 = \begin{pmatrix} \cdots & (x, y) & \cdots \\ \cdots & (x + a_1, y + b_1) & \cdots \end{pmatrix}$$

$$T_2 = \begin{pmatrix} \cdots & (x + a_1, y + b_1) & \cdots \\ \cdots & (x + a_1 + a_2, y + b_1 + b_2) & \cdots \end{pmatrix}$$

Then, omitting the intermediate position of the typical point, we obtain

$$T_1 T_2 = \begin{pmatrix} \cdots & (x, y) & \cdots \\ \cdots & (x + a_1 + a_2, \, y + b_1 + b_2) & \cdots \end{pmatrix}$$

Using the same method, let us now evaluate $T_2 T_1$, that is, T_2 followed by T_1. We have

$$T_2 = \begin{pmatrix} \cdots & (x, y) & \cdots \\ \cdots & (x + a_2, \, y + b_2) & \cdots \end{pmatrix}$$

$$T_1 = \begin{pmatrix} \cdots & (x + a_2, \, y + b_2) & \cdots \\ \cdots & (x + a_2 + a_1, \, y + b_2 + b_1) & \cdots \end{pmatrix}$$

so that

$$T_2 T_1 = \begin{pmatrix} \cdots & (x, y) & \cdots \\ \cdots & (x + a_2 + a_1, \, y + b_2 + b_1) & \cdots \end{pmatrix}$$

Since addition of real numbers is commutative, $a_2 + a_1 = a_1 + a_2$, $b_2 + b_1 = b_1 + b_2$, and $T_2 T_1 = T_1 T_2$. Thus, succession of translations is *commutative*. Let us note that (x, y), (x', y'), (x'', y''), (x''', y'''), etc., are usually used to represent successive coordinate pairs for a typical point under a succession of transformations of any kind. Then we could have computed $T_2 T_1$ as follows:

$$T_2 = \begin{cases} x' = x + a_2 \\ y' = y + b_2 \end{cases} \qquad T_1 = \begin{cases} x'' = x' + a_1 \\ y'' = y' + b_1 \end{cases}$$

Substituting the first set of equations in the second, we obtain

$$T_2 T_1 = \begin{cases} x'' = x + a_2 + a_1 \\ y'' = y + b_2 + b_1 \end{cases}$$

In summary, "is followed by" is a *binary commutative operation* on the set of all translations. That this operation is *associative* follows from the fact that succession of transformations is always associative.

Continuing with our proof that the translations form a group, we indicate that there is an *identity* translation, I, namely,

$$I = \begin{cases} x' = x \\ y' = y \end{cases}$$

Finally, every translation has an *inverse* within the set of translations; that is, if T is any translation, there exists a translation T^{-1} such that $TT^{-1} = T^{-1}T = I$. Thus if

$$T = \begin{cases} x' = x + a \\ y' = y + b \end{cases} \qquad T^{-1} = \begin{cases} x'' = x' - a \\ y'' = y' - b \end{cases}$$

then

$$TT^{-1} = {}^{2}\begin{cases} x'' = x + a - a = x \\ y'' = y + b - b = y \end{cases} = I$$

Since succession is commutative for translations, $T^{-1}T$ is also equal to I. In conclusion, the translations constitute an *infinite abelian two-parameter group* with respect to succession.

Sets of transformations do *not*, in general, qualify as groups, and if they are groups, they are not necessarily abelian (commutative) groups. For example, let us consider the one-parameter set of *reflections* in the lines $x = \frac{1}{2}a$ (parallels to the Y-axis), namely,

$$\begin{matrix} x' = a - x \\ y' = y \end{matrix} \qquad \text{with inverse} \qquad \begin{matrix} x'' = a - x' \\ y'' = y' \end{matrix}$$

If one examines the succession of the two transformations of the set, namely,

$$\begin{matrix} x' = a_1 - x \\ y' = y \end{matrix} \qquad \text{and} \qquad \begin{matrix} x'' = a_2 - x' \\ y'' = y \end{matrix}$$

the result is

$$\begin{matrix} x'' = a_2 - (a_1 - x) \\ y'' = y \end{matrix} \qquad \text{or} \qquad \begin{matrix} x'' = (a_2 - a_1) + x \\ y'' = y \end{matrix}$$

But even if the value $a_2 - a_1$ is assigned to the parameter in the representative formula of the set, the "product" of the successive motions is not a reflection in any line parallel to the Y-axis. The result does *not* fit the required formula (except for points of the Y-axis for which $x = 0$). The transformation formulas call for *subtracting* x from a constant, whereas the combination of two successive motions *adds* x to a constant. The resultant of two motions of the set is, in general, a position unattainable by any *single* motion in the set. (Note that the position can be attained by *translation* through $a_2 - a_1$, parallel to the X-axis). Hence succession is *not* a binary operation on the set and it is *not* a group.

In a modern treatment of Cartesian geometry, the Pythagorean formula is usually taken as an axiom, and then the invariance of distances and angles for all displacements is proved. Euclid's procedure was the reverse. He assumed the invariance and ultimately proved the Pythagorean theorem. If we accept the Pythagorean theorem, then, as we have seen in an earlier chapter, Figure 7.9 yields the distance formula

$$s = \sqrt{(\Delta x)^2 + (\Delta y)^2}$$

After a translation of the two points in the diagram to the new positions (x_1', y_1') and (x_2', y_2'), the distance between them is

$$s' = \sqrt{(x_2' - x_1')^2 + (y_2' - y_1')^2}$$

Substituting the formula for a translation,

$$s' = \sqrt{(x_2 + a - x_1 - a)^2 + (y_2 + a - y_1 - a)^2}$$
$$= \sqrt{(x_2 - x_1)^2 + (y_2 - y_1)^2} = s$$

and the distance after translation is equal to the original distance. It is also possible to prove by algebraic methods that *angles* are invariant under the group of all translations.

It can be shown that the formulas for all rotations about the origin as pivot are

$$x' = x \cos \theta + y \sin \theta$$
$$y' = -x \sin \theta + y \cos \theta$$

where θ, a parameter, is the angle through which the original frame of reference is rotated counterclockwise.

Again, it can be proved that the above set of rotations is a group that leaves distances and angles invariant. To give a partial demonstration, let us show that distance from the origin is invariant. Originally the distance of any point (x, y) from the origin $(0, 0)$ is

$$s = \sqrt{(x - 0)^2 + (y - 0)^2} = \sqrt{x^2 + y^2}$$

Since the origin is the pivot of the set of rotations, its coordinates remain unchanged. (This can be proved by substituting $x = 0$, $y = 0$ in the rotation formulas.) A rotation changes the coordinates (x, y) to (x', y') as given by formulas above. Hence the distance after a rotation, in the new frame of reference, is

$$s' = \sqrt{(x \cos \theta + y \sin \theta - 0)^2 + (-x \sin \theta + y \cos \theta - 0)^2}$$
$$= \sqrt{x^2(\cos^2 \theta + \sin^2 \theta) + y^2(\sin^2 \theta + \cos^2 \theta)}$$

Elementary trigonometry teaches that $\sin^2 \theta + \cos^2 \theta = 1$ for all values of the angle θ. Therefore

$$s' = \sqrt{x^2(1) + y^2(1)} = \sqrt{x^2 + y^2} = s$$

that is, the distance after rotation is the same as the original distance.

The invariance of distance under rotation is not surprising, since it is in accordance with our everyday experience with rotating wheels. But the algebraic formulas for the rotation group can also be interpreted as expressing the group of Lorentz transformations of the special theory of relativity, providing x, y, and θ are given suitable physical interpretations as follows:

$x =$ the position on a straight line at which some event takes place

$y = it$, where t is the time at which the event takes place and i is the imaginary unit, $\sqrt{-1}$

$\cos \theta = \dfrac{1}{\sqrt{1 - u^2}}$, where u is a relative velocity (measured in suitable units)

$\sin \theta = \dfrac{iu}{\sqrt{1 - u^2}}$

Since "imaginary" numbers are involved in this interpretation, a Lorentz transformation can be conceived in a pure mathematical sense as a rotation of the frame of reference through an "imaginary" angle. An actual *physical* meaning for such a transformation will be revealed in the next chapter. Just as the coordinates (x, y) of a point vary and are *not* usually invariant if the frame of reference is rotated, (x, it), that is, position and time, are not invariant or "absolute" in physics for observers in the different frames of reference with which the Lorentz group is concerned. We have proved above that $s = \sqrt{x^2 + y^2}$ is invariant under rotation. If we perform the substitution that converts rotations into Lorentz transformations,

$$s = \sqrt{x^2 + y^2} = \sqrt{x^2 + i^2 t^2} = \sqrt{x^2 - t^2}$$

is the corresponding invariant. Physicists term $\sqrt{x^2 - t^2}$ an "absolute" entity and indicate that its measurement is the same for all observers in uniform motion with respect to one another (Chapter 18). This is the fundamental invariant of the special theory of relativity. In the discussion above, $x^2 + y^2 = x^2 - t^2$ was proved invariant, but its negative, $-x^2 - y^2 = -x^2 + t^2 = t^2 - x^2$, could equally well have been proved invariant. In relativity the latter invariant may be used, and, in that case, $\sqrt{t^2 - x^2}$ is termed the *space-time interval* or *separation* between two events. Observers in all frames of reference (in uniform relative motion) will obtain identical measurements of the space-time separation, even though disagreeing on distance and time coordinates.

To return to the Program, the proper rigid motions which combine rotations and translations are described analytically as the *three*-parameter group

$$x' = x \cos \theta + y \sin \theta + u$$
$$y' = -x \sin \theta + y \cos \theta + b$$

and the similarity group is obtained by multiplying the right members of these formulas by a real parameter k. *Improper* rigid motions combine the proper ones with a reflection, which has the effect of changing the signs of the first two terms in the right member of the above formula for y'.

Affine geometry is governed by the group of linear transformations

$$x' = ax + by + c$$
$$y' = dx + ey + f$$

Because these transformations might be considered as the succession of

$$x' = ax + by$$
$$y' = dx + ey$$

and the *translation*

$$x'' = x' + c$$
$$y'' = y' + f$$

anything that is *novel* can be obtained by studying the *homogeneous* or *centered* affine group

$$x' = ax + by$$
$$y' = dx + ey$$

where a, b, d, and e are real parameters and $ae - bd \neq 0$. (The reason for this last condition will be indicated later.) The adjective "centered" is applicable because the origin or "center" is invariant under all transformations of the group, as the reader may check by substituting $x = 0$, $y = 0$. Note that rotations are special affine transformations where $a = e = \cos \theta$, $b = \sin \theta$, $d = -\sin \theta$, $ae - bd = \cos^2 \theta + \sin^2 \theta = 1$.

To prove that the set of homogeneous affine transformations does constitute a group involves considerable algebraic manipulation, and this very difficulty is a motivation for the abbreviated methodology of modern *linear algebra*. Let us merely suggest what is involved. First, one must show that succession is truly a binary operation on the centered affine set, or that if T_1 and T_2 are homogeneous affine transformations, then T_1T_2 is such a transformation. If

$$T_1 = \begin{cases} x' = ax + by \\ y' = dx + ey \end{cases} \quad \text{and} \quad T_2 = \begin{cases} x'' = Ax' + By' \\ y'' = Dx' + Ey' \end{cases}$$

then T_1T_2 can be obtained by substituting the equations for T_1 in those for T_2. Thus

$$T_1T_2 = \begin{cases} x'' = A(ax + by) + B(dx + ey) \\ y'' = D(ax + by) + E(dx + ey) \end{cases}$$

and

$$T_1T_2 = \begin{cases} x'' = (Aa + Bd)x + (Ab + Be)y \\ y'' = (Da + Ed)x + (Db + Ee)y \end{cases}$$

Now T_1T_2, however complicated in appearance, has the *form* of a centered affine transformation, and hence the set of such transformations is closed under succession. In other words, "is followed by" is actually a binary operation on the set.

Before continuing with our proof that the set is a group under succession, let us indicate the important by-product in terms of modern *linear algebra*. Now our study of the theory of games has made us familiar with the notion of a *matrix* or rectangular array. Then instead of considering the homogeneous affine transformations above, we can focus on the matrices of their coefficients. Thus

$$M_1 = \begin{pmatrix} a & b \\ d & e \end{pmatrix} \qquad M_2 = \begin{pmatrix} A & B \\ D & E \end{pmatrix}.$$

We shall see shortly why the transformations can be symbolized as

$$X' = M_1 X \qquad \text{and} \qquad X'' = M_2 X'$$

If this is correct, then substitution of the first formula in the second yields for the product $T_1 T_2$ the formula

$$X'' = M_2 M_1 X$$

But if this formula is to agree with the one previously obtained, then $M_2 M_1$ must be the matrix of coefficients in that previous formula. Thus

$$M_2 M_1 = \begin{pmatrix} Aa + Bd & Ab + Be \\ Da + Ed & Db + Ee \end{pmatrix}$$

If we think of $M_2 M_1$ as meaning the *product* of the matrix M_2 by the matrix M_1, the following definition of such multiplication is suggested:

$$\begin{pmatrix} A & B \\ D & E \end{pmatrix} \begin{pmatrix} a & b \\ d & e \end{pmatrix} = \begin{pmatrix} Aa + Bd & Ab + Be \\ Da + Ed & Db + Ee \end{pmatrix}$$

This is, in fact, the definition of multiplication used for such matrices in linear algebra. We observe a simple rule for forming the *product matrix*, $M_2 M_1$. To obtain the entry, say, in the first row, second column of that matrix, one multiplies the elements of the *first row* of M_2 (namely A, B) by the elements of the *second column* of M_1 (namely, b, e), respectively, and forms the sum of these products to yield $Ab + Be$. The general rule is: To obtain the entry in row r, column s of $M_2 M_1$, multiply the elements of the rth row of M_2 by those of the sth column of M_1, respectively, and add these products. To illustrate this further, let us apply it to obtaining the entry in the second row, first column of $M_2 M_1$. The second row of M_2 is $(D\ E)$ and the first column of M_1 is $\begin{pmatrix} a \\ d \end{pmatrix}$. Therefore $Da + Ed$ should be the proper entry in $M_2 M_1$. To apply the rule further, let us see why we used the symbolism

$$X' = M_1 X \qquad X'' = M_2 X'$$

If

$$M_1 = \begin{pmatrix} a & b \\ d & e \end{pmatrix} \quad \text{and} \quad X = \begin{pmatrix} x \\ y \end{pmatrix}$$

(where X is a 2×1 matrix), then the rule we gave leads to the first row, first column entry of M_1X by multiplication of the elements of $(a\ b)$ by those of $\begin{pmatrix} x \\ y \end{pmatrix}$ to yield the entry $ax + by$. Likewise second row, first column of M_1X should be $dx + ey$. Since X has only one column, there will be no entries in M_1X other than those we have computed. Hence

$$X' = \begin{pmatrix} ax + by \\ dx + ey \end{pmatrix}$$

or if

$$X' = \begin{pmatrix} x' \\ y' \end{pmatrix}$$

this means

$$x' = ax + by$$
$$y' = dx + ey$$

which is the meaning we desire. We leave to the reader the task of applying the rule for multiplication of matrices to the proper interpretation of the symbolism, $X'' = M_2X'$.

The algebra of matrices and, in particular, the rule for matrix multiplication are due to the noted British algebraist Arthur Cayley, whose creation of a special type of hypercomplex number was noted in an earlier chapter (Chapter 4). The multiplication rule extends to matrices of higher orders than those considered. We observe that to carry it out there must be as many elements in a row and hence as many *columns* in the first matrix as there are *rows* (elements in a column) in the second. Cayley's rule will give the product of an $m \times n$ matrix by an $n \times k$ matrix. Since matrix multiplication mirrors "multiplication," that is, succession of homogeneous affine transformations, and that multiplication must be associative, the same is true of matrix multiplication. Let us indicate that matrix multiplication is not commutative. In other words, if we seek the product T_2T_1 which is defined by the matrix product, M_1M_2, the results, in general, will be different from those for T_1T_2 which was given by M_2M_1. Thus, applying the multiplication rule,

$$\begin{pmatrix} a & b \\ d & e \end{pmatrix} \begin{pmatrix} A & B \\ D & E \end{pmatrix} = \begin{pmatrix} aA + bD & aB + bE \\ dA + eD & dB + eE \end{pmatrix}$$

which is, for most values of the constants a, b, A, B, etc., a different result from M_2M_1.

For practice in matrix multiplication the reader can compute

$$\begin{pmatrix} 2 & -1 \\ 1 & 3 \end{pmatrix} \begin{pmatrix} 1 & 4 \\ 1 & -2 \end{pmatrix}$$

and then find the product when the order of factors is reversed, thereby computing T_1T_2 and T_2T_1, respectively, where

$$T_1 = \begin{cases} x' = x + 4y \\ y' = x - 2y \end{cases} \qquad T_2 = \begin{cases} x'' = 2x' - y' \\ y'' = x' + 3y' \end{cases}$$

But we must now complete the proof that the centered affine transformations form a group. It is obvious that there is an *identity* transformation in the affine set, namely, $\{x' = x,\ y' = y\}$, with *identity matrix*

$$I = \begin{pmatrix} 1 & 0 \\ 0 & 1 \end{pmatrix}$$

The reader can show that this matrix is actually a multiplicative identity by verifying that

$$\begin{pmatrix} a & b \\ c & d \end{pmatrix} \begin{pmatrix} 1 & 0 \\ 0 & 1 \end{pmatrix} = \begin{pmatrix} 1 & 0 \\ 0 & 1 \end{pmatrix} \begin{pmatrix} a & b \\ c & d \end{pmatrix} = \begin{pmatrix} a & b \\ c & d \end{pmatrix}$$

As for inverses, let us illustrate how to find them in the case of T_1 above. If (x, y) goes into (x', y') under T_1, then, to "invert" the situation, (x', y'), should go back into (x, y). To find how this should be done, we can solve the simultaneous equations for T_1 to obtain x and y in terms of (x', y'). This would yield

$$x = 1/3\, x' + 2/3\, y'$$
$$y = 1/6\, x' - 1/6\, y'$$

Then the reader can verify that if

$$T_1 = \begin{cases} x' = x + 4y \\ y' = x - 2y \end{cases} \qquad \text{and} \qquad T_1^{-1} = \begin{cases} x'' = 1/3\, x' + 2/3\, y' \\ y'' = 1/6\, x' - 1/6\, y' \end{cases}$$

then $T_1T_1^{-1} = I$. At any rate, we can symbolize the matrix of T^{-1} by

$$M_1^{-1} = \begin{pmatrix} 1/3 & 2/3 \\ 1/6 & -1/6 \end{pmatrix}$$

This matrix is said to be the *inverse* of the matrix M_1. We can prove that $M_1M_1^{-1} = M_1^{-1}M_1 = I$, the identity matrix. Thus the reader can check that

$$\begin{pmatrix} 1 & 4 \\ 1 & -2 \end{pmatrix}\begin{pmatrix} 1/3 & 2/3 \\ 1/6 & -1/6 \end{pmatrix} = \begin{pmatrix} 1 & 0 \\ 0 & 1 \end{pmatrix}$$

and then reverse the order of factors to obtain I once again.

But to return to the centered affine set, every transformation

$$x' = ax + by$$
$$y' = dx + ey$$

has the inverse homogeneous affine transformation

$$x'' = \frac{e}{ae - bd}\, x' - \frac{b}{ae - bd}\, y'$$

$$y'' = \frac{-d}{ae - bd}\, x' + \frac{a}{ae - bd}\, y'$$

providing $ae = bd \neq 0$, which is the condition stated on page 86. This completes the proof that the system of homogeneous affine transformations is a group.

Since the multiplicative system of all 2×2 matrices,

$$\begin{pmatrix} a & b \\ d & e \end{pmatrix}$$

in which $ae - bd \neq 0$, (the *invertible* 2×2 matrices) is *isomorphic* to the homogeneous affine group, the system of matrices is also a group.

The multiplicative system of $n \times n$ (*square*) invertible matrices is also a group when $n = 3$ or 4 or 5, etc. and that group is *isomorphic* to the homogeneous affine group in the Euclidean 3-space or 4-space or 5-space, etc.

Since a 2×2 or $n \times n$ matrix may not have a multiplicative inverse, some sets of such matrices are *not* groups with respect to multiplication. Also, although matrix multiplication is always associative, it is *not* necessarily commutative on a set of matrices. These facts make multiplicative systems of matrices available as concrete interpretations of some of the modern abstract algebraic structures whose multiplication is noncommutative. Also since square matrices are not all invertible a multiplicative system of such matrices may not admit division as a binary operation.

Cayley's algebra of matrices contains a definition of "scalar multiplication," a *unary operation* on matrices, and also a definition of *addition*, a binary operation on matrices. For an example of scalar multiplication one can treble all payoffs in the game whose matrix is given on page 352 of Volume One. Thus

$$3 \begin{pmatrix} 3 & 1 & 2 \\ 6 & 0 & -3 \\ -5 & -1 & 4 \end{pmatrix} = \begin{pmatrix} 9 & 3 & 6 \\ 18 & 0 & -9 \\ -15 & -3 & 12 \end{pmatrix}$$

Here the original matrix has been multiplied by the "scalar" (ordinary number) 3. This example illustrates that multiplication of a matrix by a scalar (number) is carried out by multiplying each matrix entry by that scalar.

For an illustration of addition of matrices, let us suppose that two children, who have been encouraged to keep small savings accounts, use the matrix form to tabulate interest received in a particular year. They add two matrices to total interest receipts for two years. Thus, if the matrices for the two years are

	Bank A	Bank B	Bank C				
Helen	2	3	1	and	2	4	2
James	4	1	1		5	2	3

then

$$\begin{pmatrix} 2 & 3 & 1 \\ 4 & 1 & 1 \end{pmatrix} + \begin{pmatrix} 2 & 4 & 2 \\ 5 & 2 & 3 \end{pmatrix} = \begin{pmatrix} 4 & 7 & 3 \\ 9 & 3 & 4 \end{pmatrix}.$$

This example illustrates that two matrices of the same species, that is, having the same number of rows and the same number of columns, can be added by adding corresponding entries.

After the properties of matrix addition and scalar multiplication have been analyzed, one has available many examples of algebraic systems whose elements are *not* merely the numbers of ordinary algebra. Thus, let S represent the set of all 2×2 matrices (or all 3×3 matrices or all 4×4 matrices or all square matrices of any finite order) with entries that are real numbers or complex numbers or elements of some field. Further, if $\bullet$ represents scalar multiplication on the matrices of S (that is, the multiplication of these matrices by a number in some field), and $+$, $\times$ represent addition and multiplication on S, then the system $\{S, +\}$ is an *abelian group*, the system $\{S, +, \bullet\}$ is a *vector space* (Chapter 4), the system $\{S, +, \times\}$ is a *noncommutative ring* which is special because it has a multiplicative unit or identity, and $\{S, +, \times, \bullet\}$ is an "algebra," or a *linear associative algebra*. We have already examined the "algebras" of ordinary complex numbers, of quaternions, of Cayley numbers (Chapter 4).

To return to the homogeneous affine transformations which motivated our discussion of matrix algebra, their geometric effect, if one takes the "alias" point of view, is to change from a rectangular Cartesian coordinate system to an *oblique system* (Chapter 7). Later on, we shall see the importance of this fact for differential geometry, general relativity, and post-relativity geometries, in which the "local" geometry of some surface or space may be affine. In relativity, the geometry of the homogeneous affine group is called *Euclidean* because a transformation to an oblique coordinate system does not change essential facts. If one takes the "alibi" instead of the "alias" viewpoint, the effect can be considered to be a stretching or distortion of the Euclidean plane to fit a "neighborhood" in one of the curved surfaces of differential geometry.

Plane projective geometry is the study of properties invariant under the linear fractional transformations,

$$x' = \frac{ax + by + c}{gx + hy + k}$$

$$y' = \frac{dx + ey + f}{gx + hy + k}$$

where

$$aek - afh + bfg - bdk + cdh - ceg \neq 0$$

The apparently (but not actually) complicated restriction on the coefficients is analogous to the condition $ae - bd \neq 0$

for the affine transformation, and is part of the "linear algebra" of the situation. Incidentally, if one substitutes $k = 1$ and $c = f = g = h = 0$, the new projective transformations reduce to the homogeneous affine transformations and the above limitation becomes $ae - bd \neq 0$. But the original inequality on the coefficients insures that every projective transformation is a one-to-one mapping of the plane onto itself with an *inverse* that is a projective transformation. Then it is a simple matter to show that the projective (linear fractional) transformations form a group.

The rigid motions constitute a subgroup of the similarity group which is a subgroup of the affine group which is a subgroup of the projective group. As the generality and the number of parameters increase, the number of invariants decreases, but there are still significant invariants under projective transformation. The *degree* of the equation of any curve is preserved. Thus first-degree equations, which represent straight lines, remain first-degree equations; that is, the property of being a straight line is invariant. To prove this, suppose that the equation of a straight line is

$$mx + ny + p = 0$$

Each point (x, y) on this line will have new coordinates (x', y') after a projective transformation, that is, after the point moves to the new position prescribed by such a transformation. Can one provide a Cartesian equation for the set of new positions? If the parameters are restricted in the way we have indicated, the formulas for a projective transformation can be solved for x and y in terms of x' and y', to yield the *inverse*,

$$x = \frac{Ax' + By' + C}{Gx' + Hy' + K}$$

$$y = \frac{Dx' + Ey' + F}{Gx' + Hy' + K}$$

where the letters A, B, C, etc. are, in general, different from a, b, c, etc. Substituting the inverse formulas in the equation of the line will express a relation between x' and y', the new coordinates, namely,

$$m\left(\frac{Ax' + By' + C}{Gx' + Hy' + K}\right) + n\left(\frac{Dx' + Ey' + F}{Gx' + Hy' + K}\right) + p = 0$$

or

$$(mA + nD + pG)x' + (mB + nE + pH)y' \\ + (mC + nF + pK) = 0$$

This is a linear equation in x' and y', and hence indicates a straight line to be the configuration of points in the new positions.

In the same way, a second-degree equation in x and y remains a second-degree equation, that is, the property of being a conic section is preserved under projective transformation. A circle might be transformed into an ellipse or a parabola or a hyperbola, however, and any conic section may be changed into a conic of a different type.

If one considers any three points P_1, P_2, P_3 of a straight line, they will be converted by any projective transformation into three collinear points P_1', P_2', P_3' but, in general, both distances and ratios of distances will be changed. However, if the fate of *four* collinear points is examined, it can be proved that for every projective transformation the "ratio of ratios" or "double ratio" of distances is an invariant, that is,

$$\frac{P_1P_3}{P_2P_3} : \frac{P_1P_4}{P_2P_4} = \frac{P_1'P_3'}{P_2'P_3'} : \frac{P_1'P_4'}{P_2'P_4'}$$

We shall not establish the invariance in the general case of the *double ratio* or *cross ratio* or *anharmonic ratio*, as it is variously called, but we shall illustrate it for special cases. Thus the invariance is evident (by virtue of similarity properties) in the case of the special "central projection" of Figure 17.9.

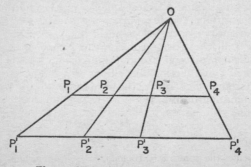

Figure 17.9   Central projection

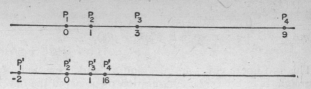

Figure 17.10

The points P_1, P_2, P_3, P_4 with Cartesian coordinates 0, 1, 3, 9, respectively, in a straight-line "space" (Figure 17.10) have the double or cross ratio $3/2 : 9/8 = 3/2 \cdot 8/9 = 4/3$. Now consider a one-dimensional projective transformation in the straight-line "space," namely,

$$x' = \frac{2x - 2}{x + 1}$$

Substituting 0 in this formula,

$$x' = \frac{0 - 2}{0 + 1} = -2$$

so that P_1' has the coordinate -2 in the new frame of reference. Substitutions of 1, 3, 9 give the coordinates of P_2', P_3', P_4', and the four new coordinates are -2, 0, 1, 1.6, respectively, with cross ratio $3/1 : 3.6/1.6 = 3/1 \cdot 16/36 = 4/3$, so that in this particular case the cross ratio has been shown to be invariant.

Klein and Cayley made use of the cross ratio in giving analytic interpretation to the non-Euclidean geometries of Lobachevsky and Riemann. They defined Lobachevskian geometry on a line by means of a special subgroup of the projective group $x' = (ax + b)/(cx + d)$, the subgroup leaving invariant two specified points of the X-axis. They defined a *plane* Lobachevskian geometry by means of a subgroup of the plane projective group, the subgroup leaving invariant a specified conic section—an ellipse or a circle, say.

In a straight-line space, the projective group has a one-parameter subgroup,

$$x' = \frac{ax + 100}{x + a}$$

which leaves the points $x = 10$ and $x = -10$ invariant. The reader can verify this by substituting $x = 10$ and $x = -10$ to obtain

$$x' = \frac{10a + 100}{10 + a} = \frac{10(a + 10)}{a + 10} = 10$$

and

$$x' = \frac{-10a + 100}{-10 + a} = \frac{-10(a - 10)}{a - 10} = -10$$

Since the equation $x^2 - 100 = 0$, when solved, yields $x = 10$ and $x = -10$, this equation is equivalent to the point pair. Moreover, it is a *second-degree* equation, and is therefore the one-dimensional analogue of a conic section, which is the figure to be left invariant in the two-dimensional Lobachevskian geometry. Cayley termed the invariant point pair or conic the *absolute*.

To define *distance* in their non-Euclidean geometries, Cayley and Klein proceeded by analogy with a discovery of Laguerre (1834–1866), who had shown that the distances and angles of ordinary *Euclidean* geometry can be expressed in terms of cross ratios, in other words, that Euclidean *metric* geometry is clearly a specialization of *projective* geometry. The concept of the "absolute" and the definition of distance unified Euclidean and non-Euclidean geometries into a single all-embracing theory.

In the Cayley-Klein non-Euclidean geometries, the distance from Q to P in a straight-line "space" (Figure 17.11)

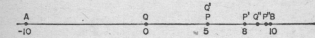

Figure 17.11

was defined in terms of the cross ratio of A, B, P, Q, where A and B are *invariant points* forming the Cayley "absolute." The distance was taken as

$$k \text{ logarithm } (ABPQ)$$

where k is some constant and $(ABPQ)$ symbolizes the cross ratio. The reason for using the logarithm was the customary one, namely, that a product is thereby converted into a sum, and this makes it true that

$$\text{distance } PQ + \text{distance } QR = \text{distance } PR$$

which is a property that one expects of anything described as a "distance." Thus, in accordance with this definition, if the invariant points A and B are $x = -10$ and $x = 10$, P is $x = 5$, Q is $x = 0$, the distance QP (Figure 17.11) is

$$k \text{ logarithm} \left(\frac{5 + 10}{5 - 10} \cdot \frac{0 - 10}{0 + 10} \right) = k \text{ logarithm } 3$$

(The constant k can be selected to suit special purposes, and logarithms to any base can be used.) If we select $k = 10$ and use common logarithms, the distance is $(10)(0.48) = 4.8$, which is not very different from our Euclidean measurement of the distance between 0 and 5.

Now let us carry out some transformation of the subgroup defining our Lobachevskian geometry. For example, in the formula for the subgroup, let $a = 20$. Then

$$x' = \frac{20x + 100}{x + 20}$$

Substitution of $x = 5$ and $x = 0$ shows that P and Q will be shifted to

$$x' = \frac{20(5) + 100}{5 + 20} = 8 \quad \text{and} \quad x' = \frac{20(0) + 100}{0 + 20} = 5$$

The Cayley-Klein distance between these new points will be

$$10 \text{ logarithm} \left[\frac{8 + 10}{8 - 10} \cdot \frac{5 - 10}{5 + 10} \right] = 10 \text{ logarithm } 3 = 4.8$$

which is the same distance as that between the original points, thus checking the invariance of distance. By *Euclidean* standards, the distance between the points 5 and 8 would be only 3 units, thus indicating the non-Euclideanism of our special geometry. To emphasize it still more, consider the transformation where $a = 11$, namely,

$$x' = \frac{11x + 100}{x + 11}$$

Then $x = 5$ and $x = 0$ are transformed into $x = 9 \ 11/16$ and $x = 9 \ 1/11$, respectively. In the Lobachevskian geometry these points are still 4.8 units apart whereas, by Euclidean standards, the distance is only 0.6 unit. If one marks off successive Lobachevskian lengths of 4.8 units, the corresponding Euclidean lengths get smaller and smaller as one approaches either $x = -10$ or $x = +10$. The Lobachevskian distance of either of these points (forming the "absolute") from any other point is "infinite." Thus, the Lobachevskian distance from 0 to 10 is

$$10 \text{ logarithm } \frac{10 + 10}{10 - 10} \cdot \frac{0 - 10}{0 + 10} = 10 \text{ logarithm } \frac{-200}{0}$$

It is impossible to divide -200 by 0, but if we divide -200 by a negative number very close to 0, the quotient will be very large and will have a large logarithm. By taking the divisor sufficiently close to 0, both the quotient and its logarithm can be made larger than any given number, however huge that number may be. That is what is meant when $-200 \div 0$ or its logarithm is said to be "infinite."

If a two-dimensional Lobachevskian geometry is set up, one chooses a conic like the ellipse in Figure 17.12 as the *absolute*, or figure to be left invariant. The results are analogous to those in one dimension. All points within the absolute are at an infinite distance from that curve. Then if one defines parallel lines as lines meeting at infinity, Figure 17.12 shows how the world within the ellipse is a realization of Lobachevsky's geometry (Chapter 3). Through point P there are two "parallels" to P_1P_2, that is, two lines meeting it on the ellipse, and an infinite number of "nonintersectors."

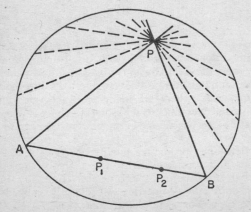

Figure 17.12   A Lobachevskian plane geometry

Klein showed that the Riemannian species of non-Euclidean geometry can be developed in a fashion completely analogous to the Lobachevskian type by choosing an "imaginary" absolute, that is, an "imaginary" point pair or conic, and an imaginary value of the constant k. Euclidean geometry can also be treated in the same way by choosing a "degenerate" point pair or conic. In one dimension the point pair "degenerates" by having the points come closer and closer together until they are coincident. Thus $x^2 - 1 = 0$ represents a real point pair suitable for the absolute of a Lobachevskian geometry. If $x^2 - 0.01 = 0$ is selected, the absolute is still real, but the points $x = +0.1$, $x = -0.1$ are close together. If $x^2 = 0$, there are two coincident points, $x = 0$, $x = 0$, and this is the sort of absolute corresponding to Euclidean one-dimensional geometry. In the variation of absolute just described, the constant in the equation increased from -1 to -0.01 to 0. If a further increase to $+0.01$ and then to $+1$ is envisioned, the equations $x^2 + 0.01 = 0$ and $x^2 + 1 = 0$ will describe *imaginary* absolutes, namely, the point pairs $x = \pm 0.1\, i$ and $x = \pm i$, respectively, and these will correspond to one-dimensional Riemannian geometries. Thus Euclidean geometry is intermediate between the two types of non-Euclidean geometry. Similarly, Euclidean plane geometry is intermediate between the two-dimensional non-Euclidean geometries. A *real* absolute, like the circle $x^2 + y^2 = 1$, can be changed to the circle $x^2 + y^2 = 0.01$ with the tiny radius 0.1, and then can degenerate into $x^2 + y^2 = 0$, a circle of zero radius, and this can change further into the imaginary circles $x^2 + y^2 = -0.01$, $x^2 + y^2 = -1$, etc. The transitions we have indicated emphasize a point implied in the previous discussion, namely, that although there is essentially *only one* Euclidean geometry in each dimension (since one "degenerate" absolute is congruent to any other), there are many Lobachevskian and Riemannian geometries since the absolutes—the point pairs, the ellipses, etc.—can be chosen in an infinite number of different ways.

Klein developed projective geometries of 3, 4, 5, . . . , n dimensions and associated with them the various higher-dimensional non-Euclidean geometries. But he also considered groups and geometries not directly related to the projective type. For example, around 1840, A. F. Moebius (1790–1868), whose name will appear frequently in the chapter on topology, the most modern of all "geometries," began a study of *inversive* geometry. To Klein this was merely the geometry associated with the one-parameter transformation group

$$x^2 = \frac{a^2 x}{x^2 + y^2}$$

$$y' = \frac{a^2 y}{x^2 + y^2}$$

The invariants (and hence the geometry) of this group differ from those in the projective case. Straight lines are not invariant but are converted into circles. The property of being a circle is invariant however—that is, inversion transforms every circle into a circle—and angles between lines and curves are also invariant. The latter property is described by saying that inversive geometry is *conformal*. This particular geometry is of great importance in the branch of analysis known as "functions of a complex variable."

The Erlanger Program, however significant from the point of view of bringing economy of thought into the treatment of geometry, does not cover everything that is called geometry today. It does include special relativity, but the *general* theory introduced by Einstein around 1916 cannot be described by Klein's 1872 definition of geometry, and the "post-relativity" geometries stimulated by the search for a "unified field theory" do not fit into the Erlanger Program. In all these geometries, the idea of *invariance* is still important, but the associated sets of transformations are not, in general, groups.

The discussion of these more general geometries will be postponed to a later chapter, and now a further excerpt from Young's biography of Klein will be offered. From the present point of view, possibly the most important facts in the extract are those concerned with the Göttingen mathematics institute and Klein's association with the Norwegian mathematician (Marius) Sophus Lie (1842–1899). Klein started a precedent at Göttingen that was to make it the mathematical center of the world until Hitler's day, when the mathematical division of our own Institute for Advanced Study carried on and improved the best features of Klein's plan. It is said that Klein and Sophus Lie, as young men, decided to divide the world of groups between them so as not to encroach on one another's territory. During most of his lifetime Klein received more recognition than Lie, whose greatest fame was probably posthumous. Today some of Klein's notions have been modified or replaced, and a few are considered passé. But one need merely examine current research periodicals in order to read about Lie groups, Lie algebras, etc. It is Lie's ideas that have stood up well under the critical test of time. But for a general reader who wants all the traditional geometries—Euclidean, non-Euclidean, conformal, etc.—in a nutshell, along with an elementary approach to the group concept, the Erlanger Program is still an eye-opener.

From the small Bavarian university of Erlangen, Klein passed in 1875 to the Technische Hochschule at the Bavarian capital, Munich. In Germany, where the different levels of society were kept rigidly distinct by what was termed the "Kastengeist," the level of professors at the technical schools was regarded as lower than that of university professors; but Klein looked at things from a broader standpoint. He says himself that there hovered before his mind's eye the vision of a polytechnic school like those of Paris and Zurich, and, in accepting this "call," he felt that he was taking a great step in advance.

The years at Erlangen had been only a preparation; it was at Munich that Klein began to feel his feet; here, to use his own words, he "worked himself through to a real mathematical individuality." But, in doing so, he undermined his health, and, at Leipzig, to which university he was called in 1880 as Professor of Geometry, he became seriously ill. His breakdown was probably accelerated by the antagonism he experienced at Leipzig. He was much younger than his colleagues, and they resented his innovating tendencies. In particular, there was opposition to his determination to avail himself of the vaunted German "Lehrfreiheit," and to interpret the word "Geometry" in its widest sense, beginning his lectures with a course on the Geometric Theory of Functions.

Klein was now at the acme of his mathematical powers. The theorem, which Klein himself prized highest among his mathematical discoveries, known as the "Grenzkreis-theorem" in the theory of automorphic functions, flashed upon his mind suddenly at the seaside, in the small hours of the morning, as he sat, propped up on a sofa, because of his asthma. This was at Easter, 1882. The stimulus to this important extension of his earlier work on the icosahedron and the modular functions had been given by Poincaré's three notes in the "Comptes Rendus" of February and March, 1881.

It is interesting to note that the turning point in Klein's recovery from his breakdown at Leipzig was marked by his being invited to Baltimore, to take the chair vacated by Sylvester in 1884. Indeed, he attributed to this invitation, and to the attractive vistas which it opened to his fancy, the tonification of his mind enabling him to throw off his malady. He eventually declined the invitation, which was not the last he received from an American university. But the days of his great productivity were over, although he had only reached what Dante calls "the middle of our walk in life"; from this time, for many years, he devoted himself to the development of his mathematical school.

In 1886 he was called to Göttingen. The great city was indeed no home for the true German, and it was with enthusiasm that the Kleins migrated to "the little garden-town," which at the time was still a medieval poem. It was here that the happiest home-days of the family were passed, in the comfortable villa, all their own, built by themselves, in its cool shady garden. On one side it was close to the Auditorium, on the other, near by, was the magnificent forest, the Göttingerwald, stretching to the Harz Mountains. Every day, after midday dinner and a short siesta, Klein used to walk up into the forest in mathematical converse with his colleagues and friends, after which he received his special students upstairs in his book-lined study, and discussed their work, or he prepared his own lectures.

Göttingen did not disappoint Klein and he refused every call elsewhere. He saw the university raised once more to a world-celebrity which even in the days of Gauss had never been surpassed, and to a material magnificence which had never been even imagined. The turning-point came when, as he himself humorously pointed out at a Christmas gathering of his students in 1893, the centre of the universe veered round to Göttingen, following as it always must, the advent of Eve's daughters. In fact, Prussian university life had been gently invaded. Two American women, inspired by Klein's visit to Chicago that year, had followed him to Europe, and a Girton girl (Grace Chisholm) had appeared at the same time independently; it was she who became eighteen months later the first female Doctor of Philosophy at a Prussian University.

At the Auditorium, on the top floor, was Klein's lecture room; in the days of his best lectures it rarely contained more than a dozen hearers, and these nearly all foreigners, but at the beginning of the present century there were near on a hundred students, mostly Germans, in his audience. Hard by was the wonderful mathematical reading-room, with the adjacent room lined with glass-cases full of models; here the professor held, after his lecture, his "Sprechstunde," when any of his pupils could come to him with requests or questions. For a very small fee the student received a pass-key enabling him to enter the reading-room at any hour and avail himself of the books, which, unlike those at the University Library, might not be taken out, and of the manuscript and lithographed notes of lectures; in particular he could consult the written "Ausarbeitung" of Klein's lecture of the day before, made by Klein's assistant and previously submitted to himself; it happened, not infrequently, that rash statements of the professor were in this way controlled and corrected, these assistants, particularly the too early lost Ernst Ritter, being for the most part mathematical collaborators of a high order. All this, which had been organized by Klein, was later developed into a Mathematical Institute in a separate building.

Klein was the principal promoter of the Enzyklopädie der Mathematischen Wissenschaften. The Enzyklopädie was, from Klein's point of view, an effort to render accessible the bulk of existing mathematics. The progress of mathematics, he said, using a favourite metaphor, was like the erection of a great tower; sometimes the growth in height is evident, sometimes it remains apparently stationary; those are the periods of general revision, when the advance, though invisible from the outside, is still real, consisting in underpinning and strengthening. And he suggested that such was the then period. What we want, he concluded, is a general view of the state of the edifice as it exists at present. Klein undertook, for his own part, in accordance with his pronounced taste for Applied mathematics, the editorship of the volume on Mechanics.

Klein's appetite for work was such that, before there was any prospect of the Enzyklopädie being completed, finding he was obliged to leave much of the organization in other hands, he had turned to the international question of mathematical teaching in the schools. He turned perhaps to something more concrete, which brought him into contact with minds other than those of the mathematical expert, something more comprehensible in fact than the huge colossus which was threatening to remain nothing but a torso. In the matter of the International Mathematical Teaching Commission Klein, as President, formed one of a triumvirate, of which another, the pioneer of the movement was a world-travelled American, David Eugene Smith, and the third, as General Secretary, a native Swiss professor, Henri Fehr. This international work was checked and rendered abortive by World War I.

It is impossible even to touch on all Klein's schemes, yet we cannot but allude to a vast undertaking, still uncompleted, in which he was the prime mover, the editing and issuing of Gauss's Works. For Klein, Gauss represented the universal in Mathematics, and in this connexion he held Gauss before himself as the master to be copied.* But, if Gauss was here the prototype, it was buried in his individual person; the apostle of universality in Mathematics was Klein, and, without hyperbole, he may be termed the founder of what the 20th Century means by Mathematical Science, raised equally above departmental specialism and narrow nationalism. Indeed, during a period when the forces of material progress were,

---

* There was hardly a new mathematical idea formulated, but Klein would cite a passage from Gauss in which it had been foreshadowed.

at first secretly, but afterwards openly, undermining the basis of the unity of civilised nations, generating jealousy, and inciting to war, Klein embodied the contrary principle, and, by his great power in his own country, and his wide-spread influence in the world of intellect, constituted one of the greatest forces tending to international amity and peace. In particular, it was he who revived the practice—prevalent in the Middle Ages, when Latin was the universal tongue of Learning—of inviting distinguished men from other countries to come and give lectures.*

In looking through Klein's Autobiography, one is struck by his constant references to his friendships. It was characteristic of him that they all bore directly, or indirectly, on his mathematical development and on his power of organisation. He was indeed a man without a hobby; in particular, and this is curious and interesting from a psychological point of view, although a German, and although endowed with an excessive acuteness of hearing,† he could not distinguish one tune from another.

Social intercourse for Klein meant the interchange of ideas, and for that he was as eager as an ancient Athenian. It was in such give-and-take that his own conceptions took form. There is, perhaps, no contradiction in saying that Klein was never the originator of his own ideas. He had not the generating force of a Cauchy or a Georg Cantor, but he had a phenomenal power of grasping the import of a suggestion, and working it out on a grander scale than any before him had imagined.

We have already mentioned incidentally several of those close friendships that directly influenced and even inspired Klein as a mathematician. The most striking of all, his friendship with Lie, merits a place by itself. It takes us back to his stay at Berlin in 1869. Klein writes: "The most important event of my time in Berlin was certainly that, towards the end of October, at a meeting of the Berlin Mathematical Society, I made the acquaintance of the Norwegian, Sophus Lie. We had, in our work, been led from different points of view finally to the same questions, or, at least, to kindred ones. Thus it came about that we met every day and kept up an animated exchange of ideas. Our intimacy was all the closer, because at first we found very little interest for our geometrical interests in our immediate neighbourhood."

In the summer of 1870 Klein and Lie went together to Paris, where they had rooms side by side, and lived in the closest bonds of friendship. Their intention was to go on to England in the

---

* In particular Poincaré came to Göttingen in 1894 or 1895, and gave a lecture in French to the mathematical professors and students.

† This enabled him to catch the faintest whisper during his lectures. Also, commonly, when away from home, he could not go to sleep unless he stopped up his ears with cotton-wool; this was the case, for instance, during his short stay at Trinity College in 1897, on the occasion of his receiving his honorary degree at Cambridge.

winter, but the outbreak of the Franco-German War prevented it. In this connection Klein writes: "This striving after the greatest possible breadth of scientific outlook, for which an acquaintance with what was being done in foreign countries seemed important, was very little understood at that time in Germany. Thus, for instance, when, urged by my father, I tried to obtain letters of recommendation from the Minister of Education in Berlin, I received the official answer: We have no use for French or English mathematics."

In Paris the two friends did not attend lectures, but worked together. It was, however, undoubtedly by the personal contact with the younger French mathematicians, particularly Camille Jordan, that the attention of the pair was directed to Galois' theory of groups. Jordan's treatise on the "Theory of Substitutions" had just appeared, and was to the two young men "a book with seven seals." We continue in Klein's own words: "It was, however, with Darboux that we were most intimate. At that time the French had been occupied with new investigations in metrical geometry (inversion, constant use of the circle at infinity), and this was quite unknown in Germany. Now it appeared that these were most closely related to our own work in line geometry. . . . For Lie, what was perhaps most interesting was the researches of the French into the geometrical theory of differential equations. It was by the coalescence of the two circles of ideas that Lie came to discover the connection between lines of curvature and minimal lines on a surface."

And here Klein gives a vivid sketch from this period of his life: "I had risen early one morning at the beginning of July, 1870, and I was just going out, when Lie, who was still in bed, called me into his room, and began explaining to me what he had found out during the night, the connexion between lines of curvature and minimal lines. I did not understand one word. Anyway, he assured me that it followed that the minimal lines on Kummer's surface must be algebraic curves of the 16th order. In the course of the morning it flashed upon me, while I was seeing over the Conservatoire des Arts et Métiers, that these must be the same curves of the 16th order which had already appeared in my theory of the Line-complexes of the first and second degree, and I succeeded at once in carrying out the geometrical proof, independently of Lie's transformation. When I got back in the afternoon, at 4 o'clock, Lie had gone out, and I left a letter for him containing my proof."

The outbreak of the war, Klein's consequent hasty departure, leaving his Norwegian friend behind, then the continuation of their mathematical conversations by letter, have an interest beyond that of the immediate consequences to Lie. While Lie remained at Paris, all went well; but when, in the heat of August, he started for Italy on foot, he was arrested at Fontainebleau as a spy, and kept in durance for four weeks, till, in fact, their friend

Darboux had succeeded in explaining the inoffensive mathematical nature of the mysterious letters, in German, and in Klein's notoriously illegible handwriting, found in Lie's possession.

This episode was one of the manifestations of the unbroken continuance during the Franco-German war of friendly scientific relations between himself and his newly-won French friends, which made such an indelible impression on Klein's mind. We may say that those were still the days of scientific chivalry. When World War I broke out in 1914, Klein was incapable of conceiving any other state of affairs, but he was, as he had in fact been in 1870, carried away by the wave of patriotic fervour of the moment. When he therefore began to perceive that there was serious danger of what he regarded as a purely political cataclysm affecting international scientific relations, he lost, for one unfortunate moment, that dignified poise of judgment which was one of his most striking characteristics. Invited by telephone to sign a document, which, according to the impression left on his mind was to make an appeal to the scientists of Europe to maintain an objective attitude during the struggle, he impetuously acceded to the request. He did not see the text of the document until it appeared in the daily papers with his signature, as one of 93, printed below. It was very damaging to Klein's international position that he permitted his name to appear without protest at the foot of a document whose tenor was so entirely antagonistic to the whole tone of his life. And he was too proud, even after the Armistice, to withdraw publicly his signature. He desired his friends to know, and to tell, how it had been obtained, but he felt that, for himself, he stood upon his whole career, and not upon an isolated and misinterpreted action.

Lie was seven years older than Klein, but their standing in mathematical productivity was about the same. Lie had only begun mathematics seriously at 26, whereas Klein, at the age of 20, when they first met, had been for three years recognised as a mathematician and a writer. Lie was excessively tenacious of his own rights to his own ideas, and resented, as is well-known, any suggestion that they were in any sense second-hand. He quarrelled with Klein, his early friend, on this very point, and in the introduction to the third volume of the "Transformationsgruppen" he repudiates the notion that he was a pupil of Klein's; "rather," he says, "the contrary was the case." This irritated Klein, and justly. His generous nature was incapable of making the former of these suggestions, and his frank and healthy self-confidence prevented his accepting the latter of them. It is so rare in this world of ours that misunderstandings are ultimately cleared up, that it is a real pleasure to know that this was the case with Klein and Lie. In the vivid picture which Klein gives in his Autobiography and in the Collected Mathematical Papers of the interweaving of his own work with that of Lie, there is no bitterness.

Mrs. Klein wrote: "The relation to Lie was an intimate friendship in mathematical and in personal respects. That remained the same also later, when Lie visited us in Leipzig. And I, too, was fond of him, the powerful Northman with the frank open glance and the merry laugh, a hero in whose presence the common and the mean could not venture to show themselves.

"Then he became my husband's successor at Leipzig, and there he was seized with home-sickness. How well I understand that! He, the free, accustomed to his rough but beautiful northern home, how could he stand the great smoky city, the high houses, the narrow streets, the puny Saxon people. He suffered from melancholia, he was taken to a sanatorium, but there things only became worse, for they robbed him of his work and of his freedom. There, in his embittered state of mind, it must have been that he wrote the malicious things about my husband which were both painful and incomprehensible to him.

"But soon he understood that his best friend was ill and that he could not be held responsible for his actions. It was not only magnanimous and good, but also wise of my husband, not to enter into any polemic, but to let the thing simply rest. And he was not mistaken in his friend.

"One summer evening, as we came home from an excursion, there, in front of our door, sat a sick man. 'Lie!' we cried, in joyful surprise. The two friends shook hands, looked into one another's eyes, all that had passed since their last meeting was forgotten. Lie stayed with us one day, the dear old friend, and yet changed. I cannot think of him and of his tragic fate without emotion. Soon after, he died, but not before the great mathematician had been received in Norway like a king."

As for Klein himself, gradually, but irresistibly, the nervous malady of which from time to time he had had serious warnings, mastered and prostrated him. It was, he thought, partly due to heredity on his mother's side, partly to his own unbridled expenditure of mental energy—an energy which remained so indomitable that, even during the last two years of his life, when he lay helpless, becoming daily weaker and weaker in body, he never complained, and remained clear to the end, working and even correcting proofsheets.

Chapter 18

A Special Group and Its Application

A pure mathematician might state that the special or restricted theory of relativity, as presented by Einstein in 1905, was nothing more than one of Klein's "geometries," that is, the study of the invariants of a particular transformation group. As already explained for the case of observers in a linear cosmos, the group in question is the set of Lorentz transformations, or alternatively the group of *rotations*, providing the time coordinate is taken with an "imaginary" factor and the angle of rotation is also "imaginary." Although such imaginary entities are entirely acceptable from an abstract point of view, they do not completely satisfy the applied mathematician, the physicist, or the general reader. If relativity is to be associated with the world of reality, a different treatment is required. Therefore the present chapter will examine the classic concepts which required revision at the hands of Einstein, and will point out how he applied the group of Lorentz transformations to the resolution of paradoxes that plagued the nineteenth-century physicists.

Those men adhered to the postulates of Newton and to the theorems derived from his assumptions—the immense structure of classical physics. By 1880 this edifice began to topple. Just as the parallel postulate was the bone of contention which ultimately required a revolution in mathematical ideas, Newton's postulation of an *absolute space* and an *absolute time* was the source of the trouble that called for a new theory of the universe. The term "absolute" is akin to the concept of "invariant," but is somewhat more general. An examination of technical works on relativity would reveal the use of the word *covariant* to provide the greater generality. To illustrate an *absolute* quantity, one need only point to a result of counting. All observers would agree that a certain pamphlet contains 45 pages or that 8 people are seated at a table. The adjective *absolute* is applied to a physical phenomenon on which all observers are in agreement, in contrast to a *relative* result whose estimation may vary from observer to observer. Chicago is *west* for observers in New York City but *east* for those in Omaha. The purchasing power of a dollar is relative, because it varies with place and time.

Since Newtonian dynamics deals with motion, one must ask whether any judgments related to motion can be absolute. If you are a passenger in a subway train and another train is on the adjacent track, you may not be able to tell, momentarily, whether your train is at rest, moving backwards, or moving forward slowly. Only after the other train has passed and you see the platform of the station, can you realize that your train is at rest. But if two ships should pass in mid-ocean, an observer on one of them could not decide whether one or both ships are in motion; both might be moving in the same direction, one more rapidly than the other; they might be moving in opposite directions; one might be at rest and the other in motion. The same thought can be extended to celestial bodies. Since there are no landmarks or signposts in the far regions of space, there must be inevitable difficulty in deciding which bodies are at rest and which in motion. An astronomer may talk about the velocity of the sun relative to the "fixed stars," but are there any stars that are really stationary, or is there anything in the universe we can be certain is fixed?

It would appear that the answer is negative and that all motion is relative. Velocity could only be absolute if there should exist one frame of reference for which the laws of nature would appear simpler to observers stationary in it than for those using any other background. Then this would constitute a *unique* or fixed frame of reference that could be singled out by any observer in the universe, and motion referred to it could be considered absolute. Newton and his successors knew that the laws of mechanics could furnish no such frame, since the laws appear the same, for example, to observers on earth and to those moving at uniform speeds with respect to the earth. Scientists thought it might be otherwise with electromagnetic phenomena, in particular those involving light.

The "wave motion" of light was assumed to take place in a medium called the *ether*, which was pictured as filling all of space. The ether theory was gratifying because the ether could be thought of as carrying electromagnetic waves and because it seemed to offer some fixed frame of reference with respect to which there might be absolute motion. In 1887, however, the American physicists Michelson and Morley performed a crucial experiment whose outcome refuted this notion.

To understand the basis of the classic experiment they performed, consider the mundane matter of rowing a boat on a stream that flows at the rate of 3 ft. per sec. between parallel banks 120 ft. apart. Two oarsmen, who both row at the rate of 5 ft. per sec. in still water, set out from a point on one of the banks. The first man rows 120 ft. downstream and back. The current helps him on his way down and hinders him on his return. His rates of rowing are 8 ft. per sec. and 2 ft. per sec., respectively, in going and returning, and the total time is

$$\frac{120}{8} + \frac{120}{2} = 75 \text{ sec.}$$

The second oarsman sets out simultaneously with the first, proceeding straight across to a point on the opposite bank, and then rows back. To row straight, he heads diagonally backward (Figure 18.1) in order to allow for the effect of the current. While he pushes the boat 5 ft., the current

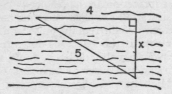

Figure 18.1

carries it 3 ft. (as in Figure 18.1), and his advance across the stream can be found by using the Pythagorean theorem:

$$x^2 + 3^2 = 5^2$$
$$x = 4$$

His rate of progress across the stream will be 4 ft. per sec. and the time required will be $120/4 = 30$ sec. The story will be the same for the return trip; therefore his total time will be 60 sec. and he will return ahead of the other oarsman.

In classical physics it was assumed that as the earth moves there is an "ether current" somewhat like the breeze when a man is driving a car. To measure the speed of the ether wind, Michelson and Morley devised an experiment in which the "oarsmen" were to be two light rays, one of which was to go down the ether stream and back, while the other was to travel the same distance across it and back. The rays were sent on the journey back by reflection from suitably placed mirrors. Instead of resulting in the earlier return of the transverse light ray, both rays arrived back *at the same time!* The experiment was repeated again and again to take account of any possible errors. Refinements were added so that an ether current as small as 1/5 kilometer per second would have been detected. The results were still negative! To all appearances, the earth stood permanently at rest in the ether, which, of course, contradicted the known fact that it speeds around the sun at nearly 20 miles a second.

Fitzgerald and Lorentz (Chapter 17) arrived independently at the same explanation of this phenomenon. They suggested that distances must *contract* in the direction of motion by an amount just sufficient to compensate for the handicap of the longitudinal light ray. If the rival rays have a normal speed of 5 units per second (each unit equal to about 37,200 miles) in some stream with a speed of 3 units per second, a contraction of longitudinal lengths to 4/5 of their original size would explain the simultaneity of return. The transverse ray would require 60 seconds for a 120-unit crossing and return. If the 120 units downstream contracted to $4/5 \times 120 = 96$, then the total trip down and back would take $96/8 + 96/2 = 60$ seconds, which checks with the outcome of the Michelson-Morley experiment.

Nineteenth-century physics indicated that the difficulties revealed by the Michelson-Morley experiment were not isolated failures of classical physical theories but actually pervaded electricity and optics. Although Lorentz and Fitzgerald pointed out a partial solution for the apparent contradictions, it was left to Einstein to proclaim in his revolutionary paper of 1905 that paradoxes could best be resolved by also scrapping the traditional concepts of space and time.

The axioms of the special, or *restricted theory of relativity*, as enunciated by Einstein are:

I. *The principle of relativity:* The laws of physics are the same whether stated in one frame of reference or any other moving with uniform rectilinear velocity relative to the first.

II. The *velocity of light* is *constant*, that is, the same when measured by all observers in the universe, and is independent of its source.

The reason the theory is *special* is that the velocities considered are not general in nature since the relative speeds are assumed to be uniform or *constant* and motions must take place in a straight line.

The first of the above assumptions is equivalent to the impossibility of defining absolute motion, for to do so one would have to single out a special frame of reference and give evidence of laws holding only in this frame and no other; this would of course be contrary to postulate I, which calls for every natural law to hold in all systems in uniform motion relative to one another. As for the second axiom, if one considers it a *physical law* that light should have a certain velocity, its constancy would follow from postulate I and no second assumption would be needed. That the speed of light is independent of the source is confirmed by some empirical evidence. To understand this experimental basis, we recall that classic theory considered light a wave phenomenon in the ether. *Sound* is just such a phenomenon, since it is transmitted by waves propagated in air or some other material medium, and numerous examples can be adduced to show that its speed is neither increased nor decreased by motion of the source. In supersonic flight, planes arrive before they are heard. The velocity of the plane does not increase the speed of the sound it emits. This is in contrast to what happens to a bomb or some other material object dropped from a plane. Such an object acquires the same forward speed as the plane and, if there is little air resistance, hits the ground just below it. If the object is thrown forward, its speed of propulsion is added to that of the plane and it hits the ground in front of the plane.

Although the velocity of sound is uninfluenced, the plane's motion has some effect on sound issuing from it. It seems not to hurry the "spheres of disturbance" caused by the vibration but to push them closer together, that is, shorten the wavelength or *raise the pitch* of the sound advancing in the direction of the plane. For sound in the opposite direction, the spheres are pulled away so that pitch is lowered. A trained ear can actually discern whether a train is approaching or receding by the sound of its whistle. Light waves do not move in a material medium, but Einstein assumed the same independence of the source that exists for sound waves. That the "pitch" of light waves is affected by motion is backed up by the experimental *Doppler effect*, the shift in the spectrum of rapidly moving stars or nebulae. The same sort of change in spectrum can be observed for all types of electromagnetic waves, and this phenomenon is being used today for the *Doppler tracking* of man-made satellites and, in a sort of reverse procedure, for the new navigation by satellite. There is some empirical evidence, too, of the lack of effect of the source on the speed of light. *Double stars* are stars of about the same mass, close together and revolving about one another. If the speed of the source helped or hindered, then the time taken for light to reach the earth from the member of the pair moving toward us would be shorter than that for the receding partner. Actual observations show that there is no such effect.

By logical deduction from his two postulates Einstein arrived at the Lorentz transformations of Chapter 17. These are the formulas

$$x' = \frac{x - ut}{\sqrt{1 - u^2}} \qquad t' = \frac{t - ux}{\sqrt{1 - u^2}}$$

where the meaning of the letters is the same as in the previous explanation. The distance x and the time t are measurements made by an observer within a linear "cosmos." The consequences of the special theory of relativity indicate that distance and time are relative, and hence measurements of them by different observers need not agree. Now suppose that a second observer resides in a straight-line cosmos which is moving parallel to the first linear universe, with constant speed u. Then the distance and time measurements made by this second observer are x' and t', which are related to x and t by the Lorentz formulas. To simplify the form of these basic transformations, the *unit* of velocity has been taken to be the speed of light. In other words, a value $u = 1/10$ would signify a velocity one-tenth the speed of light, or in everyday units, a speed of about 18,600 miles per second.

The denominator, $\sqrt{1-u^2}$, in the Lorentz formulas, indicates that for physical *reality*, u must be numerically less than 1. If $u = 1$, the denominators are zero and the formulas become meaningless. If u is numerically greater than 1, the denominators are imaginary. The exclusion of values for u numerically equal to or greater than 1 signifies that *no material body can have a velocity equal to or greater than the speed of light*. This is an important theorem of the special theory of relativity.

Consider a case where the speed of another observer, relative to us, has the permissible value $u = 3/5$. Consider the following two events:

$$\text{event I} \quad x = 0 \quad t = 0$$
$$\text{event II} \quad x = 4 \quad t = 2$$

This means that the first event occurred at our origin at "zero hour" and the second occurred 2 seconds later 4 units away ($186{,}000 \times 4 = 744{,}000$ miles away). Then, using the Lorentz transformation, we can find out what the other observer has to say. For event I,

$$x' = \frac{0 - \tfrac{3}{5} \times 0}{\sqrt{1 - (\tfrac{3}{5})^2}} = 0 \qquad t' = \frac{0 - \tfrac{3}{5} \times 0}{\sqrt{1 - (\tfrac{3}{5})^2}} = 0$$

We agree on this event, but for event II,

$$x' = \frac{4 - \tfrac{3}{5} \times 2}{\sqrt{1 - (\tfrac{3}{5})^2}} = 3\tfrac{1}{2} \qquad t' = \frac{2 - \tfrac{3}{5} \times 4}{\sqrt{1 - (\tfrac{3}{5})^2}} = -\tfrac{1}{2}$$

According to the other observer's space standards, the second event is not as far away. Even more startling is the estimate $t' = -\tfrac{1}{2}$, which signifies that in his opinion not only is the time interval between the two events much shorter, but event II occurred before event I, as indicated by the minus sign, since a positive t signifies time *after* the zero hour, and a negative t, time *before*. Thus we see that two observers in the universe may be in complete disagreement on *space* and *time* measurements as well as on the order of events.

When Einstein first pronounced these facts, a Vienna daily carried a headline "Minute in Danger!" To combat such a fear, we must point out that $u = \tfrac{3}{5}$ is not an ordinary speed like that encountered in everyday motions like walking, driving, flying, etc. because it represents $\tfrac{3}{5} \times 186{,}000 = 111{,}600$ mi. per sec. Even the earth as it speeds through the heavens covers a mere 20 mi. per sec. relative to the sun! And so the startling relativity results apply not to observers in trains, planes, even rockets, but to beta particles, for example, which are electrons shot out of the nuclei of radioactive atoms at speeds almost as huge as that of light. The point of view of an individual imagined to inhabit a beta particle would differ so radically from that of the scientist observing him that social life between them could be nothing but a series of violent disagreements!

To see if these observers can agree on anything or, in other words, to try to find some absolute or *invariant* entities, let us consider a set of observers moving with the respective speeds

$$u = \frac{4}{5}, \quad -\frac{4}{5}, \quad \frac{3}{5}, \quad \frac{12}{13}, \quad -\frac{7}{25}$$

relative to us, positive and negative velocities signifying motion to our right and left, respectively. Let our observations give

$$\text{event I} \quad x = 0 \quad t = 0$$

$$\text{event II} \quad x = 8 \quad t = 10$$

As before, all observers will agree on event I. Substitution in the Lorentz transformation will yield the following different estimates of the where and when of event II.

speed	u	0	$\frac{4}{5}$	$-\frac{4}{5}$	$\frac{3}{5}$	$\frac{12}{13}$	$\frac{7}{25}$
distance	x	8	0	$\frac{80}{3}$	$\frac{5}{2}$	$-\frac{16}{5}$	$\frac{135}{12}$
time	t	10	6	$\frac{82}{3}$	$\frac{13}{2}$	$\frac{34}{5}$	$\frac{153}{12}$

No invariant is obvious from the table, but if we compute t^2, x^2, and $t^2 - x^2$ in each case, we obtain

t^2	100	36	$\frac{6724}{9}$	$\frac{169}{4}$	$\frac{1156}{25}$	$\frac{23409}{144}$
x^2	64	0	$\frac{6400}{9}$	$\frac{25}{4}$	$\frac{256}{25}$	$\frac{18225}{144}$
$t^2 - x^2$	36	36	36	36	36	36

Thus, although time and space measurements vary from observer to observer, all will agree that

$$t^2 - x^2 = 36$$

$$\sqrt{t^2 - x^2} = 6$$

It can be shown that this is a general truth, that no matter what the speed u of an observer is, and no matter what event (x,t) we measure, his measurement (x',t') will be such that

$$(t')^2 - (x')^2 = t^2 - x^2$$

This can be proved by performing a little algebraic manipulation on the Lorentz transformation.

This means that although time and space are relative, a certain *mixture* of them is absolute. It is an error to think that because Einstein's theory is called Relativity, all measurements are relative. The mathematician Whitehead chose the name "separation" for the absolute invariant $\sqrt{t^2 - x^2}$. We can see why and can gain more understanding of this new space-time mixture if we chart events on a Cartesian graph. Figure 18.2 shows that when the events $(0, 0)$ and

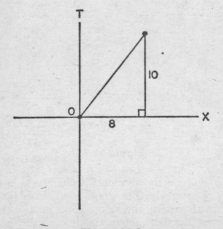

Figure 18.2

$(8, 10)$ are points on such a graph, the actual *distance* between them as given by the Pythagorean theorem is

$$\sqrt{10^2 + 8^2} = \sqrt{164}$$

The separation is obtained by changing the sign in the Pythagorean theorem

$$\sqrt{10^2 - 8^2} = 6$$

and can be thought of as a sort of "pseudodistance."

Plotting events on a Cartesian graph and recognizing separation as algebraically similar to distance give one justification for the name of this invariant. The picture introduces another new element, for we see that to graph events occurring at points of a one-dimensional world gives rise to a two-dimensional picture. If we extend the world of events to all those taking place in a single *plane*, the Cartesian picture will be three-dimensional. If we picture the floor of a room as part of the plane of events (Figure 18.3), then the values

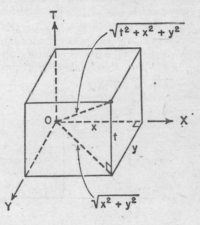

Figure 18.3

of x and y will be the distances from the side (left) and back walls, respectively. The graph of an event (x, y, t) will be a point in the room, the value of the time t being represented by the distance above the floor. The graph of an event will be somewhere in the room on a vertical line through the point in the floor where it occurs.

If the two events are $(0, 0, 0)$—the corner at "zero hour" —and (x, y, t)—anywhere, anytime—then

$$\text{Pythagorean distance} = \sqrt{t^2 + x^2 + y^2}$$

$$\text{separation} = \sqrt{t^2 - x^2 - y^2}$$

Again, algebra will prove that Pythagorean distance varies with the observer, but that separation is invariant.

To picture events occurring at points of a three-dimensional space, a four-dimensional scheme would be necessary. We are not compelled to resort to visualization in this case, but can nevertheless use the associated invariant,

$$\text{separation} = \sqrt{t^2 - x^2 - y^2 - z^2}$$

numerically and algebraically, thus accepting the idea advanced in 1908 by the mathematician Minkowski. He was the first to state that it is logically simpler to regard the universe as a four-dimensional *space-time continuum* rather than to divide our experiences artificially according to unrelated spatial and temporal aspects, especially since different observers will hold divergent opinions on how the division should be effected.

To return to our one-dimensional world and two-dimensional space-time picture, let us compute the separation of (0, 0) and (4, 2). It is equal to

$$\sqrt{4 - 16} = \sqrt{-12}$$

This is an *imaginary* separation! Whenever x is greater in numerical value than t, the separation will be imaginary. Since the unit is equal to the speed of light, $x = 4$ is the distance light will travel in 4 seconds. Then, with the pair of events (0, 0) and (4, 2), if a light signal were sent from the place where the first event occurs (the origin), describing that event, it could not arrive at the place where the second event occurs *prior to* this second occurrence. Whatever happens at the first locality cannot be a "warning" to the second, influence it, or exert a "force" on it in any way. In other words, there can be no *causal* connection between the two events.

A little earlier we saw that a different observer would measure the event (4, 2) as (3½, −½). Still he would obtain the separation as

$$\sqrt{\frac{1}{4} - \frac{49}{4}} = \sqrt{-12}$$

and so would all observers in uniform relative motion. Now we see why the fact that the second observer does not agree on the order of the two events does not matter in this case. The points where the events occurred will, in any frame of reference, be too far apart for causal connection or exertion of any "force," since the distance will have to be numerically greater than the time to ensure a negative value of $t^2 - x^2$ and an imaginary separation. This is just another way of saying that *no force can be propagated with a speed greater than that of light*.

In general, then, an imaginary separation signifies no causal connection. By contrast, a real separation would permit signaling. It can be shown algebraically, by using the Lorentz transformation, that in this particular case, although observers may disagree on the length of time intervals, they will never disagree on the *order* of events. When separation is real, then, a causal connection between two events is possible.

We have been considering events occurring at *different* places. If we were following the life history of an individual, however, different events might occur at the *same* place as far as his measurements are concerned. (If the individual were a human being with reference frame on earth, his personal motion in space would be so tiny in comparison with our unit of 186,000 miles that for practical purposes, he could consider himself permanently at rest.) Then for him event I $= (0, 0)$ and event II $= (0, t)$, and

$$separation = \sqrt{t^2 - 0^2} = t$$

The separation of the events would be identical with his measure of the time between them. Hence, for self-observation, *separation is a synonym for time*, and the choice of name for this invariant has additional justification. We remark, in passing, that separation could never be imaginary for events happening to the same individual, since $x = 0$ in such a case, and hence only t^2, which has to be positive, contributes to the value under the square root sign.

For an observer whose world is moving past with speed u, if $x = 0$,

$$t' = \frac{t - u \cdot 0}{\sqrt{1 - u^2}} = \frac{t}{\sqrt{1 - u^2}}$$

or the first observer's time t is given by

$$t = t'\sqrt{1 - u^2}$$

and hence is *less* than the time as recorded by any other observer because the factor $\sqrt{1 - u^2}$ is less than 1 in value.

The measurement by an individual of the time interval between two events occurring at the same place is called the *proper time* for the individual and, as just indicated, is less than the estimate made by any other observer. It is the time as measured by his own clock and, as it gives much smaller estimates of intervals than the clocks of observers moving at tremendous speeds relative to him, the latter observers will say his clock "runs slow."

In the early days of relativity, spinners of popular science yarns had as a favorite plot the tale of two friends parted in youth, one of the pair traveling into space at a velocity close to that of light, while the other remained quietly at home on earth. When the wanderer eventually returned from his lengthy journey he was still to all appearances a boy in his teens, although by earthly reckoning he had to be counted an octogenarian. His stay-at-home friend looked old enough to be his great-grandfather.

The explanation of this apparent paradox was that the traveler took his clock with him. It was at rest relative to his surroundings and measured his proper time. If we think of his speed as being 0.99 (that is 99% of the velocity of light), then he will think of himself as at rest and consider the earth to be receding from him with this speed. If the boys part at the age of eight, and 70 years elapse on earth, then the proper time for the wanderer as measured by his own clock will be given by

$$t = t'\sqrt{1 - u^2}$$

$$= 70\sqrt{1 - (0.99)^2}$$

$$= 70 \times 0.14$$

$$= 9.8 \text{ years}$$

and he will be only eighteen years of age by his own standards, whereas his friend will be seventy-eight.

This is naturally a fantasy, but has some scientific justification in the fact that the human heart vibrates and so, like a pendulum, is a clock. Hence its beating should also be affected by rapid motion if we are to be consistent about the relativity of time. If an individual is in rapid motion relative to the earth, then by his own standards his heart may beat 72 times per minute. Since the results of *counting* are absolute, we will count 72 heart vibrations, but in a longer interval as measured by our own clocks, for the traveler was considering one minute of his proper time. In other words, we consider all his clocks to run slow, his heart being one of them. Since the same retardation affects all the metabolic processes in the body, it can be said that the wanderer "ages" less than the person remaining at home.

To consider other consequences of the special relativity theory, let us return for a moment to Minkowski's space-time picture, limiting ourselves once more to events on a one-dimensional straight line as graphed in a two-dimensional chart. Let the creatures existing in the one-dimensional space be insects crawling along OX (they cannot jump or fly). The events occurring in the life of an insect will form a continuous curve, the graph of each event lying on a line perpendicular to OX at the point x, where the event occurs. In Figure 18.4, P is the graph of the event at p, Q the rep-

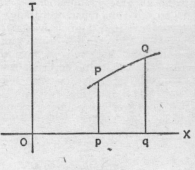

Figure 18.4

resentation of that at q, etc. Different insects will have different curves of events, or *world-lines*, as Minkowski called them. If this picture is generalized, individuals existing in 3-dimensional space will have world-lines in a 4-dimensional space-time continuum, which is a convenient mathematical abstraction, not something to be visualized.

In the 2-dimensional space-time continuum, an insect that remains permanently at rest at the origin will have the T-axis (OT) as its world-line, and if it is at rest at any other point, the world-line will be parallel to the T-axis. There are no world-lines parallel to the X-axis because this would signify that time stands still while the insect moves! Such lines are not world-lines, but can be considered "cross-sections" of the insect's space-time. They give all possible insect locations for a specific time, since t is constant along these lines, while x varies.

If the insect starts at the origin and moves to the right with a constant speed of ½ unit per second, its progress chart will be

$$t \quad 0 \quad 1 \quad 2 \quad 4 \text{ etc.}$$
$$x \quad 0 \quad \tfrac{1}{2} \quad 1 \quad 2$$

This is no ordinary insect, to be sure, but some nuclear particle moving at ½ unit = 93,000 miles per second. Then the formula connecting distance and time for this "insect" is

$$x = \tfrac{1}{2}t$$

This is the equation of its world-line, which is straight. If the insect moves with variable speed, its world-line is broken or curved. If its speed is any constant k, the equation of its world-line is

$$x = kt$$

Since material things can never achieve the speed of light, k must be numerically less than 1. The equations

$$x = t \quad \text{and} \quad x = -t$$

represent the world-lines of light rays moving right or left from the origin. All other world-lines, straight or curved,

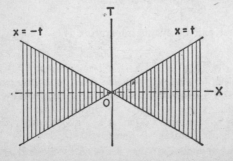

Figure 18.5

are thus restricted to the unshaded sector of the space-time continuum pictured in Figure 18.5. Only a portion of space-time is allotted to material objects. If we use a more *human* scale in our graph, this restriction will appear slight. If the unit on the X-axis is taken as 1 mile instead of 186,000, the shaded or "forbidden" area will look like that in Figure 18.6, except that it will be a much thinner sector, and therefore exclude only a small portion of the space-time continuum.

If we study a particular world-line like

$$x = \frac{5}{13} t$$

the chart for insect progress is

t	0	13	26	39	52	. . .	104
x	0	5	10	15	20	. . .	40

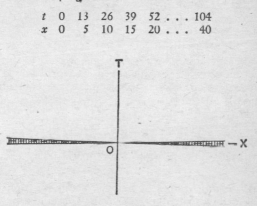

Figure 18.6

For the first pair of events, *separation* is

$$\sqrt{13^2 - 5^2} = 12$$

and since the intervals are equal, it will be 12 for every consecutive pair. Computing the separation of the first and last events

$$\sqrt{104^2 - 40^2} = 96$$

which is what common sense leads us to expect, since there are 8 intervals of 12 each.

In Euclidean geometry a straight line segment is the

shortest distance between two points. In contrast to this it can be proved that separation obeys an opposite law. A straight line segment represents the *longest* separation between two points. If a world-line is curved or broken (Figure 18.7), the separation of the last event from the first is

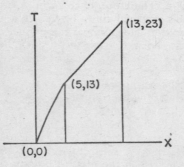

Figure 18.7

greater than the sum of the separations between successive events measured along the world-line. We shall not give a general proof but, for the sake of simplicity, we shall limit ourselves to an illustration. Take the events $(0, 0)$, $(5, 13)$, and $(13, 23)$. The separations are

I to II $\sqrt{13^2 - 5^2} = 12$

II to III $\sqrt{10^2 - 8^2} = 6$

I to III $\sqrt{23^2 - 13^2} = \sqrt{360} = 18.96$

The separation of I and III is almost 19, whereas the sum of the separations is only 18. To realize the significance of this fact, notice that the world-line from I to II represents a motion covering 5 units of distance in 13 seconds of time, that is, a motion with speed 5/13. Similarly, the world-line from II to III pictures a motion with speed 4/5. Then the broken world-line from I to II to III shows the progress of an insect moving *nonuniformly*. It would start with one velocity and later change abruptly to a more rapid one. By contrast, the straight world-line from I to III represents a *uniform* motion with speed 13/23.

So it is that insects whose world-lines are straight, signifying that they are either *at rest* or in *uniform* motion, will have greater separations than if these lines were broken or curved. For an object at rest, separation has been shown to signify personal or proper time. If a body is in uniform motion relative to an observer, relativity permits an individual situated on this body to judge himself at rest and the observer in motion. Therefore, once again separation becomes that individual's personal time. In the light of this equivalence of separation and personal time, the fact that separation is greatest along a straight line can be stated thus: *Proper time between two events will be a maximum for bodies at rest or in uniform motion.* This rule of behavior has sometimes been called the "law of cosmic laziness," and in relativity theory takes the place of the "path of least resistance."

One consequence of the Einstein theory is that, in addition to the fact that distance and time measurements depend on the observer making them, there is relativity of *mass* as well. Newton described the mass of a body as the quantity of matter it contains and defined it by means of his second law of motion in terms of "force" and change in *velocity*. Since velocity is no longer absolute in relativity, and "gravitational force" is ruled out by the general relativity theory, which we shall shortly discuss, we should expect a modification of the concept of mass.

Long before Einstein, physicists J. J. Thomson and W. Kaufmann had found that the movement of electrons with a very high velocity u causes an apparent increase of mass equal to approximately $\frac{1}{2}mu^2$. The mathematics of relativity agrees with this, for it indicates that if m is the mass of a body at rest in a particular frame of reference, which has speed u relative to an observer, this observer will obtain

$$\frac{m}{\sqrt{1 - u^2}}$$

as his estimate of the mass. Since $u = 1$ for the speed of light, u is a fairly small fraction even for high electron speeds. For such small values of u, algebra indicates that

$$\frac{m}{\sqrt{1 - u^2}} = m + \frac{1}{2}mu^2 \text{ (approximately)}$$

This means that the original mass m is increased by $1/2mu^2$, the same fact obtained in the experiments of Thomson and Kaufmann.

For example, if $m = 1$ and $u = 7/25$,

$$\frac{m}{\sqrt{1 - u^2}} = \frac{25}{24} = 1.04$$

$$m + \frac{1}{2} mu^2 = 1 + \frac{49}{1250} = 1.04 \text{ (a 4\% increase in mass)}$$

The expression $1/2mu^2$ is called the *kinetic energy* of a body, that is, the amount of work it is capable of doing by virtue of its motion. The term *potential energy* is used for the work it can do by virtue of its position, for example, the work possibility inherent in a compressed spring or a rock at the edge of a cliff. In the expression $m + 1/2mu^2$, if the second term is *energy* and the terms are to be combined, the first term must also represent some sort of energy. Since m is the *rest* mass, it is like a rock or spring at rest, and hence m can be thought of as potential energy. Then, in the expression above, the observer's measure of the mass of a body is partly potential and partly kinetic energy, but it is energy of one kind or another. This is the principle of the *equivalence of mass and energy* used in nuclear theory.

The term $1/2mu^2$ is a good approximation if u is small, but even if u is as small as $1/1000$, for example, its value in ordinary units like centimeters per second would be huge—3×10^7—and when squared, tremendously greater—9×10^{14}. If this figure is multiplied by $1/2m$ even for m as tiny as electron mass, the value of $1/2mu^2$, increase in mass, will be enormous in terms of ordinary energy units.

Although the Einstein formula

$$E = mc^2$$

is used in a somewhat different connotation, where matter is "annihilated" and converted into energy, there is a kinship in form to

$$\tfrac{1}{2}mu^2$$

in that we square a speed to obtain the energy associated with a mass, the speed c signifying that of light, which is 1 unit in relativity reasoning but 3×10^{10} measured in centimeters per second. Hence $c^2 = 9 \times 10^{20}$, so that even if m is the tiny mass of a nuclear particle, the product of its size by 9×10^{20} will be enormous, a fact basic in nuclear bombs as well as in more peaceful uses of nuclear energy.

The general theory of relativity, launched by Einstein in 1917, takes into account frames of reference with *variable* velocity relative to one another. The mathematics involved is not, as originally claimed, so difficult that it is comprehensible to only a dozen mortals, and in the next chapter, we shall give details of its fundamental concepts.

Chapter 19

Geometry for Universe Builders

The purpose of the general theory of relativity, like that of the special theory, is to distinguish the subjective impressions of individual observers from the reality of the thing being observed. By the addition of only one new postulate called the principle of equivalence, Einstein developed a physical concept more adequate than Newton's law of gravitation and one which is able to explain experimental facts that had defied classic theory and puzzled physicists and astronomers for a long time.

To see why "gravitational force" is not absolute but a matter of relative opinion depending on who is making the observation, consider the example of Newton and the famous falling apple. Suppose that you, instead of Newton, are an observer and that you are located in an elevator with opaque, shut doors. Unknown to you, the supports break and the controls fail. Emulating Newton, you let go of an apple. It appears to remain at rest, poised in mid-air, and hence *you* observe *no force* on it. But we say that this happens because you, the elevator, and the apple are all falling in the same way without your knowledge of it.

In your frame of reference, then, things do not fall, and no special force or influence makes its presence known. In relation to your frame of reference, there is no gravitation. Just as +32 will balance —32 in addition, giving zero as sum, so gravitational force, as we conceive it, is apparently neutralized by the elevator's motion, and hence must be numerically equivalent to it, but opposite in effect.

This is the basis of Einstein's *principle of equivalence*, which states: If attention is confined to a small region of space, *a gravitational field at rest is equivalent to a frame of reference moving with uniform acceleration in a field free of gravitation*, and it is impossible to devise any experiment that will distinguish between the two.

This means that any observer, like the man in the elevator, can select a frame of reference moving in such a way that in his *immediate neighborhood* all gravitational effects are neutralized, and consequently, in this small vicinity, the *restricted theory of relativity holds true.* By a small neighborhood we mean a tiny *space-time* region surrounding a point or event in his world-line, so that to apply the special theory in the presence of matter and its accompanying "gravitational field," the observer can pick a neutralizing frame of reference, but that will serve for a short time only. He must change that frame as time passes, for he will be in a new space-time region even if he considers himself at rest. For example, in the 2-dimensional space-time previously pictured, an observer at rest had a world-line parallel to the T-axis. As time passes, the events would be pictured on different portions of this line and would occupy different neighborhoods of the 2-dimensional space-time world.

In the observer's opinion, if his world-line is straight, signifying rest or uniform motion, his separation will be a maximum, as previously explained. Since separation is invariant, other observers will also agree that it is a maximum, but may not consider the world-line straight because they may not be in the same space-time neighborhood. Thus observers who exist far apart in 3-dimensional space or are widely separated in time—in other words, those who are remote when the customary mixture of space-time measures their separation—will agree on maximum properties but not on "straightness" versus *curvature.*

As a result, one fact of the restricted theory must be modified, namely, the "law of cosmic laziness." The route for maximum separation need not be straight. In the general theory, one says that the presence of matter *distorts* space-time in its neighborhood, and for that reason the world-line of maximum separation (the customary mathematical name for such a line is *geodesic*) is distorted into a *curve*. Let us picture a crumpling of the flat 2-dimensional space-time in which the world-lines of Chapter 18 were drawn. Then the straight lines in the diagrams would be wrinkled, possibly distorted into curves.

According to Newton, a planet describes an elliptic path around the sun because there is an attractive "gravitational force" between sun and planet, but according to the general theory of relativity, the matter in the sun causes distortion of the space-time in its neighborhood, and the planet's world-line of maximum separation has to be curved in order to conform to the curved continuum on which it is drawn. Thus the notion of gravitational force is relinquished. Curved paths or other effects (attributed to gravitation in Newtonian theory) occur only because following particular routes leads to maximum separation in space-time or, stated otherwise, because bodies follow the "law of cosmic laziness." Our education has conditioned us to believe to such a degree in a force tugging at things and making them fall that it is hard to get away from the idea. Surely it is easier to believe that our earth or the other planets are just lazy and fall "into the groove," than to believe that the sun exercises some remote control, holding invisible reins 93,000,000 miles or more in length.

Perhaps we can help ourselves out by an analogy. Before 550 B.C. the belief that our earth was flat was almost universal. Even later, the idea of sphericity was slow in gaining acceptance. Early maps made in accordance with the theory of a flat earth served very well until the new countries discovered and added to the flat map began to introduce inconsistencies. A *Mercator's projection* is a flat map whose distortions suggest what can happen. If you examine such a map, you will notice the apparent hugeness of Greenland in comparison to its size as mapped on a globe. The earliest cartographers did not use a sphere to map the earth, and hence in the days before Ptolemy, who understood the problem, people would have supposed that the flat maps gave the true size of faraway countries like Greenland. Inevitably, explorers of such a region would report that journeys there seemed much shorter than the maps indicated. Believing the map to be a correct representation of geographic facts, they might invent a theory that there was a *force* in this part of the world causing distances to shrink whenever explorers appeared on the scene. Our modern knowledge of the spherical shape of the earth would eliminate this theory, show that no force of the sort exists, and indicate that the effect is caused by the curvature of the earth. This is a 2-dimensional analogy indicating how a phenomenon produced by curvature might appear, at first conjecture, to be caused by some "force."

Space-time is curved here and there, wherever matter is

present. The 2-dimensional analogy would be the surface of the skin with blisters on certain spots, or a golf course with hummocks drawing a ball off its straight course. The combined distortion of space-time by all the matter in the universe causes it to bend back on itself and close. As a crude 2-dimensional analogy, if we take a flat sector of a circle (Figure 19.1) and curve it sufficiently, we can close it so

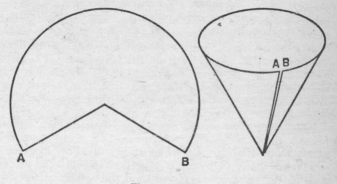

Figure 19.1

as to get a conical drinking cup. A cross-section of this cup would be circular or oval, a geometric curve that might be described as *finite, but unbounded,* since we can go round and round it in spite of its limited length. This is a one-dimensional cross-section of a closed 2-dimensional continuum. In the Einstein theory, *space* is considered a *finite but unbounded* 3-dimensional cross-section of a closed 4-dimensional space-time continuum. (It is not closed in the *time* direction, much as the conical drinking cup is not, for some of its cross-sections would be two straight lines in V-formation meeting at one end and open at the other.)

Still another item of the general relativity theory becomes clearer through a 2-dimensional analogy. If we consider geometry on the surface of a sphere, straight lines would be replaced by great-circle arcs, for these would be shortest distances, or geodesics (term used for minima *or* maxima, that is, for extrema). A triangle would be bounded by three great-circle arcs, and the sum of its angles would be greater than 180°. We can visualize, for example (Figure 19.2), the spherical triangle formed by the half of the prime meridian extending from North Pole to Equator, the same part of the meridian through New York City, and the slice of the Equator between the feet of these meridians. The angles at the feet would each be 90°, and the angle at the Pole would equal 74°, the longitude of New York, so that the total would be 254°. On the sphere we have a 2-dimensional continuum with a non-Euclidean geometry of the Riemannian type. If, however, we think of the space inside and outside the sphere, we have a 3-dimensional continuum with straight-line geodesics, and we can go back to Euclid after all. By analogy, in the 4-dimensional space-time continuum of relativity, distances obey a non-Euclidean geometry.

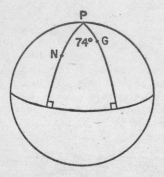

Figure 19.2

Again, Euclidean geometry can be employed by going outside, but in this case, six extra dimensions have to be added. Since it is all a matter of abstract terminology, we do not have to trouble ourselves about how this would look.

The ultimate test of a theory is its application, and the Einstein theory has been amply backed up in this way. Where speed is small compared to that of light, or "weak" gravitational fields exist because of "small" masses like the earth, Einstein's predictions agree with Newton's. To find phenomena inconsistent with Newtonian mechanics, Einstein had to go beyond mundane space-time neighborhoods. His first case was that of the planet Mercury, close to the sun, a relatively large mass with a considerable gravitational field to which Mercury is strongly exposed. This planet does not move exactly as predicted by Newton's theory, for then it would describe virtually the same elliptical orbit over and over again in relation to the fixed stars. Newton allowed a slight "perturbation" or shift in the orbit because of the influence of other planets, but the *observed* amount of shift in the orbit was greater than the classic theory permitted, and the discrepancy had never been satisfactorily explained. The calculations of the orbit based on the Einstein theory agree more closely with observation.

The second test of the Einstein theory was more impressive because it was a matter of *complete prediction* from the theory, of facts never before observed. It concerned the effect of the curvature of space on the path of light rays. If the corpuscular theory of light is accepted, then as light from a distant star passes near the sun, it must, according to Newton, be bent toward the sun, because that body exerts gravitational attraction on the corpuscles. The amount of this deflection as computed by Einstein's general theory was double that figured from Newtonian theory. This cannot be checked ordinarily, since the sun's brilliance makes it impossible to see the star rays passing near, but total eclipses furnish an opportunity. British expeditions to observe such eclipses in Brazil and West Africa in 1919, as well as observations of later eclipses, confirmed Einstein's prediction beyond a doubt.

The third of the tests was connected with a fact mentioned in the previous chapter, namely, that the vibration of an atom is like the oscillation of a clock pendulum. The mathematics of the general theory indicates that the atom clock is slowed up near the sun, in comparison to a clock of the same atom on earth. The effect should be a shift in its spectrum toward the slow or red end. For the sun, this shift is too slight to lend itself readily to experimental verification, but there is a companion star of Sirius, known as a "white dwarf," for which it is believed that the density is as much as a ton per cubic inch. Consequently it sets up a gravitational field of so great an intensity in its neighborhood as to make it ideal for testing the hypothesis of spectral shift. Observations made by the astronomer Adams at Mt. Wilson agreed with Einstein's prediction. Very fine measurements made by Evershed in 1927 gave evidence of a shift toward the red even in the vicinity of the sun, where the shift is small.

Having sketched, in outline, the major features of the general theory of relativity, we shall now present some of the actual details of the mathematics involved. As in the case of restricted relativity, the subject matter can once more be described as *geometry*, in this case, the kind of geometry developed by Gauss and Riemann. Klein's ideas are still pertinent, because transformations and invariants are still important. However, the sets of transformations involved will not, in general, be groups.

Just as the surveying procedures of antiquity provided the physical basis for the principle of relativity of Euclidean metric geometry, modern geodetic problems stimulated the theoretic geometry that is the first step toward general relativity. Let us then consider what would be done by surveyors required to make measurements and subsequently to map a hilly region overgrown with forests. The transit would be of little use to them because the density of growth would make it difficult to make proper sights. It would become a matter of chaining—stretching the steel tape along the ground, setting up and measuring triangles. One triangle is contiguous with the next one, and a step-by-step advance through the woods is made. A triangle is determined by its three sides; that is, when surveyors have measurements for the lengths of sides, it is merely a matter of trigonometric computation to find the angles and the area.

Euclidean plane geometry would not be valid in an extensive geodetic survey, because the earth is a spheroid and not a flat surface. Even when the area under study is not huge, it may be impossible to consider the whole of it as the physical analogue of some figure in Euclid's plane. But regions that are relatively tiny portions of *any* curved surface may be considered as approximately flat. Applying Euclidean metric geometry to very small successive portions of such a curved surface, and then linking each region to the next, is the surveying tactic corresponding to the abstract mathematical subject called *infinitesimal* or *differential geometry*.

Some minor, very elementary aspects of this branch of mathematics were developed soon after Newton and Leibniz, but the tool that would ultimately survey the hills of the universe was developed in 1828 by the greatest "surveyor" of them all, Carl Friedrich Gauss. Mathematicians agree that Gauss should rank first among creative mathematical thinkers of the nineteenth century, and many scientists believe that Archimedes, Newton, and Gauss are the three all-time greatest. Gauss's creativity extended to many mathematical areas and, in particular, his *Disquisitiones generales circa superficies curvas* (1827) initiated a triumphal era for differential geometry. Concerning theoretical geometry, Gauss wrote to the astronomer Bessel: "All the measurements in the world are not the equivalent of a single theorem that produces a significant advance in our greatest of sciences."

Nevertheless, geodetic counterparts of concepts and propositions are clarifying. Hence one may envision surveyors who cover part of the mountainside with a network of curved lines (Figure 19.3) and mark intersections by stakes or fortuitously situated trees. The curved streets and avenues are numbered $u = 0, 1, 2, 3$, etc., and $v = 0, 1, 2, 3$, etc. Intermediate streets and avenues are thought of as having appropriate fractional or decimal values. Thus a one-to-one correspondence is set up between points of the region and u-v coordinate pairs. This seems very much akin to Descartes' scheme. The difference is that *Gaussian* coordinates give location but tell nothing about distance. Neither the u-curves nor the v-curves are necessarily equidistant and, in general, u-curves do not intersect v-curves at right angles. The values of u and v are just numbers that assign an order to the network curves. But when we state that a point P (Figure 19.3) has Gaussian coordinates $(3, 4)$, we give no information about its distance from the origin or any other point. If these were Cartesian coordinates, we would know at once that the distance from the origin is 5 units.

That Gaussian coordinates serve to *locate* but *not to measure* should not seem strange to city dwellers, for if we state that the Metropolitan Museum of Art is located at 83rd Street and 5th Avenue in New York City or has coordinates $(83, 5)$, we cannot automatically find its distance from $(42, 8)$, since New York City blocks are not all the same length.

Long before Gauss's day, curvilinear coordinates were employed to locate points on the earth's surface. The meridians and the latitude circles form the traditional network; the longitude and latitude of a point are its coordinates, but do not represent distance from prime meridian or equator. Saying that a ship has traveled east through 6° of longitude does not tell us the length of the trip. Near the equator, such a journey would cover 400 miles, whereas at latitude 60°N. it would mean 200 miles. In both cases, the arc along which the voyage takes place is $6/360 = 1/60$ of the entire circle of latitude—the equator or the sixtieth parallel, respectively. When a network is made up of straight lines or circles, each line of the network is alike in all its parts, or *homogeneous*, and that is why distances along such a line change in proportion to Gaussian coordinates. In previous chapters, changes in variables were symbolized by Δx, Δy, etc. We now make use of the symbols dx, dy, etc. whenever the changes are very small. Without going too deeply into mathematical meanings, we can say that the symbol d has *approximately* the same meaning as Δ for small changes. If

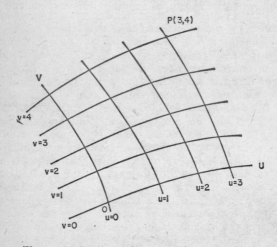

Figure 19.3   Gaussian coordinate system

the changes in distance and longitude of a ship traveling due east or west are small, they can be symbolized by ds and du (d for difference), and according to what we have just said $ds/C = du/360$ or $ds = k\ du$, where C is the length of the circumference of the circle of latitude and $k = C/360$.

In the same way, if a city block is short, and houses along it are fairly uniform in size, then (the front door of) number 810 will be approximately at the center of a block whose corner houses are numbered 800 and 820. If the block is 90 yards in length, 810 will be about 45 years from either corner. In this case,

$$ds = 4.5\ du$$

and for other small blocks of the same sort,

$$ds = k\ du$$

where in each particular block k is a constant depending on the length of the block and the number of houses on it.

In general, the curves of a Gaussian network are not homogeneous. Since we are studying *infinitesimal* geometry, however, each mesh is relatively tiny (compared to the entire surface) and is considered, for purposes of approximation, to be a Euclidean parallelogram. Then distances along two sides of a single mesh—for example, $OABC$ in Figure 19.4—follow the same rule as for short city streets, and

$$ds = k_1 du \qquad \text{(along } OA \text{ or parallel to it)}$$

$$ds = k_2 dv \qquad \text{(along } OC \text{ or parallel to it)}$$

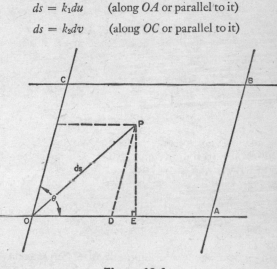

Figure 19.4

The surveyors now measure OA and OC and find their lengths to be 16.2 and 11.4 meters, respectively. Suppose that the rulings of the meshwork are numbered by consecutive integers. Then

$$du = 1 \qquad \text{and} \qquad dv = 1$$

Therefore, in parallelogram $OABC$,

$$16.2 = k_1(1) \qquad \text{and} \qquad 11.4 = k_2(1)$$

Hence

$$ds = 16.2 \, du \text{ along } OA \text{ or parallel to it}$$

and

$$ds = 11.4 \, dv \text{ along } OC \text{ or parallel to it.}$$

To obtain the distance from O of *any point* P within the small parallelogram, one can apply the Pythagorean formula (Figure 19.4) to right triangles OPE and DPE in order to derive what is called the *law of cosines* in trigonometry. From this law (which, we wish to emphasize, is merely a corollary of the Pythagorean theorem) it follows that

$$(ds)^2 = (OP)^2 = (OD)^2 + (DP)^2 + 2(OD)(DP)\cos\theta$$

where θ represents the size of angle AOC of the parallelogram. But OD and DP are distances along OA and parallel to OC, respectively. Hence

$$OD = 16.2 \, du \text{ (meters)}$$

and

$$DP = 11.4 \, dv \text{ (meters)}$$

Our surveyors may be able to measure angle AOC by using a theodolite. If this is difficult, they will measure OB by chaining. Then the three sides of triangle OAB will be known, and it will be possible to compute the size of angle A by a trigonometric formula. Suppose Angle A is found to measure $108°$. Then angle AOC is $72°$. Now cosine $72° = 0.309$ (approximately) and the above formula for ds^2 becomes

$$ds^2 = 262.44 \, du^2 + 114.13 \, du\, dv + 129.96 \, dv^2$$

This formula applies to every point of the small parallelogram; for example, if Q is the point for which $du = 0.2$, $dv = 0.1$, substitution in the distance formula gives

$$ds^2 = 14.08$$

and

$$ds = 3.75 \text{ meters}$$

The surveyors will now proceed from mesh to mesh, and by measuring two adjacent sides and an angle, or two sides and a diagonal, obtain a distance formula for each infinitesimal parallelogram. If it should happen that in some region the surveyors construct meshes that are *square*, then $k_1 = k_2$

and $\theta = 90°$, so that cos $\theta = 0$. If $k_1 = k_2 = 1$, then in this region,

$$ds^2 = du^2 + dv^2$$

which is just the ordinary Pythagorean formula. This would occur for *all* meshes only in very special surveys, as we shall see. Again, in general, the proportionality factors k_1 and k_2 will vary in different meshes (as they do on different city blocks). Hence the *coefficients* of du^2, $du\,dv$, dv^2 will differ from mesh to mesh. These coefficients depend on the position of the infinitestimal parallelogram, or, in technical language, they are *functions* of the position, that is, of u and v.

The reader will be correct if he judges field work to be a long drawn-out process. But Gauss's *theory* of differential geometry is pure mathematics. Abstract surfaces are idealizations of the reality, and can be described by simple algebraic formulas. Then calculus, instead of the surveyor's tape, is used to obtain the coefficients of the local distance formula, which is usually symbolized by

$$ds^2 = g_{11}du^2 + 2g_{12}du\,dv + g_{22}dv^2$$

where one or more of the coefficients g_{11}, g_{12}, g_{22} may be constants for some surfaces, but generally are expressions involving u and v, for, as we have just remarked, the coefficients usually vary with position on the surface. In other words, in Gaussian differential geometry, a *single* formula for ds^2, called the *metric*, in which g_{11}, g_{12}, and g_{22} are functions of u and v, serves for measurement in *all* small meshes of the surface.

For example, it can be shown that, if u and v represent the longitude and latitude of a point on a spherical surface whose radius is one unit of length, then

$$ds^2 = \cos^2 v\,du^2 + dv^2$$

Here $g_{11} = \cos^2 v$ and hence depends on v, the latitude; $g_{12} = 0$ and $g_{22} = 1$.

Again, on a surface called a *hyperbolic paraboloid* (whose appearance resembles the saddle of Figure 10.1) it is possible to select the curves of a network to be two sets of parabolas such that the metric for the surface (with the mesh system chosen) is

$$ds^2 = (1 + 4u^2)du^2 - 8uv\,du\,dv + (1 + 4v^2)dv^2$$

and

$$g_{11} = 1 + 4u^2$$
$$g_{12} = -4uv$$
$$g_{22} = 1 + 4v^2$$

so that all three coefficients vary with position on the surface, as is generally the case for the metric of a surface.

Since the values of g_{11}, g_{12}, g_{22} at each point of a surface determine the measurements in a small region surrounding the point, we may say that the expressions for the g's represent the entire metric geometry of the surface. As an illustration, consider on the above hyperbolic paraboloid the point for which $u = 1$, $v = 2$. The generalized Pythagorean theorem for a small region of the paraboloid close to this point is found by substituting these values of u and v in the above expressions for g_{11}, g_{12}, g_{22} to obtain 5, -8, 17, and

$$ds^2 = 5\,du^2 - 16\,du\,dv + 17dv^2$$

This specific formula will give any distances required in surveying or mapping the small area in question. If, however, one is interested in measuring distances on the part of the surface near $u = 2$, $v = 3$, then

$$ds^2 = 17du^2 - 48\,du\,dv + 37dv^2$$

that is, a different distance formula obtains. From the metric, all local distance formulas can be obtained by substituting particular values of u and v. Therefore the metric or general expression for ds^2 contains in a nutshell the entire geometry of a surface.

Since the two systems of curves forming a network are selected in a rather *arbitrary* fashion, it is remarkable that a single formula for the metric ds^2—that is, a set of coefficients g_{11}, g_{12}, g_{22}, resulting from a scheme chosen almost *at random*—should fix the measurement of an *entire* surface and thus determine, as it were, the nature of a 2-dimensional "space." That this is the case, however, has been indicated above and will now be emphasized in several different ways.

Each type of geometry discussed in a previous chapter required a special principle of relativity, with a group of permissible transformations of the network. The geometric properties of figures were the *invariants* for all transformations of the group, that is, for all permissible mesh systems. Except that transformation sets need *not* be groups, a similar relativistic point of view holds good for differential geometry. Different networks of curves may be chosen on a mountainside being surveyed. Thus meridians and latitude circles are not a unique framework for locating points of a sphere. By transforming a meshwork to another permissible frame of reference, one obtains a different set of coefficients, g_{11}', g_{12}', g_{22}', for the metric, but since the same distance is involved, ds^2 must be *invariant*. In differential geometry, there are transformations which express the new coefficients in terms of the original g_{11}, g_{12}, g_{22}. The curvilinear systems permitted by Gauss were of infinite variety and quite arbitrary except for two requirements—first, that they be continuously curved and, second, that they cover the surface singly without gaps. Similarly the transformations to other mesh works $u' = \phi(u, v)$, $v' = \psi(u, v)$ have great freedom, being restricted only by the need to have certain desirable analytic properties. Thus the functions $\phi(u, v)$, $\psi(u, v)$ must have continuous partial derivatives (Chapter 9) of the first and second orders.

While we are discussing Gaussian mesh systems, let us indicate that we may have *straight* lines in the framework even when a surface is curved. For example, the "meridians" on a cylinder or cone are straight. From another point of view, we can employ non-rectangular networks in the *plane*, like the *oblique* and *polar* systems in Figures 7.3 and 7.18 which have the respective metrics

$$ds^2 = du^2 + 2g_{12}\, du\, dv + dv^2$$

and

$$ds^2 = du^2 + u^2\, dv^2$$

In summary, then, the expression for the metric of any surface is dependent on two entirely different factors, the first being a "relative" matter—the particular network or frame of reference—and the second an "absolute" issue—the nature of the surface itself, that is, whether it is a plane or a sphere or an ellipsoid or a paraboloid, etc.

In discussing the methods of differential geometry, emphasis has been placed on the advantages of curvilinear networks for location and measurement on curved surfaces. But the feature of Gaussian geometry that has become most important in relation to relativity is its *intrinsic* nature, the fact that the surface leaves its stamp on the metric. The set of possible frameworks and the g's are *internal* aspects of the surface and have nothing to do with surrounding space. Longitude and latitude, for example, and all the geographical facts connected with them are defined in terms of the earth's surface. If one were to use, instead of a curvilinear network of longitude and latitude lines on the surface, a Cartesian system with origin at the earth's center and axes along three mutually perpendicular diameters, one would have to refer to *extrinsic* or external points, lines, and planes. This would be very inconvenient since it would necessitate the taking of measurements below the earth's surface, near its hot center, etc., and thus things are simplified by having reference frames right on the surface. When it is a matter of applying geometry to relativity theory, understanding is enhanced if one can avoid the conception of points external to physical 3-dimensional space or of points outside Minkowski's 4-dimensional space-time continuum. In the latter case, *intrinsic* observations of x, y, z are made by means of measuring rods, and clocks furnish the values of t; there is no notion of looking at things from a vantage point in some mystic, nonphysical 5-dimensional continuum.

A special advantage of intrinsic geometry is its ready generalization. Since it requires *two* coordinates (u, v), to locate a point on an ordinary surface, we say that a surface is a two-dimensional "space" or *manifold*. If Cartesian coordinates are used, a relation among *three* of them, (x,y,z), is needed in order to describe such a manifold. For example, the equation $x^2 + y^2 + z^2 = r^2$ describes the surface of a sphere. Similarly, a 3-dimensional continuum would require four Cartesian coordinates for its expression but only three Gaussian coordinates (u_1, u_2, u_3). Again, four Gaussian coordinates (u_1, u_2, u_3, u_4) give location in abstract 4-dimensional spaces or manifolds. In a pure mathematical sense, we can have manifolds with any number, n, of dimensions. It was Riemann who extended Gauss's theory of 2-dimensional surfaces to cases where $n > 2$.

Location in an n-dimensional manifold is accomplished by a one-to-one correspondence between its "points" and the Riemannian n-tuples $(u_1, u_2, \ldots, u_n)$. But such location is mere charting, and there is need to know the "structure" of the manifold if it is to possess a geometry. For a *metric* geometry, the requisite is a distance formula, that is, a set of g's for the small n-dimensional region around each point. Just what algebraic form and mathematical properties a metric should have, that is, the generalization to n dimensions of ordinary 2-dimensional metric differential geometry, was worked out by the twenty-eight-year-old Riemann in 1854.

Riemann's explanation was given in the essay "On the Hypotheses at the Basis of Geometry," which is considered one of the greatest masterpieces in mathematical literature. This was his *Habilitationsschrift* (probationary essay) for the position of *Privatdozent* (lecturer) at the University of Göttingen. In compliance with academic tradition, the young mathematician had submitted three possible titles to the Göttingen faculty. He hoped one of the first two would be chosen, because he was well prepared to write and talk on these. In youthful fashion, he took his chances by listing as the third possibility a profound issue to which he had given very little thought, namely, the foundations of geometry. Fate, in the form of Gauss, designated this third topic for Riemann's probationary ordeal. The selection of the most difficult question was probably not a sadistic impulse on the part of the great master—but rather the natural desire, with his death imminent, to witness the torch he had kindled being carried forth brilliantly into the future.

The aging mathematician, never generous with praise, nevertheless found Riemann's doctoral dissertation of 1854 a work of gloriously fertile originality. Gauss fought weakness and pain to hear the *Habilitationsschrift* delivered, and pronounced it a surprise beyond his utmost expectations to see how such a difficult subject could be handled by such a young man. The words of the Titan were apparently unheard by mathematicians and physicists. Riemann achieved but modest recognition in his brief lifetime. His great essay on the foundations of geometry was published posthumously, and its applicability to physics was not fully realized until the day of general relativity.

Because men are 3-dimensional beings, they were able to realize, early in history, that the earth's surface is curved. This was revealed, for example, by the gradual appearance or disappearance of a ship in relation to the horizon. But could such a conclusion be reached by a 2-dimensional being confined to a spherical surface? If such a surface-dweller were to talk of "curvature" in any physical sense, he would be referring to the difference between straight lines and curves. He might provide analytic formulas to measure deviation from straightness. Then, *generalizing* these formulas so as to include more algebraic variables, he might, for the sake of clarification, describe the generalizations in quasi-geometric terminology. He might state how his generalizations would indicate whether or not his world or some other 2-dimensional cosmos is bent or "curved" in some enveloping 3-dimensional space which surface-dwellers cannot visualize. Going further he would derive formulas which would indicate whether 3-dimensional spaces are bent in some 4-dimensional continuum, which in turn may be curved in some external space, whose possible deviation from "flatness" might again be of interest, and so on *ad infinitum.*

Instead of speaking of a "curvature" which one cannot observe, one can express statements in alternative fashion by describing how a surface-dweller would be able to discover by suitable measurements whether or not the geometry of the triangles, polygons, circles, etc. in his cosmos is the Euclidean geometry of a "flat" surface or plane. Two-dimensional beings might plan a "geodetic" survey to settle the issue, in much the same spirit as Maupertuis, Clairaut, and La Condamine led expeditions into Lapland and Peru, to measure meridional arcs near the North Pole and the equator with the express purpose of choosing between oblate or prolate spheroid as the earth's shape. These great eighteenth-century scientists had wished to decide between Newton and Cassini. The former had indicated on purely *theoretic* grounds that the earth must be flattened at the poles. Cassini, the leading French astronomer of the day, based the alternative hypothesis of the prolate form on his geodetic measurement of the meridian arc between Dunkerque and Perpignan.

Let us imagine that a number of expeditions are organized by surface-dwellers and sent to survey widely separated regions of their space. One group, working in a desert, finds few obstacles to its operations and attempts to cover the ground with a Cartesian network of straight lines. To see whether the desert region is Euclidean (flat), the surveyors make distance measurements for points in the small meshes and substitute in the Pythagorean formula $ds^2 = du^2 + dv^2$. If the substitutions fail to check even approximately, this is no reason for rejecting the hypothesis of Euclideanism. The 2-dimensional scientists know that even in Euclidean geometry there are infinitely many different Gaussian networks with varying distance formulas and hence they proceed to a reexamination of the framework. Perhaps the surveying operations have not actually marked out rectangular meshes.

The field workers start anew, measuring adjacent sides and diagonals in a sequence of infinitesimal parallelograms, in order to determine for each mesh the proper set of values for g_{11}, g_{12}, g_{22} and the appropriate distance formula

$$ds^2 = g_{11}\,du^2 + 2g_{12}\,du\,dv + g_{22}\,dv^2$$

After forty or fifty repetitions of this procedure for different infinitesimal parallelograms, the set of values obtained for g_{11} is examined. Suppose that the figures run somewhat as follows: −0.97, 1.02, 1.06, 1.00, 0.96, 0.94, 1.01, 0.98, 1.04, 1.03, 0.95, . . . and that when all fifty are averaged and rounded off to two significant figures, $g_{11} = 1.0$. Let us say that g_{12} and g_{22}, like g_{11}, fluctuate very little from mesh to mesh and that, on the average,

$$g_{12} = 0.12 \qquad g_{22} = 1.0$$

Then a statistical metric for the entire region is

$$ds^2 = du^2 + 0.24\,du\,dv + dv^2$$

But this fits the standard form previously listed for an oblique network, and is merely an expression of the law of cosines. Therefore in each parallelogram of the mesh, the cosine of one of the angles has the value 0.12, and this angle is 83° in size. Then in every mesh two of the angles measure 83°, and the other two 97°, so that the lines of the mesh system do *not* meet at right angles. But the desert region can be pronounced Euclidean (flat) and the surveyors realize that this fact was obscured at first because they had erroneously believed the frame of reference to be rectangular.

While the first expedition has carried on as described, a second group is at work in totally different territory. Obstacles have made it impossible to set up markers for a Cartesian reticulation, but with a polar scheme of radiating lines and concentric circles it has been possible to skirt impassable areas. Measurements substituted in the plane polar distance formula

$$ds^2 = du^2 + u^2\,dv$$

check and thus confirm that the framework used is actually a polar one.

The net result of the two geodetic surveys is that the two regions measured are *Euclidean* or, from the viewpoint of 3-dimensional observers, flat. If very numerous surveys of a similar sort were conducted in areas all over the world of the 2-dimensional folk, and in every case led to a metric formula possible for some permissible network in a plane, then the infinitesimal geometry of the 2-dimensional cosmos would be pronounced Euclidean by its inhabitants.

It is possible to imagine a Gaussian "survey" of the Minkowski 2-dimensional space-time of the previous chapter. Then the derivation of the metric would start with the "Pythagorean formula" of special relativity.

$$s^2 = t^2 - x^2$$

and with the simplest mesh system one would have

$$ds^2 = dt^2 - dx^2$$

or, using the transformation

$$u = ix$$
$$v = t$$

one would obtain the usual Pythagorean formula and the corresponding metric,

$$s^2 = v^2 + u^2 = u^2 + v^2$$

or

$$ds^2 = dv^2 + du^2 = du^2 + dv^2$$

so that the space-time continuum of *special relativity* has a *Euclidean* or flat geometry. Because imaginary numbers are used in the above transformation to a Euclidean meshwork, just as in converting the Lorentz transformations to Euclidean rotations of axes (Chapter 17), some mathematicians refer to the restricted relativity space-time continuum as "pseudo-Euclidean" or "semi-Euclidean."

To us, in 3-dimensional space, a 2-dimensional surface that is pronounced flat or Euclidean by surveys like those just considered would *not* necessarily look like a plane. If the 2-dimensional beings lived on the surface of a cylinder or a cone, millions of surveys of different regions would all lead to the verdict "Euclidean." But to 3-dimensional observers, cylinders and cones are *not* planes. However, the local or differential geometry of such a 2-dimensional cosmos is Euclidean, because very small regions are for all practical purposes flat, exactly like parts of a plane. Hence 2-dimensional surveys of many small regions would yield the same sort of results for worlds that are cylindric or conic as for those that are plane, and would not lead to any distinction among them or between a plane and any other surfaces that are locally Euclidean. To find any failures in Euclideanism, the 2-dimensional folk would need to attempt surveys of *large* areas, as we shall see.

To see why the infinitesimal geometry of a cylinder or cone is the same as that of the plane, we can think of rolling a plane rectangular sheet of paper into a cylinder, or a plane sector into a cone. In fact, if a surface can be constructed from any plane paper pattern without stretching or tearing this pattern, its local geometry will be Euclidean. If any network is drawn on the plane pattern, it will remain after the pattern is rolled into a surface. Since there is no stretching or tearing in the process, the distances and the corresponding metric formula are also unaltered. All surfaces that can be formed from plane patterns in this way are termed *developable*, because from an opposite point of view such surfaces can be unfolded into plane forms, or *developed* on a plane (see Figure 19.5).

Although many surveys of small regions will not enable creatures bound to the surface of a cylinder to distinguish it from a plane, "global" operations would bring awareness. We imagine the radius of a cylindric world to be relatively large, so that in the early stages of the 2-dimensional civilization there are many unexplored and unmeasured regions. But a time arrives when there are means of transportation that make long journeys possible. Then it is observed that in certain cases a lengthy trip in one direction brings the traveler back to his starting point. In Figures 19.1 and 19.2, traveling "east" or "west" will ultimately bring an individual home. This sort of thing *cannot* happen in a plane, since trips "east" or "west" carry the traveler to ever-new territory. In a cylindric or conic universe, the 2-dimensional creatures would say that although the local geometry of their world is flat or Euclidean, its "global" or macroscopic geometry is not that of the Euclidean plane.

One point at issue is how the small parts of a 2-dimensional universe are connected with one another. The nature of a surface *in toto* depends on its *connectivity*, that is, the effect created by connecting any two points of the surface by a continuous path, or of drawing some closed, continuous path like the circumference of a circle or ellipse. If one were to draw such a closed path on the surface of a sphere, for example, the Arctic circle on the earth, then the cir-

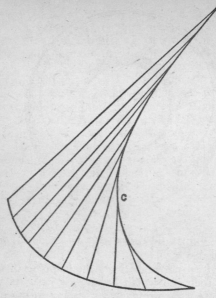

Figure 19.5   Developable surface generated by tangents to a twisted curve C. (A *plane* curve with its tangents can be twisted or "fluted" to form the surface pictured and, conversely, the surface can be flattened out.)

cumference would act as a sort of fence dividing the surface into two parts, so that one could not pass continuously from one part to the other because the fence would interfere. To make a journey from a point in the North Frigid Zone to some point in the Torrid Zone (or vice versa) and remain on the surface of the earth, it would be necessary to cross the Arctic circle. On the other hand, on the surface of a doughnut (Figure 19.6) certain closed curves would *not* fence in the portions of the surface and would not interfere with the possibility of connecting points with one another. The doughnut or *torus* is said to possess different connectivity from the sphere. All such "global" issues, however, are outside the province of classic differential geometry. The discussion of *topology* in a later chapter will provide a fuller treatment of geometry "in the large" whereas the present chapter will be limited to geometry "in the small."

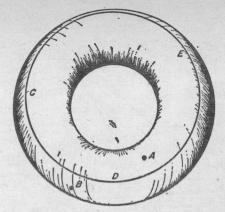

Figure 19.6   Connectivity on a torus. Curve *CDE* does not fence off an area since *A* can be connected with *B* by a path proceeding around the inside of the torus.

If the task of cartographers were the mapping of *developable* surfaces, their job would be an easy one. As we have mentioned, there is no stretching or tearing in the unrolling of such surfaces. Not only are distances invariant under such "development," but relative directions are also unchanged. The countries of the cosmos would not necessarily have the correct shape, but they would have the correct area in the development on a plane. But, alas for human mapmakers, the earth's surface is not developable! Spheres, spheroids, paraboloids and, in fact, most surfaces are *not* developable, and therefore not even locally flat. Because the methods of Gaussian differential geometry are internal or *intrinsic*, their practical counterpart—surveying in a 2-dimensional manifold—would enable beings confined to a nondevelopable surface to discover that the local geometry of their world is non-Euclidean, in other words that no one of the many different forms of ds^2 that apply to different Gaussian networks in a plane can fit the local distance measurements of their cosmos.

Let us return to the previous picture, where members of a geodetic survey attempted to cover a region with a polar network. If things had turned out differently, and distance measurements had *not* checked in the polar Pythagorean formula, it would have been necessary, as it was in the desert survey, to use statistical methods to arrive at the correct

metric. Now imagine that, in this new situation, a sequence
of forty or fifty determinations of g_{22} for different meshes
yields measurements all close to one another in value and
that they average 1.0, whereas measurements of g_{12} are either
zero or close to zero. This would mean that the cosine of
the angle between curves of the network is zero, so that this
angle measures 90° and the curves are orthogonal (perpendicular). Now suppose that the values of g_{11} do not exhibit
the same sort of statistical concentration as g_{12} and g_{22}, but
gradually decrease as the v-coordinate of meshes increases
through positive values $v = 1, 2, 3, 4, 5, \ldots$. This would
indicate that the value of g_{11} depends on the value of v or
that g_{11} is a function of v. Advanced mathematical methods
can be used to find the function that is the "best fit," in the
statistical sense, of the set of figures for g_{11}. Now suppose
that the function that fits is $g_{11} = \cos^2 v$. Then the metric
would be

$$ds^2 = \cos^2 v \, du^2 + dv^2$$

This happens to be the distance for a longitude-latitude network on an ordinary spherical surface, and hence the region
being surveyed would be declared "spherical." The surface-
dwellers might not have the word "sphere" in their vocabulary, but their knowledge of differential geometry would tell
them that, even with the infinite variety of plane Euclidean
mesh systems, there is not a single one to which the above
distance formula corresponds. In other words, they would
be able to show that no permissible transformation of coordinates would convert the above metric into the simple Pythagorean formula

$$ds^2 = du^2 + dv^2$$

They would therefore say that the region being surveyed is
non-Euclidean.

Gauss provided an exact definition of the property that he
termed *curvature*, the one we have described as the "non-
Euclideanism" of a surface in a region surrounding some
point. Gauss was able to prove that this attribute can be expressed in terms of g_{11}, g_{12}, g_{22} and their partial derivatives of
the first and second orders, a fact that he called a *theorema
egregium* (a most remarkable theorem). An alternative way
of stating Gauss's *theorema egregium* is to say that curvature or non-Euclideanism is an *intrinsic* or *absolute* characteristic of a surface. And, in general, any property of a

surface involving the g's, their derivatives, and arbitrary functions of u, v, the Gaussian coordinates, is considered *absolute*. Still a third way of expressing all these facts is to say that ds^2 and "non-Euclideanism" are *bending invariants*, characteristics unchanged by deformations of small regions of a surface.

In all the hypothetical experiments we have assigned to the surface inhabitants, we have had them base their tests on infinitesimal operations and the definition of the fundamental metric. But to find out whether a surface geometry is Euclidean or non-Euclidean, or from a 3-dimensional viewpoint, flat or curved, we can in theory perform a *crucial test* based on any metric theorem that is valid for Euclidean geometry only, for example, the proposition asserting that the sum of the angles of a triangle is equal to 180°. As mentioned in Chapter 3, Gauss himself measured the triangle formed by the peaks of three mountains, Brocken, Höher Hagen, and Inselberg, in order to test whether our space is Euclidean (flat). Since the angle sum came out close to 180°, he could not tell whether the deviation from the Euclidean sum was an error of observation or the result of non-Euclideanism.

We think of a Euclidean triangle as a figure bounded by three straight-line segments. But what would a triangle or a "straight line" be on the surface of a sphere? From the modern abstract point of view the term "straight line" can be left completely undefined and can be given appropriate interpretations in particular applications of an abstract geometry. Hence, 2-dimensional surveyors may use their own special idea of what a straight line is. We imagine them to hold the tape taut in laying out a "straight line." But if they are working on a spherical surface their straight line would thus appear to 3-dimensional observers as a great-circle arc. In any case, whether on a Euclidean plane or on some curved surface, a surveyor's "straight-line" segment is the shortest distance between two points of a small area. In differential geometry such a line is called a *geodesic*, and a triangle is a figure bounded by three geodesics. On a sphere, the sides of a triangle will be three great-circle arcs. Now suppose once more that on a sphere (Figure 19.2), a triangle is formed by joining the North Pole to two points on the equator so that the sum of the angles of this triangle is 254°. Hence, measurements of angles in such a triangle or, at any rate, in some fairly large triangle, made by creatures limited to a spherical surface, would indicate that the "global" geometry of their world cannot be that of a Euclidean plane or a developable surface.

But beings on a spherical surface would be able to conduct other experiments to reveal that their universe is not even locally Euclidean, providing always that they did not limit themselves to a very small region of their world. They need not involve themselves in "global" considerations but must go beyond the small neighborhood of each individual point. Starting from such a point, let us say that they measure off numerous "straight-line" segments of equal length, and join the end-points of these segments to form a circle. They are aware that in Euclidean plane geometry the length of the circumference should conform to the formula $C = \pi d$, or that for every circle the ratio of the circumference to the diameter is the same number, the constant π. But they

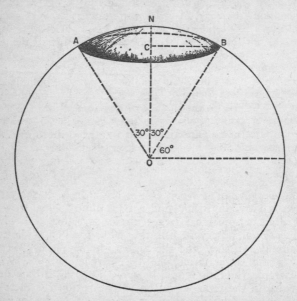

Figure 19.7(a)   The *intrinsic* diameter of the 60th parallel is ANB, a 60° arc of a great circle. If the radius of the sphere is taken as the unit of measure, $ANB = 1/6 \cdot 2\pi = \pi/3$, $CB = \frac{1}{2}$, and the circumference of the 60th parallel measures $2\pi \cdot \frac{1}{2} = \pi$. Thus the ratio of the circumference to the intrinsic diameter is 3:1.

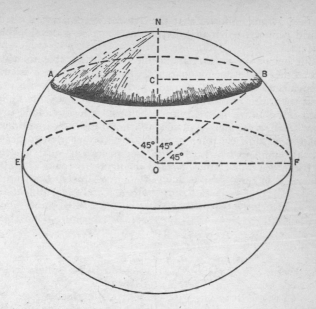

Figure 19.7(b) *ANB,* **the intrinsic diameter of the 45th parallel, measures $\frac{1}{4} \cdot 2\pi = \pi/2$; $CD = \sqrt{2}/2$ and the circumference of the parallel $= 2\pi(\sqrt{2}/2) = \pi\sqrt{2}$. The ratio of the circumference to the intrinsic diameter is $2\sqrt{2} : 1 = 2.83$ (approximately).**

find that, in their universe, the ratio of the circumference to the diameter is *not* constant but varies with the diameter of the circle, and in every case is less than π. If the circle drawn is very tiny, they find a ratio almost equal to π. If they draw a somewhat larger circle, say, that one which 3-dimensional observers call the 60th parallel of latitude (Figure 19.7a), they find the ratio to be 3. If they were to draw a still larger circle, the 45th parallel (Figure 19.7b), for example, the ratio would be about 2.83, and if they drew the equator, the ratio would be 2. The reason for these results is that in relativity all observers must agree on measurements, and in the diagrams the lengths of various "straight lines" like the "diameters" have been deduced from the realization that these are extrinsically great-circle arcs, and extrinsic length must equal intrinsic length.

Riemann dealt with a 3-dimensional spherical space which

is analogous to the 2-dimensional spherical world just considered. Then by analogy with the procedures above, we, the creatures who live in a 3-dimensional cosmos and cannot view it from some external point in a 4-dimensional space, could nevertheless discover whether the geometry of our world is Euclidean or not, and in the latter case whether it is spherical. Thus, starting at a point, we might mark off very numerous "straight-line" segments of equal length so that their end-points would form a 2-dimensional spherical surface. If tiny squares are applied to this surface and enumerated as a device for measuring its area, it will turn out in cases where the radius is very small that the area $A = \pi d^2$, where d is the "straight-line" diameter. If the diameter is then increased in size, the formula may always remain the same, and this would prove that the portion of space being surveyed is Euclidean. If, however, our entire space should be a Riemannian 3-dimensional spherical surface, the area A would turn out to be less than πd^2 for any diameter that is not tiny; that is, the ratio of A to d^2 would be less than π, and would diminish as the diameter of the sphere is increased.

In all the illustrations we have given, spherical spaces were chosen for the sake of simplicity. The uniformity of a spherical space causes the experiments to yield the same results for every region of such a universe. This uniformity would not occur for other types of non-Euclidean space, but detection of non-Euclideanism would nevertheless be possible. The theorems, however, would vary with the locality. If the universe were an elongated ellipsoid, for example, the value of the ratio C/d would depend not only on the size of d but on the location of the circle on the ellipsoidal surface. Or 2-dimensional creatures might live on a surface somewhat irregularly curved, but not too different from a plane, a cosmos that to 3-dimensional observers would look like the rippled surface of a lake, or like a flat surface with a few ridges, blisters, and puckers. The intrinsic measurements in the former case would show the surface to be approximately Euclidean, whereas in the latter case, Euclideanism would be established except for specific regions which would manifest various degrees of non-Euclideanism.

At long last, what does all the preceding discussion of the intrinsic geometry of spaces have to do with relativity? The answer is that if we substitute Riemann for Gauss, a Minkowski 4-dimensional space-time manifold for a 2-dimensional surface, *ourselves* for the surface creatures, certain observations from nineteenth- and twentieth-century experimental physics for surveying procedures, then we shall have Einstein's general relativity of 1916. The theoretical and empirical steps by which the great universe-builder arrived at his theory of gravitation are, *mutatis mutandis*, the 4-dimensional analogues of the operations carried out by creatures confined to an ordinary surface.

For differential geometry on a surface, Gauss provided the metric or fundamental form

$$ds^2 = g_{11}du_1du_1 + g_{12}du_1du_2 + g_{21}du_2du_1 + g_{22}du_2du_2$$

with the understanding that $g_{12} = g_{21}$, and the order of all multiplications is immaterial. Since it is the *coefficients*, the g's, that determine the formula, it is customary to omit the du_1 and du_2 and write the coefficients in a square arrangement, or square *matrix:*

$$\begin{pmatrix} g_{11} & g_{12} \\ g_{21} & g_{22} \end{pmatrix}$$

When this matrix is accompanied by the law of transformation to g_{11}', g_{12}', etc., that is, the set of transformations to all permissible mesh systems or frames of reference, then it is termed a *tensor*, and g_{11}, g_{12}, g_{21}, g_{22}, are called *components* of the tensor. Thus we see that the whole issue of Euclidean versus non-Euclidean geometry, flat versus curved space for surface-dwellers, depends on the tensor components, and it is the hypothetical surveyor's task to determine these components as functions of u_1 and u_2.

Analogous considerations apply to the 4-dimensional spaces of Riemann. In relativity, which is a physical geometry, it seems meaningless to speak of 3-dimensional or 4-dimensional "surfaces" because this would seem to imply that they are "surfaces" of something, in other words that there is some sort of external 4- or 5-dimensional space in which they are embedded. Hence it is preferable to refer to a *continuum* (of any number of dimensions) with an *intrinsic* geometry.

The physicists surveying the 4-dimensional space-time continuum have, corresponding to the *points* where 2-dimensional surveyors place markers, *events* (x, y, z, t); the x, y, z of an event are determined by measuring rods, and the t by a clock. In the arbitrary curvilinear Gaussian or Riemannian networks used in general relativity, one may specify an event by (u_1, u_2, u_3, u_4). But the mere specification of points or events does not make a geometry. In other words, the space-time continuum is amorphous, structureless, until ds^2 is specified. In the case of a general Riemannian 4-dimensional continuum, this is a matter of furnishing the *matrix* (or the *tensor*, when the all-important transformation law is included) which is

$$\begin{pmatrix} g_{11} & g_{12} & g_{13} & g_{14} \\ g_{21} & g_{22} & g_{23} & g_{24} \\ g_{31} & g_{32} & g_{33} & g_{34} \\ g_{41} & g_{42} & g_{43} & g_{44} \end{pmatrix}$$

where $g_{12} = g_{21}$, $g_{13} = g_{31}$, $g_{14} = g_{41}$, $g_{23} = g_{32}$, $g_{24} = g_{42}$, $g_{34} = g_{43}$. When the first g in each of these equations is substituted for the equivalent g in the matrix above, the number of g's is reduced from 16 to 10. The corresponding metric is

$$ds^2 = g_{11} du_1{}^2 + 2g_{12} du_1 du_2 + 2g_{13} du_1 du_3 + 2g_{14} du_1 du_4 + g_{22} du_2{}^2 \\ + 2g_{23} du_2 du_3 + \cdots + g_{44} du_4{}^2$$

There are now *ten* g's to be fixed instead of the three of ordinary surface theory, and this is one reason why Einstein's task was so difficult. In our previous discussion, after the g_{11}, g_{12}, g_{22} functions for a surface had been determined, its intrinsic geometry was complete; all the rest would have been inference from the fundamental formula. Einstein's restriction on his ten g's, and their formulation as functions of space and time provide the complete story of our physical universe as far as "gravitational" phenomena are concerned.

In the earlier discussion of the special theory of relativity, there was the metric (separation formula), $s^2 = t^2 - x^2$. This metric was used in describing a 1-dimensional motion as recorded in a 2-dimensional space-time continuum. Generalizing this metric so that it can be used to describe *local* motion in 3-dimensional space, one obtains the formula in the 4-dimensional space-time continuum, namely,

$$ds^2 = dt^2 - dx^2 - dy^2 - dz^2$$

or, in Riemannian form, if we take time as the *fourth* coordinate,

$$ds^2 = -du_1{}^2 - du_2{}^2 - du_3{}^2 + du_4{}^2$$

Comparing this with the general form above, we see that all elements of the matrix except the diagonal ones are equal to zero, that is, $g_{11} = g_{22} = g_{33} = -1$, $g_{44} = +1$, and all the other g's are zero. This is a specially simple Riemannian tensor, and the corresponding metric is Euclidean or pseudo-Euclidean (page 146) because a permissible transformation of coordinates (involving imaginaries) will transform it to the Pythagorean distance formula

$$ds^2 = du_1^2 + du_2^2 + du_3^2 + du_4^2$$

In 2-dimensional Gaussian differential geometry, the metric of any surface can be derived, as explained earlier in this chapter, by applying the Pythagorean formula (or its corollary, the law of cosines) to measurements made on the infinitesimal meshes of a Gaussian network. Einstein's *principle of equivalence* furnishes the analogous starting point for deriving the metric of the 4-dimensional space-time continuum of general relativity. It will be recalled that the principle of equivalence, reduced to geometric form, states that in infinitesimal regions of space-time the restricted theory of relativity holds; that is, in such regions, if a suitable local frame of reference is chosen, it is true that

$$ds^2 = dt^2 - dx^2 - dy^2 - dz^2$$

One may apply this rule to a small "curvilinear" Riemannian mesh of space-time, much as was done with Gaussian meshes on a surface where $k_1 du$ and $k_2 dv$ represented distances "parallel" to the sides of the mesh, the proportionality factors k_1 and k_2 being determined by surveying. By analogy, general relativity must make use of $k_1 du_1$, $k_2 du_2$, $k_3 du_3$, $k_4 du_4$, where the k's are determined by "surveying" a particular mesh in space-time. Application of the Pythagorean formula gave the *local* values of g_{11}, g_{12}, g_{22} in

$$ds^2 = g_{11} du^2 + 2g_{12} du\, dv + g_{22} dv^2$$

Similarly, in general relativity, application of the formula $ds^2 = dt^2 - dx^2 - dy^2 - dz^2$ will give the *local* values of the *ten* coefficients or ten tensor components, g_{11}, g_{12}, g_{13}, . . . , g_{44}.

We conceived of the Gaussian surveyors as proceeding from mesh to mesh obtaining different coefficients, or g's for each locality, and finally expressing the g's as *functions* of u and v to obtain a formulation of ds^2, the metric in which the entire geometry of the surface is implicit. Similarly, to obtain the metric of the space-time continuum of general relativity is a matter of proceeding from mesh to mesh of space-time, "surveying" to obtain the k's or proportionality factors, and applying again and again the restricted relativity formula for ds^2, the space-time separation formula of the previous chapter. After we have discussed the g's abstractly, this "surveying" problem still remains.

Einstein postulated the principle of equivalence in order to make the metric of special relativity applicable to the surveying of small regions of space-time. But, in order to determine the g's, the tensor components, for all points of the space-time continuum and all possible Riemannian frames of reference, he found it necessary to make additional assumptions based on theoretical or empirical facts of physics and astronomy. The *invariance* of ds^2, the metric tensor, under arbitrary transformations of the Riemannian coordinates is one axiom governing the selection of suitable functions of u_1, u_2, u_3, u_4 for the various g's. Another restriction arises from the distribution of material bodies in space, since "gravitational" phenomena are to be explained as the effect of such bodies on space-time structure, that is, on the g's. Einstein made a third assumption, based on the views of the great mathematical physicists who had preceded him, namely, that the laws of physics, in particular the "field" laws, are partial differential equations of the second order, and hence that the g's must satisfy such equations, this in effect being the expression of the new law of gravitation. The "surveying" of those regions of space-time where the presence of matter produces "gravitational" phenomena, or, alternatively, non-Euclideanism in the geometry, becomes a matter of *solving* the associated differential equations for the g's. To find *particular* or specific solutions calls for boundary and/or initial conditions (Chapter 9).

The physicist M. Schwarzschild succeeded in solving the partial differential equations for radially symmetric "gravitational fields" like those around the sun. In the boundary conditions, he introduced m, the "gravitational mass" of the sun (or other particular material body involved), and also specified that for events at a great distance from the body there would be no "gravitational" effects, that is, that the space-time in such regions would conform to the metric of special relativity so that $g_{44} = 1$, $g_{11} = g_{22} = g_{33} = -1$ and all the other g's would be zero for the values of u_1, u_2, u_3, u_4 in these regions. Using polar coordinates with the origin at the center of mass of the body, he obtained the following solution of the differential equations:

$$g_{44} = 1 - \frac{2m}{r}$$

$$g_{11} = -\frac{1}{1 - 2m/r}$$

$$g_{22} = -r^2$$

$$g_{33} = -r^2 \sin^2\theta$$

The corresponding metric is

$$ds^2 = \left(1 - \frac{2m}{r}\right) dt^2 - \frac{dr^2}{1 - 2m/r} - r^2 d\theta^2 - r^2 \sin^2\theta d\phi^2$$

or, if one wishes to use the symbols u_1, u_2, u_3, u_4,

$$ds^2 = \left(1 - \frac{2m}{u_1}\right) du_4^2 - \frac{du_1^2}{1 - 2m/u_1} - u_1^2 du_2^2 - u_1^2 \sin^2 u_2 du_3^2$$

If u_1, that is, r, the radial distance, is very large, then $2m/u_1$ will be negligible and the metric will reduce to that of special relativity (in polar coordinates) as required by the boundary condition. This will also occur for space-time regions where $m = 0$, that is, where no matter is present. Hence the Schwarzschild metric is very general, applying to events occurring near masses like the sun as well as to occurrences remote from matter.

One might have expected that with the acclaim of the general theory, Einstein could have rested from his labors, but instead he continued along the lines of still further generalization in order to include electromagnetic phenomena, since he believed that electric and magnetic field strengths are also *relative* and not absolute. Students of elementary classical physics learn that there is an analogy between certain mechanical and electromagnetic laws. To take a specific instance, consider Newton's formula for gravitational attraction,

$$F = G \frac{Mm}{d^2}$$

where M, m are the masses of the two attracting bodies, d is their distance apart, F is the force of attraction, and G is a constant depending on the particular units of mass, distance, force that are used.

This becomes Coulomb's law of *magnetic* attraction between the poles of two magnets if we replace M and m by the magnitudes of the poles and G by a suitable magnetic constant. It becomes *electric* attraction if we replace M and m by electric charges and G by another suitable constant. Moreover, if we take Newton's law and think of it as applied to constant masses like those of the earth and sun, it reduces to the inverse-square law, the attraction between the earth and sun varying inversely as the square of the distance between them. But we have seen that the inverse-square law also arises in the theory of light. Thus, phenomena in gravitation, magnetism, electricity, and light seem to be manifestations of one general principle. Matter and electromagnetic entities exert influences or create a *field* in the space around them.

Most of the present chapter was devoted to the mathematics which enabled Einstein to handle the gravitational field, that is, the influence of matter on the space-time continuum. For thirty years or so, Einstein, Hermann Weyl, Sir Arthur Eddington, and others tried to obtain a single theory that would include gravitational and electromagnetic fields as two special cases. Finally, in February 1950, Einstein released to the world a "unifield field theory," which still awaits the sort of experimental verification that Einstein's earlier work has had. There is no doubt, however, that the new theory, expressed in the language of *tensors*, is one of the greatest contributions to mathematical physics in modern times.

If we trace facts to their sources, then we must say that Einstein's signal contribution to modern physics was made possible by one of the many very great advances in modern mathematics made by Carl Friedrich Gauss, that towering figure whose diversified mathematical achievements are, of necessity, described at many points of our story. We have already discussed his fundamental discoveries in algebra, astronomy, non-Euclidean geometry, complex analysis, probability theory, and differential geometry. His contributions to number theory and topology will be discussed later. Thus there is actually no most appropriate subject with which to unify the story of his life. Although he himself pronounced number theory the "queen" of mathematics, general readers may be more impressed by how he paved the path to relativity. Hence, having reached the end of that road, we are presenting his biography at its terminus.

Gauss was born in Braunschweig (Brunswick) in 1777, where his father, a bricklayer and gardener, would have been quite willing to have his son follow the same pursuits. The boy's exceptional numerical talent manifested itself very early—in fact, before he was three years of age, as legend has it. At that early age he found an error committed by his father in making out the payroll for the bricklayers whom he supervised.

The child prodigy's school experiences were fortunate in one respect, for the assistant schoolmaster was none other than Johann Martin Bartels (1769–1836), whose later influence on Lobachevsky has already been mentioned (Chapter 3). When Gauss was ten and Bartels was eighteen, they became acquainted, and from then on studied elementary and advanced mathematics together. Bartels soon recognized that Carl was no ordinary child but a full-fledged genius who could improve on the analytic techniques of Newton, Euler, and Lagrange. The young teacher publicized his student's mathematical feats by recounting them to prominent citizens of Braunschweig. Eventually the stories reached (Carl Wilhelm) Ferdinand, Duke of Braunschweig, to whom Gauss was presented at the age of fourteen. At once the Duke became the kindest and most generous of patrons. He financed all of Gauss's education for the next eight years, right through the doctorate at the University of Helmstädt in 1799. The Duke paid for the publication of his protégé's doctoral dissertation, and granted him a small regular allowance thereafter in order to enable him to carry on mathematical research without the need to teach or seek some other means of earning a living. When Gauss married in 1805, his patron increased the amount of the annual stipend. This support ceased only in 1807, after Duke Ferdinand died from wounds received in the battles of Auerstädt and Jena.

In 1807, then, Gauss was faced with the practical problem of finding a job. This was, in fact, no problem at all, since his renown was widespread by that time and he received excellent offers from leading academic institutions all over Europe. Alexander von Humboldt (1769–1859), the famous traveler and scientist, sought to have Gauss remain in

Germany, and was influential in obtaining his appointment as director of the Göttingen Observatory. Laplace was Gauss's "reference" for the position. "Who is the leading mathematician in Germany?" von Humboldt asked Laplace. "Johann Friedrich Pfaff," was the answer. Von Humboldt was crestfallen. "What is your opinion of Gauss?" he inquired. "Oh, he is, of course, the greatest mathematician in the world," Laplace explained.

What had Gauss done to earn such a reputation? He had already made a multitude of discoveries, among them the proof of the fundamental theorem of algebra, published in his Ph.D. dissertation of 1799. Then there was the 1801 *Disquisitiones Arithmeticae*, whose contents will be discussed later (Chapter 21). Gauss was contemplating the preparation of a second volume for this work when there occurred an event which caused him to swerve from pure to applied mathematics.

Although astronomic theory had indicated the probable existence of tiny planets or "planetoids," the very first observation of such a heavenly body was made at Palermo on January 1, 1801, by the Italian astronomer Giuseppe Piazzi (1746–1826). The planetoid he discovered was named Ceres. It was possible to obtain only a very few exact observations of Ceres' positions in the course of its motion around the sun, and therefore the computation of its orbit from such limited empirical data presented a problem which aroused Gauss's interest. In formulating the issue, he had to solve (approximately) an algebraic equation of the eighth degree. Thus he provided a "practical" application of the very equations which the Babylonians of Hammurabi's day had solved merely because they enjoyed algebra.

When in 1802 Pallas, another planetoid, was discovered, Gauss embarked on the formulation and solution of the *general* problem of computing the orbit of *any* such tiny member of our solar system. The ultimate result was his 1809 *Theoria motus corporum coelestium*, in which he showed just how to chart the complete orbits of planets and comets from limited observational data; he dealt with the difficult matter of "perturbations," and provided the techniques that were to govern computational astronomy until the recent era. Observations of the diminutive planets, Ceres, Pallas, Vesta, Juno, etc. confirmed the accuracy of Gauss's methods, which were enormous time-savers as well.

Only in 1820 did Gauss develop a new interest by embarking on that theoretical research in geodesy which we have pictured as the applied background for his differential geometry. Incidental to the computational aspects of geodesy was his use of the statistical method of "least squares" which, in the *Theoria motus*, he had claimed as one of his early discoveries. However, from the point of view of publication, Adrien-Marie Legendre (1752–1833) held priority, since his exposition of the method had appeared in 1806, three years earlier.

Next Gauss made discoveries in optics, in electromagnetic theory, and in the theory of Newtonian attraction. In connection with gravitational attraction, he initiated the mathematical subject which came to be known as "potential theory." In 1833 he and his young associate, Wilhelm Weber (1804–1891), invented the electric telegraph, and used it to transmit messages. Weber, in fact, foretold the eventual importance of this method of communication.

But it was only long after Gauss's death that the mathematical world became aware of the full extent of his mathematical creativeness. In 1898 the Royal Society of Göttingen borrowed Gauss's *Notizenjournal* (scientific diary) from one of his grandsons. An analysis of the 146 brief summaries which this record contained indicated that during the period from 1796 to 1814 Gauss anticipated practically all the major discoveries of his contemporaries and immediate successors and that he held a priority he never claimed in discovering non-Euclidean geometry, complex variable theory, elliptic functions, quaternions, etc. In delaying publication, Gauss was like Newton. But whereas Newton was tardy, Gauss *never* published some of his most important findings. Why he failed to announce his discoveries has not been adequately explained. There are those who claim that Gauss did not publish because he was a perfectionist and never found his work good enough; they point to his motto, *Pauca sed matura* (Few but ripe). Others suggest that the feeling that none of his research was ever *druckreif* was due to a trauma produced by the rejection which the French Academy of Sciences accorded to his first and possibly greatest masterpiece, the *Disquisitiones Arithmeticae*.

As has been said repeatedly at other points, the purely personal aspects of the life of a man like Gauss are less significant than his role in the history of science. Nevertheless, for the sake of human interest, some facts on record should be recounted. At age twenty-eight Gauss married

Johanne Osthof of Braunschweig, who bore him two sons and a daughter. She died in 1809, shortly after the birth of the second of her sons. Her husband's letters and the statements of those who knew him well reveal that the loss of his young wife was a source of permanent sorrow to him. Museum researchers have performed chemical analyses of certain markings that appear in letters where Gauss referred to the death of Johanne. These spots have been proved to be tear stains, and it has been assumed that the tears were those of Gauss. It is true that he married Johanne's friend, Minna Waldeck, less than a year after his loss, but this appears to have been a marriage of convenience, for the sake of his three motherless children. There were two sons and a daughter by the second marriage. Two of Gauss's sons emigrated to the United States, and their numerous descendants are citizens of our country today.

Gauss was "all mathematician," as he himself said. His only nonmathematical activities were a few intellectual hobbies like studying foreign languages. He knew English and Russian, for example, and enjoyed reading literature in both languages. He liked to correspond with scientists in their native languages. Thus he carried on a correspondence with a certain Monsieur Leblanc, whose discoveries in the higher arithmetic Gauss lauded and encouraged. In 1807 the French mathematical correspondent intervened in Gauss's behalf with the French General Pernety, whose troops were occupying Hanover. This resulted in Gauss's discovery that Monsieur Leblanc was in reality a woman, Sophie Germain (1776–1831). Hers is one of the few important feminine names in mathematical history. Prior to her day there were only Hypatia, Maria Gaetana Agnesi (1718–1799), and the Marquise du Châtelet (1706–1749), the last named being more of an expositor than a creative mathematician. Sophie Germain made notable discoveries not only in number theory but also in acoustics and the theory of elasticity.

There is a record of the letter which Gauss wrote to thank Mademoiselle Germain for her intercession with the French military authorities, and to express his surprise concerning her true identity. "How can I describe my admiration and amazement in learning that the esteemed Monsieur Leblanc is now transformed into someone so important?" wrote the foremost world mathematician. ". . . A talent for abstract thought in general, and for mathematics in particular, is exceedingly rare. . . . But when a member of the sex which, according to our prejudices, must find enormous difficulties in mathematical research, actually succeeds in penetrating the most problematic issues, then one must acknowledge her extraordinary courage and her great genius. . . ." Finally, the letter closes with a date bearing a sentimental allusion, "My birthday—April 30, 1807."

Several months after this birthday, Gauss wrote to another friend: "Lagrange is deeply interested in the higher arithmetic; he considers the two special theorems I formulated 'most beautiful and most difficult to prove.' But nevertheless Sophie Germain has succeeded in proving them."

Gauss and the French woman mathematician continued to carry on their mathematical correspondence. In 1831 he influenced the faculty of Göttingen in their decision to grant an honorary doctorate to Sophie Germain, but she died just a month before the degree was to be conferred. Her illustrious mentor, who was just a year her junior, was to survive her by almost a quarter of a century. He was active in significant research almost to the day of his death, February 23, 1855.

Chapter 20

Post-Relativity Geometry

Riemann extended Gauss's notion of geometry in a way that was vital for the general relativity of 1916. But in the quest for a unified field theory, further generalizations of geometry arose. *Non-Riemannian geometry* was essentially the result of concepts shaped in 1917 by Tullio Levi-Civita (1873–1941), whose biography and contributions to mathematics will be considered in the present chapter.

That certain geometrical or physical entities are affected by motion should be no surprise to those who have read all the preceding chapters. But now come the added revelations that, in non-Euclidean or "curved" spaces, parallelism is a relative concept and it is impossible to maintain directions in the course of motion. Thus, suppose that at some point P of a curved surface like a sphere, two small rods are initially coincident so that they have the same direction, and then while one rod remains at rest the other moves by infinitesimal steps so that in each tiny displacement it maintains its direction. If the bottom of the moving rod is attached to a closed curve starting at P and if the moving rod makes the complete circuit, one might expect that on its return to P it would have the same direction as the rod that remained at rest, marking the original direction of the moving rod. But it can be proved that this is *not* the case and, if the tour of the moving rod has enclosed a considerable area, the discrepancy in direction on its return will be very large. Of course this would not happen if the rod were to move around a closed curve in a Euclidean plane (Figure 20.1) for then it would return to its exact original direction. Nontransference of direction is just another manifestation of the non-Euclideanism of a space. Levi-

Civita` attacked this problem in 1917 by generalizing the
ordinary concept of parallelism. His notion was to be
invaluable in progress toward a "unified field theory" and
a powerful stimulus to the development of post-relativity
geometries.

If, prior to the study of plane geometry, a child is ques-
tioned on the meaning of parallel lines, he will usually say
that they are lines that have the same direction, an idea
more accurately formulated by the Euclidean theorems
which prove that lines forming equal corresponding angles
with a transversal are parallel, and conversely (Figure 20.2).
We shall now, in *three* steps of increasing generality, extend
the elementary Euclidean concept to the parallelism of Levi-
Civita.

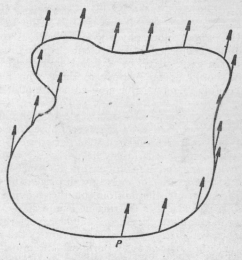

Figure 20.1

In Chapter 3 we indicated that the assumptions about
parallelism constitute the essential difference between Euclidean and non-Euclidean geometries "in the large," that is,
over an entire surface. Hence for geometry "in the small,"
that is, differential geometry, it seems logical to consider the
question of parallel motion in small regions of a curved
surface and to relate parallelism in one "neighborhood" to

that in an adjacent small area. Therefore we imagine, once
again, creatures confined to a two-dimensional curved surface, and we observe their geometric activities from our
vantage point in "outer space." If, in a small region of their
universe, they attempt to construct Figure 20.2, that is, if
they attach one end of a small "straight" rod to a "straight"
line and try to move it parallel to itself, we may see both
the line and the rod as *curved* geodesics. But then we may
decide that, for a small portion of the surface, there is little
difference between the small curved rod and a straight line
vector *tangent* to it (and the surface). Hence we agree to
reason about parallelism in terms of such small tangent
vectors.

With the point of view adopted, our first generalization
can deal with parallelism on a *developable* surface like a
cylinder, a cone, or the surface of Figure 19.5. When such
surfaces are rolled out on a plane, all their geodesics become
straight lines, and conversely. If our fictitious creatures live
on a developable surface, and if the "flattening" process
causes the successive positions of the small rod, or tangent
vector, to form a diagram like Figure 20.2 where correspond-

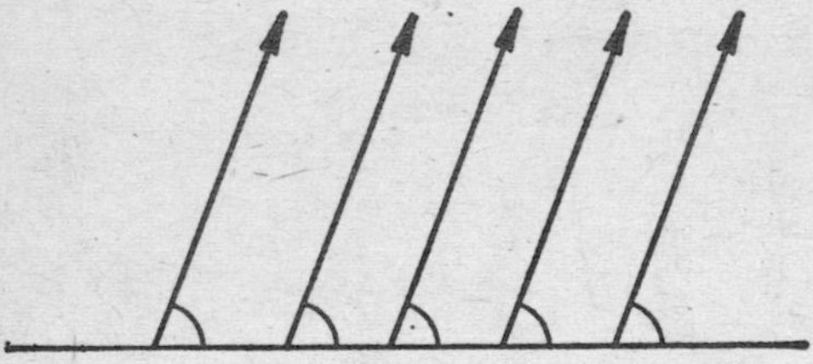

Figure 20.2

ing angles are equal, one says that the *original* tangent
vector was displaced *parallel* to itself *in the sense of Levi-
Civita.*

The next step is to generalize the above situation to a
definition of parallel displacement along a geodesic on *any
curved surface* whatsoever: A tangent vector is said to
undergo parallel displacement along a geodesic if and only
if the moving tangent vector forms equal corresponding
angles with the geodesic. The thought in this case is that,
although a general curved surface cannot be flattened out

on a plane, one can attach a developable surface that is tangent to the general surface all along the geodesic path of motion. Then when the attached surface is unrolled, the geodesic path becomes a straight line and the tangent vectors are transformed into vectors issuing from different points on the line. Since angles are invariant in the flattening process, there are equal corresponding angles in the plane figure, and the transformed vectors are parallel in the ordinary Euclidean sense.

In the process of generalization the final step is to consider parallel displacement along *any curve C* (not necessarily a geodesic) on a general curved surface. Once again the formulation uses parallelism on the developable surface attached to the general surface and tangent to it all along the curve C.

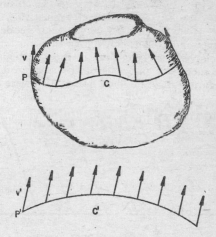

Figure 20.3   Levi-Civita parallel displacement

If that curve is twisted, that is, does not lie in a single plane, the attached surface might look something like the one pictured in Figure 19.5. When the developable surface is rolled out on a plane, the tangent vector v issuing from P of curve C is mapped onto v' issuing from point P' of curve C' in the plane (Figure 20.3). In the plane, P' traces curve C', and the vector v' is required to remain actually parallel to itself in the elementary Euclidean sense. Finally the plane is turned back into the developable surface so that all points go back to their original positions. The various positions of v' now become positions of the vectors v tangent to the surface along the curve C, and these vectors are called *parallel in the sense of Levi-Civita*. It must be emphasized that the vectors v will *not*, in general, be parallel in the usual sense. We have given a geometric description, but the *exact* expression of the Levi-Civita notion of parallel displacement is furnished in terms of differential equations.

Even the parallelism of Levi-Civita is *not* an absolute property, but is *relative* to the curve of transport. Thus, if points P and Q on a general curved surface are joined by a geodesic and a nongeodesic, then, as we have indicated, parallel displacement of a vector along the former is defined somewhat differently from that on the latter, and therefore it seems logical that the total effect on the direction of the vector might possibly be different in the two cases. Again, suppose that it did not matter along which curve the vector moves in the Levi-Civita parallel displacement from P to Q (Figure 20.4) of a curved surface. Then it would reach the

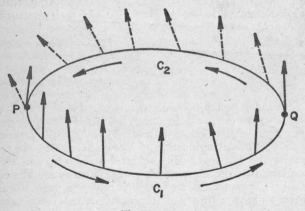

Figure 20.4

same direction at Q by moving along C_1 as along C_2. If this were true, it could be carried "parallel" to itself along C_1 and then *back* along C_2, so that it would return to its original direction, which, as stated at the beginning of this chapter, is *not*, in general, possible. Therefore, Levi-Civita parallel displacement along C_1 leads to one direction at Q, whereas parallel displacement along C_2 leads to a *different* direction at Q.

The *non-Riemannian* geometry that grew from this idea is like the Riemannian in that it deals with n-dimensional continua with different meshworks $(u_1, u_2, \ldots, u_n)$. Only there is no metric ds^2, since the new type of geometry has nothing to do with distance, but is based either on the idea of *displacement*, a generalization of Levi-Civita's parallelism, or on the concept of *paths*, a generalization of the notion of *geodesics*. The latter kind of non-Riemannian geometry was founded about 1922 by Oswald Veblen and Luther P. Eisenhart. The displacement generalization was begun about 1918 by Hermann Weyl in his attempt to create a unified field theory. He developed a logical, beautiful type of pure geometry, but it did not fit the facts of our physical universe.

Weyl worked on the effects of non-Euclideanism on non-transference of *length*. In other words, instead of concentrating on the fact that vectors will have different directions when transported from P to Q by parallel displacement along different paths, he assumed that two unit measuring rods would have different *lengths* if they were displaced from P to Q along different paths. Later, Eddington created an elegant generalization of Weyl's idea by assuming that the measuring rod would change in length not only if it were displaced from one point of the continuum to another, but also if it were rotated around one of its points as pivot. And again, although Eddington's geometry is a superior piece of pure mathematics, the associated "unified field theory" was unsatisfactory as a description of the physical world. The actual unification of gravitational and electromagnetic theories was finally achieved by Einstein in 1950, as explained at the close of the previous chapter. Since it was Levi-Civita who blazed the mathematical trail toward Einstein's ultimate theory of the universe, the fundamental concept involved was explained above, and something will now be said about the creative thinker who made the discovery. The facts are those recorded by the noted British geometer W. V. D. Hodge, with the assistance of Eddington, Whittaker, Beniamino Segre, and Enrico Volterra, the son of Vito Volterra (Chapter 23).*

* Royal Society of London, *Obituary Notices of Fellows*, Vol. 4, No. 11 (November 1942), pp. 151 ff.

Tullio Levi-Civita and Vito Volterra were both mathematicians who in the course of active lives contributed greatly to the high reputation enjoyed by Italian mathematics in general, and the school of mathematics in Rome in particular; both had made many contributions which have found a permanent place in mathematical literature, and both ended their days as victims of a political system which destroyed institutions and liberties in which they were firm believers.

Levi-Civita was born in Padua on 29 March 1873, the son of Giacomo Levi-Civita and his wife, Bice Lattis. The family was a wealthy one, well known for its strong liberal traditions. Giacomo Levi-Civita was a barrister, jurist and politician, and was for many years mayor of Padua, and a Senator of the Kingdom of Italy. As a young man he had served as a volunteer and fought with Garibaldi in the campaign of 1866, and he had played an important part in the Risorgimento.

Giacomo Levi-Civita was anxious that his son should follow in his footsteps as a barrister, but Tullio's interest in the physical and mathematical sciences was apparent even in early childhood, and when he expressed a wish to follow his own inclinations his father never opposed him; and in later years the son's eminence in the scientific world was a source of great pride to the father. Consequently, when he completed his classical studies at the Ginnasio-Liceo Tito Livio in his native city at the age of seventeen, Tullio Levi-Civita entered the faculty of science at the university of Padua as a student of mathematics, and four years later he took his degree.

Amongst his teachers at the university of Padua were D'Arcais, Padova, Veronese, and Ricci-Curbastro (known to the scientific world simply as Ricci). The two last-named were the most distinguished, and both had considerable influence on the future career of their brilliant pupil. The influence of Ricci is the more obvious, since it developed into active collaboration, but probably Veronese's influence was quite as important, since it is largely to him that Levi-Civita owed the remarkable spacial intuition and familiarity with multidimensional space which characterizes the younger man's contributions to the Ricci-Levi-Civita partnership in the absolute differential calculus.

Levi-Civita's undergraduate days were not over before he began to write mathematical papers, and his ability was quickly recognized. At the age of twenty-five he was appointed professor of mechanics at Padua. For twenty years he held that post, and these were among the most productive of his life. In 1918 he was called to the chair of mechanics at Rome, a post which he held for another twenty years, until racial discrimination, introduced into Italy in 1938, brought about his removal from office. Until then his life was uneventful, spent in the happy pursuit of his mathematical interests.

The work by which Levi-Civita is certainly best known is that on the absolute differential calculus, with its applications to relativity theory. The study of the particular class of invariants known as tensors goes back to the work of Riemann and Christoffel on quadratic differential forms (though the name tensor was only introduced by Voigt in 1898). In 1887 Ricci published his famous paper in which he developed the calculus of tensors including the important operation of covariant differentiation. For a considerable number of years following the publication of this paper he was engaged in working out his "absolute differential calculus" aided by a number of able pupils, foremost among them being Levi-Civita. The results of the work of Ricci, Levi-Civita and others were finally published in a joint memoir by Ricci and Levi-Civita which appeared in 1900 and which presented the theory of tensors essentially in the form used by Einstein and others fifteen years later.

In 1917 Levi-Civita made an advance in the absolute differential calculus of fundamental importance, with the introduction of the concept of parallel displacement. Few mathematical ideas have found such diverse applications so quickly as that of parallel displacement. It is the basis of the unified representation of gravitational and electromagnetic fields in relativity theory, and there are still more far-reaching consequences which are not yet fully recognized in physics. Levi-Civita's direct contributions to relativity theory are substantial, but they are of a less conspicuous nature. In addition to the large number of papers which Levi-Civita published on the absolute differential calculus and relativity he published two books, *Questioni di meccanica classica e relativistica* (1924) and *Lezioni di differentiale assoluto* (1925). Both of these have become standard works, and the latter was translated into English and has been widely read in the translation as well as in the original.

Although he is most famous for his work in relativity theory, Levi-Civita has had an important influence on many other branches of mathematics. It is particularly necessary to mention his work in analytical dynamics, to advance which subject he did as much as any one during the earlier years of the twentieth century. The largest individual group of these papers deals with the problem of three bodies [Chapter 25]. In 1923 Levi-Civita, in association with Professor Amaldi, published a three-volume work on rational mechanics, which is now one of the accepted classics on the subject, and which has been translated into various other languages, including Russian.

Hydrodynamics is another subject which attracted Levi-Civita's attention, and to which he made a considerable number of contributions. His work on hydrodynamics is to a certain extent bound up with his work on the general theory of systems of partial differential equations. His work on this subject forms an important addition to the well-known Cauchy-Kovalevsky theory.

It was natural that the efforts made to find a common framework to contain both quantum mechanics and the general theory of relativity should prove of the greatest interest to Levi-Civita. In 1933 he published a paper in which he proposed to replace Dirac's first order equations by a set of second order equations which took into account the gravitational field. When the two sets of equations are compared in the case in which there is no gravitational field it is found that Levi-Civita's equations are reconcilable with Dirac's when the electromagnetic field is either purely electric or purely magnetic, but not in the general case.

Though reference has been made to some of Levi-Civita's more outstanding researches there are very many which must be passed over. It ought to be mentioned, however, that in addition to his work in the realm of pure science he was frequently consulted by technicians and engineering firms on problems of practical engineering. In this way he was brought to do work of considerable value to the outside world, notably in connexion with the construction of submarine cables and the vibration of bridges.

Again, there is a great deal of evidence of Levi-Civita's interest in branches of mathematics in which he never published any researches. Old pupils frequently consulted him on their problems, and always found him acquainted with their work, even though it differed widely from anything that Levi-Civita had taught them, and he was always ready both with encouragement and with useful advice.

Levi-Civita was not at first appearances a very striking figure. The first impression received was of an exceedingly small man (he was only about five feet tall) who was very short-sighted. His bearing was quite unpretentious; but, after having talked to him for a while, one was particularly struck by the vivaciousness and precision of his discourse and his very wide knowledge extending over pure and applied mathematics, astronomy and physics, and also by his remarkable acquaintance with the literature on these subjects, both old and new. One noticed in particular his quick grip on a problem, and his passionate interest in all sorts of scientific questions.

In spite of his small frame Levi-Civita was very robust, and enjoyed excellent health until he was well over sixty. What energy he had to spare from his work was devoted to his three great hobbies—mountaineering, cycling, and foreign travel. As a young man he devoted most of his vacations to mountaineering in the Dolomites, and in spite of his physical handicaps he was a good climber. As he grew older his worsening eye-sight curtailed his climbing activities, but he kept them up as far as he could for many years. He enjoyed cycling, and was often to be seen cycling round the countryside near Padua while he was professor there, and subsequently during his frequent visits to his parents; and when he was no longer able to climb he continued to visit his beloved mountains on his bicycle.

He was singularly well placed for indulging his third passion, foreign travel. His private fortune and freedom from domestic worries removed many obstacles from his way, and opportunities were regularly given him by invitations to visit countries in all parts of the world in order to deliver lectures to scientific gatherings. These visits he enjoyed intensely; he could see new places, meet new people, and, thanks to his own personal charm, make a host of new friends. Indeed, Levi-Civita was one of the personally best known and best liked mathematicians of his time.

Levi-Civita was also fortunate in his home life. There was a strong bond of affection between his father, who died in 1922, and himself. While the father was intensely proud of his son's scientific achievements, the son was equally proud of the father's record in the Italian wars of liberation. Though not himself an active politician, Levi-Civita was extremely interested in politics, and remained true to the noble traditions of his family. A visitor to his study could be in no doubt as to his beliefs; while three of the walls were lined by bookcases, the fourth remained empty save for two solitary portraits, one of his father and the other of Garibaldi. Levi-Civita always felt a great tenderness for his mother, and visited her regularly, either at the family house in Padua, or at her villa in Vigodarzere, a nearby village where she lived for several years before her death in 1927. After her death the villa was kept on by her daughter, Ida Senigaglia, and Levi-Civita continued to spend a part of each year there.

In 1914 Levi-Civita married Libera Trevisani. She had been his pupil at the university of Padua, and had taken her doctorate in mathematics. She proved herself a clever and affectionate companion to him, and she was a very gracious hostess, not only to the many eminent scientists who came to visit them from afar, but to the more humble students who regularly visited their home. She accompanied her husband on his many travels and shared with him the many friendships which he made on these journeys. There were no children of the marriage.

For Levi-Civita, research and teaching went hand in hand, and he guided a great number of pupils in fields in which he was the pioneer. His teaching was not circumscribed by any curriculum, as was usual in an Italian university, but was freely given to all who came to consult him. During his vacations, either in the Dolomites or at Vigodarzere, his former pupils would come to be near him, and he would follow their researches with the utmost interest. With infinite patience and unselfishness he would enter into the problems which they brought to him; nothing gave him more pleasure than to have an opportunity of helping them, and it was with the greatest pride that he would present their works for publication by one or other of the many learned societies of which he was a member. Indeed, as one of his pupils once remarked, no one ever merited more than he did the title of Maestro.

He was a born teacher. His scientific papers are models of lucidity, and his books are amongst the easiest reading on their specialized topics. In conversation he could give in simple terms a very simple account of an abstract theory. In acquiring his command over such vast fields of science he was greatly aided by being the possessor of an unusually good memory.

Many honours came to Levi-Civita. He received honarary degrees from many universities throughout the world, including Toulouse, Aachen, Amsterdam and Paris. Academies in all countries of the world honoured him by election to honorary membership. The list is too long to repeat, but included the Institut de Paris and the Berlin academy, and societies in Leningrad, Madrid and South America. In his own country he was a member of the Reale Accademia dei Lincei, the Reale Accademia d'Italia and the Pontificia Accademia delle Scienze dei Nuovi Lincei. When, in 1936, Pope Pius XI dissolved the last named and replaced it by the Pontificia Accademia delle Scienze, an international body, Levi-Civita became an original member of the new academy. The Sylvester medal of the Royal Society was conferred on him in 1922, and in 1930 he was elected a foreign member. He was elected an honorary fellow of the Royal Society of Edinburgh in 1923, and of the London Mathematical Society in 1924. He was also an honorary member of the Edinburgh Mathematical Society, and attended one of its colloquia in St. Andrews.

Although he did not take any active part in politics, he could not remain indifferent to the rise of fascism in Italy, and in 1925, after the "Matteotti affair" he was, with Volterra and many other Italian scientists, a signatory of the "Manifesto Croce," which stigmatized fascism and deprecated its growing power in Italy. For some time, however, his scientific renown protected him from persecution. But in September 1938 the government issued decrees removing from office all professors of Italian universities who were of Jewish origin, and dismissing them from Italian academies. Levi-Civita, who came under the ban, found himself cut off from all that made life interesting to him. It is recorded that he learned of the decrees while staying with his sister at Vigodarzere, when someone happened to switch on the radio as they were being announced. His expression did not change, and he went out for his afternoon walk as usual. The blow soon told on him, however. His health began to fail. After he returned to Rome severe heart trouble developed, and as he was forbidden by his doctors to take any long journey he could not accept any of the offers of asylum which came to him from foreign universities. The remaining years of his life were very sad; he was confined to his room, and unable to continue his work. He died on 29 December 1941 of a stroke. At first the Roman newspapers, except the *Osservatore Romano*, the organ of the Vatican, ignored his death, and it was only after the Pontifical Academy had used its influence that the family were able to announce in the newspapers the fact of his death and the arrangements for his funeral.

If one is interested in *pure* geometry, then the ultimate generalization is to be found in the work of Élie Joseph Cartan (1869–1951), one of the foremost mathematicians of the recent period. Cartan's concept includes those of Levi-Civita, Weyl, and Eddington as special cases. For a description of the transition to post-relativity geometry, and, later, for an account of some phases of Cartan's research, we shall quote statements made by the late J. H. C. Whitehead (1904–1960), whose specialties were related to Cartan's. John Henry Constantine Whitehead who was himself a leading mathematician of our day, specialized in topology (Chapter 25) and, like Cartan, applied that subject to the study of generalized spaces. Whitehead was the author of many research papers, some written in collaboration with American mathematicians. With Oswald Veblen of the Institute for Advanced Study he wrote *The Foundations of Differential Geometry* (1932). He was born in Madras, India, and was the son of the Bishop of Madras and the nephew of the mathematical philosopher Alfred North Whitehead. J. H. C. Whitehead taught at Oxford University from 1932 to 1946, and then from 1947 to 1960. In between times he was at Princeton and the Institute for Advanced Study. He received his Ph.D. from Princeton in 1930, where he was a research fellow from 1929 to 1932, and then visiting lecturer from 1946 to 1947. He was a visiting member of the Institute in the spring of 1960, when he died suddenly on May 8 of that year. His description of the transition from pre-relativity to post-relativity geometry will now be presented.*

Let us briefly recall the state of geometry just before and just after the discovery, in 1916, of general relativity. During the period between this time and 1870 ideas concerning the foundations of geometry had been dominated by Felix Klein's Erlanger Program. Riemann's philosophical concept of geometry had been ignored by most geometers though the analytical side of his theory had been extensively developed, notably by Ricci and Levi-Civita. After the discovery of general relativity, which was based on Riemannian geometry, it was realized that the Erlanger Program was no longer adequate as a general description of geometry. The first person to understand the mathematical implications of this, in anything like their full generality, seems to have been Weyl, when he introduced generalized affine, projective, and conformal

* Royal Society of London, *Obituary Notices of Fellows*, Vol. 8, No. 21 (November 1952), pp. 71 ff.

geometries, whose relation to their classical counterparts was analogous to that of Riemannian to Euclidean geometry.

After the publication, in 1918, of Weyl's first paper in this field, and of one by J. A. Schouten, the development of the subject was guided by two rather different sets of ideas. One of these, due to Cartan, is described below. According to the other, which was first formulated explicitly by Veblen in 1928, at the Bologna International Congress, a geometry is the study of a "geometric object," such as a tensor or projective connexion, from which others can be derived by certain formal processes. One of the main objectives is to define a complete set of *invariants*, such as the curvature tensor and its successive covariant derivatives in generalized affine geometry.

Relativity may have been the "practical" motivation for Cartan's creation of generalized spaces, but his methodology in geometry and, in fact, in all his specialties, drew its strongest inspiration from the geometric and group-theory creations of Sophus Lie. Therefore, if Levi-Civita's life and mathematical contributions are one preliminary to a discussion of Cartan's work, the ideas and activities of Lie should logically form another.

Part of Lie's story was related in connection with Klein. We recall how the young mathematicians met in 1869 and then went to Paris to confer with leading French mathematicians, in particular with Darboux. Then, in 1870, when the Franco-Prussian war broke out, Klein returned to Germany and Lie, an inveterate hiker and mountain climber, set out for Italy *on foot*. Like Archimedes, he had no interest in the war being waged around him, and was unaware that military precautions might limit one's freedom to practice mathematics. Hence, at age twenty-eight, Lie *almost* duplicated the last hour of Archimedes' life. The Syracusan's mathematical notes and geometric diagrams (drawn on the sand along the Sicilian shore line) made him suspect to a Roman soldier, who stamped on the figures and slew Archimedes when he protested. Two millennia later, the Norwegian geometer paused in the first lap of his walking tour, rested in the shade of a tree, and entered in a notebook some of his thoughts on how a geometry of lines could be transformed into a geometry of spheres. He was seized by a French soldier who thought the towheaded giant was a German spy, and mistook his diagrams for copies of French military plans, his symbols for a secret code, the mathematicians named in his notes for a list of guilty parties. Lie, imprisoned at Fontainebleau, appealed for help to Darboux,

Chasles, Bertrand, and other French mathematicians who knew him. It took almost a month before they could obtain his release.

According to Darboux, the Fontainebleau prison was a comfortable place, and Lie was able to make use of his enforced leisure to enlarge on the ideas in the notes which had caused his arrest. In this way he made his first important mathematical discovery, which he presented in a short paper to the French Academy a month after he left prison. Of this brief note, Darboux said, "Nothing resembles a sphere less than a straight line and yet . . . Lie found a transformation which makes spheres correspond to straight lines and hence makes it possible to derive theorems about spheres from those about lines and vice versa."

The 1870 paper was Lie's mathematical debut, a relatively late one as mathematicians' careers go. (Marius) Sophus Lie was born in 1842 at Nordfjordeid (near Flöro), Norway, where his father was a minister. He showed no special interest in mathematics at school, and as late as 1865, when he had completed his courses at the University of Christiania (in preparation for teaching in the secondary schools), he was undecided between philology and mathematics. A reading of the works of the geometer Plücker first aroused his interest and made him aware of his own mathematical talent. After travels in Germany, Italy, and France from 1869 to 1871, he returned to Christiania, took his doctorate in 1872, and became "extraordinary" (associate) professor of mathematics, a position he held until 1886. In that year he was invited to Leipzig, where he was offered a full professorship and the directorship of the mathematical institute. He held this position until 1898. In an earlier chapter, we have had Frau Klein's account of Lie's 1898 visit to Göttingen. Shortly thereafter, the Norwegian parliament created a special chair for him at Christiania, with an exceptionally high salary. But he lived only a half year after receiving this honor, dying in February 1899, at age fifty-six.

Other recognition had come to him before that, however. He had been invited to give a special address in Paris in 1895 for the centenary of the founding of the great École Normale, which along with the École Polytechnique, has always supplied France and the world with leading mathematicians and scientists. He spoke on the importance of the work of Galois, his idol. Then, in 1898, Lie was the first recipient of the Lobachevsky Prize, an award of 500 rubles given by the Physico-Mathematical Society of the University of Kazan for the best original research work submitted in the field of geometry, preferably non-Euclidean.

The book which led to this prize was indeed a remarkable one containing in one section the solution of the so-called Riemann-Helmholtz space problem, a result important not only in group theory and differential geometry, but also in applications to physiology. What Lie did was *correct* and *rigorize* Hermann von Helmholtz's 1868 and 1884 attempts at solution. Helmholtz had sought some justification of Riemann's use of the *quadratic* metric;

$$ds^2 = g_{11}du_1{}^2 + 2g_{12}du_1du_2 + \ldots + g_{nn}du_n{}^2$$

Why, he asked, is it not equally logical to postulate ds^2 as the sum of *fourth* powers, or to express it by some entirely different type of formula? His answer to this question was a kinematic theory of space, that is, an explanation characterizing space according to the movements possible within it. (The idea is much the same as that of Klein's transformations.) Helmholtz drew the foundation of his theory from experimental sources and set down four basic postulates from which he was able to deduce Riemann's metric. Lie's 1898 treatment of the same problem was vastly superior, at least from the point of view of pure mathematics. His assumptions referred to transformations and invariants; they enabled him to establish rigorously and exhaustively the general results of Riemann and Helmholtz.

Lie's period of mathematical creativity (1870–1899) was devoted entirely to the study of *continuous* transformation groups and their invariants. He showed how these two related ideas can furnish principles for simplifying and unifying diverse mathematical subjects—geometry, the theory of *algebraic* invariants (largely the work of Cayley and Sylvester), mechanics, ordinary and partial differential equations. The "contact transformations" he conceived in 1870 during his sojourn in prison were the means of bringing all of Hamiltonian dynamics under the wing of group theory.

Application of these same contact transformations also shed light on some of the most difficult theoretical questions associated with partial differential equations. Like Poincaré, who felt that groups are "all of mathematics," and indicated that "physical laws are differential equations," Lie devoted himself to groups and asserted that "differential equations constitute the most important branch of modern mathematics."

The Norwegian was a prodigious worker, and with the assistance of his disciples, Friedrich Engel (1861–1944) and Georg Scheffers (1866–1945), he set down his ideas in full in colossal tomes. His *Theorie der Transformationsgruppen* appeared in three large volumes between 1888 and 1893. Then there were *Differentialgleichingen* (Differential Equations) in 1891, *Kontinuierliche Gruppen* (1893), and *Berührungstransformationen* (Contact Transformations) in 1896. In the era between 1900 and 1930 these works, with all their excessive detail, were studied by graduate mathematics students all over the world. But since that time Lie's group-theory and geometric notions have been distilled, and their abstract essence extracted. The "pure" part of his work is thus seen in all its profundity, and is being extended in the vigorous research in today's abstract algebra. The study of "Lie groups" and "Lie algebras" is receiving the attention of the best mathematical minds.

In personality, Lie conformed to the conventional idea of the genius. He was shy and withdrawn, but nevertheless outspoken on occasion and given to temper tantrums. In relation to Klein, we have described Lie's tendency toward depression and notions of persecution. To "relax his nerves," he went on hikes or read the novels of Walter Scott and Frederick Marryat. George Abram Miller (1863–1951), an American researcher in group theory in the early years of its development, attended Lie's classes in Leipzig, and later reminisced about them. He recounted that Lie was careless in dress, and sometimes appeared in class without collar or necktie, or even with his hat on. Miller described one of Lie's verbal outbursts, when the latter stated, "Mathematics may be the royal road to learning, but unfortunately we mathematicians do not receive royal pay." Lie's students respected him, but gossiped about his eccentricities. Nevertheless the doctoral candidates at Leipzig flocked to Lie, who assigned easy topics for research and provided a tremendous amount of assistance. But pupils found him personally crude and were wont to contrast him with the suave Klein. They pronounced the latter a "cultured gentleman" but said, "The best you can say for Lie is that he is a good fellow." The consensus today is that he was a very good fellow indeed.

Now, to link the geometric notions of Lie, Levi-Civita, and Çartan, let us recall from the previous chapter that in the small "neighborhood" of a point in a Riemannian space the geometry is approximately Euclidean, so that for an ordinary 2-dimensional surface, the geometry of the surface and that of the tangent plane are the same in the locality of the point of contact. In the case of an n-dimensional Riemannian manifold, this space can be considered as the aggregate of its tangent spaces or, in the words of Cartan, as a multitude of tiny facets each of which is a Euclidean space. But all these facets or tangent spaces must be fused into a whole, the *Riemannian manifold*. There must be a "connection" between one tangent space and a "neighboring" or "infinitesimally close" tangent space, that is, an analytic formulation of the "displacement" of the former into the latter. Cartan's generalized spaces consist of (1) an underlying manifold with (2) a tangent space at each point of this manifold in which (3) a Kleinian geometry obtains (that is, an affine or projective or conformal geometry related to the affine, projective, or conformal transformations of the tangent space, respectively), and (4) a connection or displacement formula defining the displacement of any tangent space along any curve from the point of contact to a neighboring point.

When these four points are treated less intuitively and more mathematically, the influences of Levi-Civita and Lie become more apparent. The Levi-Civita tangent spaces are Euclidean, and his parallel displacement is a special case of (4) above. As for Sophus Lie, the notions he contributed are numerous. In the first place, he emphasized the importance of the principle of *linearity* in analytic approximations. The idea is similar to the numerical integration techniques, in which one uses a chord or straight-line segment as an approximation to a small curved arc. Lie indicated that in arbitrary analytic transformations, however complicated the functional formulations, the differentials dx, dy, etc., representing the differences in the coordinates of neighboring points, undergo only a homogeneous affine transformation. In Chapter 17 the plane group of such transformations was expressed by

$$x' = a_1x + b_1y$$
$$y' = a_2x + b_2y$$

Then if u, v are Gaussian coordinates on a surface, and these coordinates undergo arbitrary analytic transformations, the corresponding Lie "infinitesimal transformations" are

$$d(u') = a_1\, du + b_1\, dv$$
$$d(v') = a_2\, du + b_2\, dv$$

where, for each analytic transformation of the entire surface, the values of a_1, b_1, a_2, b_2 depend only on the particular point of the surface, that is, are functions of u and v. The different points of the tangent plane are obtained by varying du and dv. Similarly, in a Riemannian space of n dimensions, $d(u_1')$, $d(u_2')$, ..., $d(u_n')$ would be expressible as linear functions of du_1, du_2, ..., du_n, and the points of the tangent space would be obtained by varying du_1, du_2, ..., du_n. Then to each arbitrary analytic transformation of the underlying manifold there corresponds a homogeneous affine transformation in each tangent space, and corresponding to the set of analytic transformations of the manifold there is the affine group and affine geometry in each tangent space. If the manifold is Riemannian, the metric

$$ds^2 = g_{11}dx_1^2 + 2g_{12}dx_1dx_2 + \ldots + g_{nn}dx_n^2$$

fuses the affine geometries of all the tangent spaces. The non-Riemannian geometries are not metric, and in them the generalizations of Levi-Civita's parallel displacement integrate the geometries of the tangent spaces in a different way. The Cartan generalized spaces have nonaffine geometries (projective or conformal, etc.) in the tangent spaces, and different connections or displacements from those in the Riemannian or Levi-Civita manifolds.

Concerning Élie Cartan and his mathematical work Professors Shing-Shen Chern and Claude Chevalley state[*]:

Undoubtedly one of the greatest mathematicians of this century, Élie Cartan's career was nevertheless characterized by a rare harmony of genius and modesty. He was born on April 9, 1869, in Dolomieu (Isère), a village in the south of France. His father was a blacksmith. Cartan's elementary education was made possible by one of the state stipends for gifted children. In 1888 he entered the École Normale Supérieure, where he learned higher mathe-

---

[*] Shing-Shen Chern, and C. Chevalley, "Élie Cartan and His Mathematical Work," *Bull. of the Amer. Mathematical Society*, Vol. 58, No. 3 (March 1952).

matics from such masters as Tannery, Picard, Darboux, and Hermite. His research work started with his famous thesis on continuous groups, a subject suggested to him by his fellow student Tresse, recently returned from studying with Sophus Lie in Leipzig. Cartan's first teaching position was at Montpellier, where he was *maître de conférences;* he then went successively to Lyons, to Nancy, and finally in 1909 to Paris. He was made a professor at the Sorbonne in 1912. The report on his work which was the basis for this promotion was written by Poincaré; this was one of the circumstances in his career of which he seemed to have been genuinely proud. He remained at the Sorbonne until his retirement in 1940.

Cartan was an excellent teacher; his lectures were gratifying intellectual experiences, which left the student with a generally mistaken idea that he had grasped all there was on the subject. It is therefore the more surprising that for a long time his ideas did not exert the influence they so richly deserved to have on young mathematicians. This was partly due to Cartan's extreme modesty. But in 1939, the celebration of Cartan's scientific jubilee, J. Dieudonné could rightly say to him: ". . . *vous êtes un 'jeune,' et vous comprenez les jeunes*"—it was then beginning to be true that the young understood Cartan.

In foreign countries, particularly in Germany, his recognition as a great mathematician came earlier. It was perhaps H. Weyl's fundamental papers on group representations published around 1925 that established Cartan's reputation among mathematicians not in his own field. Meanwhile, the development of abstract algebra naturally helped to attract attention to his work on Lie algebra.

Cartan was elected to the French Academy in 1931. In his later years he received several other honors. Thus he was a foreign member of the National Academy of Sciences, U.S.A., and a foreign Fellow of the (British) Royal Society. In 1936 he was awarded an honorary degree by Harvard University.

Closely interwoven with Cartan's life as a scientist and teacher had been his family life, which was filled with an atmosphere of happiness and serenity. He had four children, three sons, Henri, Jean, and Louis, and a daughter, Hélène. Jean Cartan oriented himself towards music, and already appeared to be one of the most gifted composers of his generation, when he was cruelly taken by death. Louis Cartan was a physicist; arrested by the Germans at the beginning of the Resistance, he was murdered by them after a long period of detention. Henri Cartan followed in the footsteps of his father to become a leading mathematician.

Cartan's mathematical work can be roughly classified under three headings: group theory, systems of differential equations, and geometry. These themes are, however, constantly interwoven with each other in his work. Almost everything Cartan did is more or less connected with the theory of Lie groups.

Sophus Lie introduced the groups of transformations which were named after him. The idea of considering the *abstract group* which underlies a given group of transformations came only later; it appears quite explicitly in the first paper by Cartan. Whereas, for Lie, the problem of classification consisted in finding all possible transformation groups on a given number of variables (a far too difficult problem in the present stage of mathematics as soon as the number of variables is not very small), for Cartan the problem was to find all possible abstract structures of continuous groups. He solved the problem completely for "simple" groups (those having no proper normal subgroups). Once the structures of all simple groups were known, it became possible to look for all possible realizations of any one of these structures by transformations of a specific nature, and, in particular, for their realizations as groups of linear transformations. This is the problem of the determination of the representations of a given group; it was solved completely by Cartan for simple groups. The solution led in particular to the discovery, as early as 1913, of the *spinors*, which were to be rediscovered later in a special case by the physicists.

Cartan also investigated the infinite Lie groups, i.e., the groups of transformations whose operations depend *not* on a finite number of continuous parameters, but on arbitrary functions. In that case, one does not have the notion of the abstract underlying group. Cartan and Vessiot found, at about the same time and independently of each other, a substitute notion which consists in defining when two infinite Lie groups are to be considered as isomorphic. Cartan then proceeded to classify all possible types of non-isomorphic infinite Lie groups.

Cartan also paid much attention to the study of topological properties of groups considered in the large. He showed how many of these topological problems may be reduced to purely algebraic questions; by so doing, he discovered the very remarkable fact that many properties of the group in the large may be read from the infinitesimal structure of the group, i.e., are already determined when some arbitrarily small piece of the group is given. His work along these lines resembles that of the paleontologist reconstructing the shape of a prehistoric animal from the peculiarities of some small bone.

The idea of studying the abstract structure of mathematical objects which hides itself beneath the analytical clothing was also the mainspring of Cartan's theory of differential systems. He insisted on having a theory of differential equations which is invariant under arbitrary changes in variables. Only in this way can the theory uncover the specific properties of the objects one studies by means of the differential equations they satisfy, in contradistinction to what depends only on the particular representation of these objects by numbers or sets of numbers. In order to achieve such an invariant theory, Cartan made a systematic use of the notion of the *exterior differential* of a differential form, a notion which he helped to create and which has the required property of being invariant with respect to any change of variables.

Raised in the French geometrical tradition, Cartan had a constant interest in differential geometry. He had the unusual combination of a vast knowledge of Lie groups, a theory of differential systems whose invariant character was particularly suited for geometrical investigations, and, most important of all, a remarkable geometrical intuition. As a result, he was able to see the geometrical content of very complicated calculations, and even to substitute geometrical arguments for some of the computations.

In the 1920's the general theory of relativity gave a new impulse to differential geometry. This gave rise to a feverish search for spaces with a suitable local structure, The most notable example of such a local structure is a Riemann metric. It can be generalized in various ways, by modifying the form of the integral which defines the arc length in Riemannian geometry (Finsler geometry), by studying only those properties pertaining to the geodesics or paths (geometry of paths of Eisenhart, Veblen, and T. Y. Thomas), by studying the properties of a family of Riemann metrics whose fundamental forms differ from each other by a common factor (conformal geometry), etc. While in all these directions the definition of a parallel displacement is considered to be the major concern, the approach of Cartan to these problems is most original and satisfactory. Again the notion of group plays the central role. Roughly speaking, a generalized space in the sense of Cartan is a space of tangent spaces such that two infinitely near tangent spaces are related by an infinitesmal transformation of a given Lie group. Such a structure is known as a connection.

Besides several books, Cartan published about 200 mathematical papers. His major specialties, in addition to geometry, were group theory and differential equations. Cartan's papers on group theory fall into two categories, distinguished from each other both by the nature of the question treated and by the time at which they were written. The papers of the first cycle are purely algebraic in character; they are more concerned with what are now called Lie algebras than with group theory proper. The work of Cartan's second group-theoretic period is concerned with the groups themselves, and not with their Lie algebras, and in general with the global aspect of the group.

For an account of his algebraic discoveries we return to J. H. C. Whitehead once more.*

In the years 1897, 1898 Cartan turned his attention from Lie algebras to linear associative algebras. In 1898 he proved the Wedderburn structure theorem [Chapter 28] for algebras over the real and complex fields. The methods which Wedderburn (1908) used

---

* Royal Society of London, *Obituary Notices of Fellows, loc. cit.*

in proving his theorem are more suitable than Cartan's to the problems of linear associative algebra. Indeed this paper of Wedderburn's is one of the outstanding contributions to the subject and it is reasonable to associate the theorem with his name. But the fundamental importance of Cartan's paper, which Wedderburn duly acknowledged, should not be forgotten.

During the years 1904 to 1909, there are his papers on infinite transformation groups, as defined by Lie. Such a group is "infinite" in the sense that its general transformation cannot be expressed in terms of a finite set of parameters. In general it is only defined as a local group, or pseudo-group, whose transformations operate on different open subsets of Cartesian space. Finally a (local) group, G, of this kind is defined as the totality of transformations which leave invariant a given set of differential equations. The transformations in G are themselves given by a set D, of differential equations. Since G is infinite the general solution of D is not expressed in terms of a finite set of parameters.

There have been very few, if any, new contributions to the general theory of infinite groups since these papers of Cartan. This is doubtless due to the difficulty of the subject and also to the appearance of temporary finality in Cartan's work. That is to say, there does not seem to have been much hope of greatly extending his theory with the methods which have been available during the last forty years. At the present time the obvious questions are those concerning global infinite groups, acting on n-dimensional manifolds. It may be that a theory of such groups will be constructed on the basis of Cartan's local theory. In this case it would not be surprising if the latter were eventually considered to be his greatest work.

From 1916 onwards Cartan's papers, with one or two exceptions, were on differential geometry, including the theory of generalized spaces and differential goemetry in the large. This work on differential geometry would, by itself, have been sufficient to establish Cartan among the leading mathematicians of this half-century. It is remarkable that he embarked on it when he was nearly fifty years old and maintained a steady output of first-class work throughout the subsequent thirty years.

As for Cartan's work on differential equations, probably the best authority is his own 1945 book, *Les systèmes différentiels extérieurs et leurs applications géométriques*. But we now return to the Chern-Chevalley biography for further details of Cartan's geometric work, which is the major theme of the present chapter.*

Einstein's theory of general relativity gave a new impetus to differential geometry. In their efforts to find an appropriate model

---

* Shing-Shen Chern and C. Chevalley, *loc. cit.*

of the universe, geometers have broadened their horizon from the study of submanifolds in classical spaces (Euclidean, non-Euclidean, projective, conformal, etc.) to that of more general spaces intrinsically defined. The result is an extension of the work of Gauss and Riemann on Riemannian geometry to spaces with a "connection," which may be an affine connection, a Weyl connection, a projective connection, or a conformal connection. In these generalizations, sometimes called non-Riemannian geometry, an important tool is the absolute differential calculus of Ricci and Levi-Civita. The results achieved are of considerable geometric interest. For instance, in the theory of projective connections, developed independently by Cartan, Veblen, Eisenhart, and Thomas, it is shown that when the space has a system of paths defined by a system of differential equations of the second order, a generalized projective geometry can be defined in the space which reduces to ordinary projective geometry when the differential system is that of the straight lines. Numerous other examples can be cited. The problem at this stage is twofold: (1) to give a definition of "geometry" which will include most of the existing spaces of interest; (2) to develop analytic methods for the treatment of the new geometries, it being increasingly clear that the absolute differential calculus is inadequate.

For this purpose Cartan developed what seems to be the most comprehensive and satisfactory program and demonstrated its advantages in a decisive way. This contribution clearly illustrates his geometric insight and we consider it to be the most important among his works on differential geometry. It can be best explained by means of the modern notion of a "fiber bundle."

A *fiber bundle* is merely the generalization of a simpler concept considered earlier in this book (Chapter 7), namely, the idea of a *Cartesian product*. Let us recall that if there are two sets of numbers, $A = \{1, 2, 3\}$ and $B = \{7, 8\}$, then the Cartesian product symbolized by $A \times B$ and read as "*A cross B*" consists of all possible ordered number pairs formed from selecting the first number from A and the second from B. Thus, "*A cross B*," or $A \times B$, is the set of *six* number pairs, $\{(1, 7), (1, 8), (2, 7), (2, 8), (3, 7), (3, 8)\}$. Again, if A is the set of all real numbers between 0 and 2—that is, the interval [0, 2] on the X-axis in Figure 20.5—and B is the set of all real numbers in the interval [0, 1] on the Y-axis, then $A \times B$ is the shaded rectangle in Figure 20.5.

If A consists of all points of a circle and B of all points of a line segment, then $A \times B$ is the surface of a cylinder. To clarify this, suppose that the equation of the circle A is $x^2 + y^2 = 25$ (Figure 20.6), and that B is the interval [0, 1] on the Z-axis of the diagram. One point of this circle has

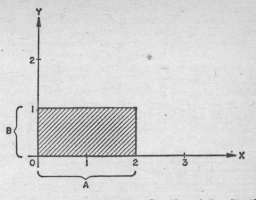

Figure 20.5 $A \times B$ for $A = [0, 2]$ and $B = [0, 1]$

$x = 3$, $y = 4$ as its coordinates. If this is combined with the point ½ of the interval [0, 1], the result is the number triple $(3, 4, ½)$, or point P of Figure 20.6. Combining $(3, 4)$ with *any* number z on [0, 1] leads to $(3, 4, z)$, a point on that *vertical* element of the cylinder which goes through $(3, 4, 0)$ $(3, 4, ½)$, $(3, 4, 1)$ etc., in Figure 20.6. Now to form $A \times B$ one must combine *every* point on the circle with *every* point of the line segment in the way just indicated, and this will lead to all points on all elements of the cylinder.

In the language of fiber bundles, the circle would be called the *fiber*, the line segment would be termed the *base space*, and the cylindric surface would be the *total* or *bundle space*, which can be transformed into the *fiber* by *projection*. But the cylindric surface is a trivial example of a fiber space because it is too special, much in the way that a plane would be a trivial instance of a surface. The *general* fiber bundle is only *locally* a Cartesian product, that is, only the small "neighborhoods" of points of the bundle are required to be Cartesian products, and the bundle as a whole need *not* be such a product. This permits the presence of "twists" or "torsion" in the bundle or total space. In fact, a fiber bundle is called a *skew product* by one of the Soviet mathematical leaders of our day, L. Pontrjagin, whose specialty is topology, a "geometric" subject in which his blindness has apparently not handicapped him in making discoveries.

In addition to having small subsets that are Cartesian products, a fiber bundle must meet certain continuity and

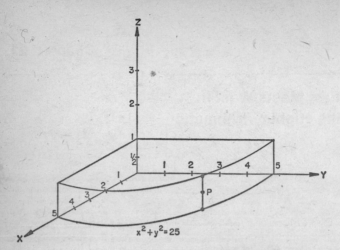

Figure 20.6 $A \times B$ for $A : x^2 + y^2 = 25$ and $B : [0,1]$. (Diagram pictures only one-quarter of the circle and Cartesian product.)

group-theory requirements concerning the way the "neighborhoods" or tiny subsets are linked with one another to make up the total space. This part of the definition will become clearer after the concepts of "analytic topology" have been developed in later chapters. The idea of a fiber bundle has been treated here not only because it is important in Cartan's ultimate answer to "What is geometry?" but also because it is fundamental in other branches of mathematics today. Its connection with elementary analytic geometry has been specified, and it is interesting to note that, although the term "fiber bundle" is not used, the idea of a Cartesian product is developed in detail and given considerable emphasis in United States high school courses in the "new mathematics" today.

Chapter 21

East Meets West in
the Higher Arithmetic

The story of geometry which reached its final abstract climax in the work of Élie Cartan started with the ideas of Gauss and Riemann. Those two nineteenth-century Titans exerted an equally powerful influence in other mathematical areas, and, as in the case of geometry, the Gauss and Riemann beginnings evolved into some of the most significant tools of twentieth-century pure mathematical research. As an instance, one can consider the effect of Gauss and Riemann on the theory of numbers (the higher arithmetic). In fact, of all the great contributions of Gauss, his number-theory discoveries are often considered the greatest of all. To him we owe the saying, now classic: Mathematics is the queen of the sciences, and arithmetic the queen of mathematics.

The "queen of mathematics," that is, the higher arithmetic, is often described as the theory of the natural numbers. In the theory one must define certain binary arithmetic operations. If subtraction is to be one such operation (or, what is the same thing, if additive inverses are to exist), then zero and the negative integers must be adjoined to the natural numbers. Hence the theory of numbers is actually the study of properties of the set of integers, {. . . , −3, −2, −1, 0, 1, 2, 3, . . .}. In the present chapter we shall discuss important aspects of that theory.

The theory of the integers is a worthwhile study for many reasons. For one thing, there is perhaps no other branch of mathematics whose issues form an unbroken chain of thought linking early man with his descendants in the nuclear age. Again, the higher arithmetic holds a strong appeal for scholar and amateur alike. The proverbial man in the street can readily understand the meaning (if not the proofs) of all theorems. There is also the intriguing and mystifying challenge of the numerous unsolved problems, issues whose "truth" seems "self-evident" to the uninitiated just because so much numerical evidence can be found to lend credence to the hypotheses involved. Another reason for devoting a detailed chapter to the theory of numbers is that the subject is the purest of *pure* mathematics and thus offers a contrast with geometry, differential equations, mathematical statistics, and all the other mathematical fields whose applications to physics and practical affairs have been stressed in previous chapters. In spite of its purity, however, number theory does have some applicability to the physical world. Finally, as the present chapter will show, the higher arithmetic offers some exceedingly simple illustrations of the advanced concepts of modern abstract algebra.

The introduction to the "queen of mathematics" involves the very elementary notion of the divisibility of one natural number by another. At school, children frequently consider that question in working with fractions. In cancellation, it is helpful to break integers down into divisors or *factors*. Such experience shows that there are two cases, the first illustrated by $5 = 5 \cdot 1$, $7 = 7 \cdot 1$, $11 = 11 \cdot 1$, $29 = 29 \cdot 1$, etc., the second by $4 = 2 \cdot 2$, $6 = 2 \cdot 3$, $12 = 2 \cdot 2 \cdot 3$, $30 = 2 \cdot 3 \cdot 5$, etc. Natural numbers like 5, 7, 11, 29, in which the factoring appears trivial since the number is expressed as the product of itself and unity (the number *one*), are called *primes*. More exactly a prime number is an integer greater than 1 whose only positive integral divisors are itself and unity. Natural numbers like 4, 6, 12, 30, which have positive integral divisors other than themselves and unity, are called *composite*. The factoring process expresses a composite natural number as the product of its prime divisors.

Let us see what an illustrious Alexandrian, Eratosthenes (*ca.* 230 B.C.), had to say about primes. His famous *sieve* was designed to remove the composite numbers from the list of positive integers and leave the set of all primes. He is probably best known for his measurement of the earth. But his talents were not limited to number theory and geography. He was also a poet, philosopher, and historian, who was summoned to Alexandria to direct the great Library. There is much lore associated with his name. For example, his colleagues at the Library and Museum appear to have endowed him with a number of nicknames. One of these was *Pentathlos*, a tribute to his "five-sided" nature, that is, to the universality of his interests; another labeled him a second Plato. At any rate, he must have had a likable personality, since a sobriquet is usually the product of friendly, informal relationships.

In constructing his sieve, Eratosthenes saw immediately that 4, 6, 8, 10, 12, . . ., that is, all *even* natural numbers greater than 2, are composite. Therefore his formula for sifting was as follows: List the integers starting with 2, and then strike out every *second* number after 2. Then from the list of integers remaining, strike out every *third* number after 3. Then return and strike out every *fifth* integer after 5, every *seventh* integer after 7, every *eleventh* integer after 11, etc. In the process, certain integers may be crossed out several times, for example, 15 will be stricken out in both the second and third siftings, 35 in the third and fourth, etc. We indicate several steps in Eratosthenes' method for straining out composite numbers.

Step 1: 2 3 ~~4~~ 5 ~~6~~ 7 ~~8~~ 9 ~~10~~ 11 ~~12~~ 13 ~~14~~ 15 ~~16~~ 17 ~~18~~ 19...

Step 2: 2 3 5 7 ~~9~~ 11 13 ~~15~~ 17 19 ~~21~~ 23 25 ~~27~~ 29
                 31 ~~33~~ 35 37 ~~39~~ 41 43 ~~45~~ 47 49...

Step 3: 2 3 5 7 ~~9~~ 11 13 ~~15~~ 17 19 ~~21~~ 23 ~~25~~ ~~27~~ 29
                 31 ~~33~~ ~~35~~ 37 ~~39~~ 41 43 ~~45~~ 47 49...

Step 4: 2 3 5 7 ~~9~~ 11 13 ~~15~~ 17 19 ~~21~~ 23 ~~25~~ ~~27~~ 29
                 31 ~~33~~ ~~35~~ 37 ~~39~~ 41 43 ~~45~~ 47 ~~49~~...

When the sifting is done, one is left with the succession of primes

2 3 5 7 11 13 17 19 23 29 31 37 41 43 47
              53 59 61 67 71 73 79 83 89 97 . . .

An observation of this list indicates that among the first six integers after 1, namely, 2, 3, 4, 5, 6, 7, two-thirds are primes; among the first twelve after 1, one-half are primes; among the first 96 after 1, only one-quarter are primes. The incidence of primes becomes less and less frequent the farther we go, for the obvious reason that more integers precede any particular number and are available as possible divisors. If, for example, one continues the list of natural numbers as far as 1,000,000,000, only about 5 per cent of the integers up to that point will be primes. With such continued thinning out of the primes, it seems possible that after a certain position in the list of integers there may be no more primes and all integers will be composite. Euclid *proved* that such a conjecture is false. His theorem is: *The number of primes is infinite.*

His reasoning, although much more rigorous, was somewhat as follows. In the above list of primes, multiply the first two prime numbers, and add 1 to this product; then multiply the first three primes and add 1, etc. This yields

$$2 \cdot 3 + 1$$
$$2 \cdot 3 \cdot 5 + 1$$
$$2 \cdot 3 \cdot 5 \cdot 7 + 1$$
$$2 \cdot 3 \cdot 5 \cdot 7 \cdot 11 + 1$$

We could compute the results of these operations and find the values 7, 31, 211, 2311, etc., but it is better merely to *reason* about the nature of the results so that we can come to conclusions about

$$2 \cdot 3 \cdot 5 \cdot 7 \cdot 11 \cdot 13 \cdot 17 \cdots 89 \cdot 97 + 1$$

without resorting to tedious multiplication.

At any rate, Euclid considered each expression above with a view to finding possible prime divisors (that are exact). Thus, in the first expression, one might perform division by 2 or by 3, with the results

$$2 \overline{)2 \cdot 3 + 1} \qquad\qquad 3 \overline{)2 \cdot 3 + 1}$$
$$3 + \tfrac{1}{2} = 3\tfrac{1}{2} \qquad\qquad 2 + \tfrac{1}{3} = 2\tfrac{1}{3}$$

Since the quotients are fractional, 2 and 3 are *not* exact divisors. In the same way it can be shown that the second expression above, $2 \cdot 3 \cdot 5 + 1$, does *not* have the primes 2, 3, or 5 as exact divisors. Finally,

$$2 \cdot 3 \cdot 5 \cdot 7 \cdot 11 \cdot 13 \cdot 17 \cdots 89 \cdot 97 + 1$$

does not have the primes 2, 3, 5, 7, 11, 12, 17, . . . , 89, or 97 as exact divisors. Hence if one were to "multiply out" to obtain the value of the above expression, the result might be composite, but in this case its prime factors would not be any of the prime numbers in the list from 2 to 97, and could only be primes greater than 97.

Now, Euclid argued, if at any stage in listing the primes in order of size (as Eratosthenes did), one believes he has arrived at the "last prime," let him form an expression like those above, that is, the product of all the primes up to the point in question, increased by 1, thus:

$$N = 2 \cdot 3 \cdot 5 \cdot 7 \cdot 11 \cdot 13 \cdot 17 \cdots 89 \cdot 97 \cdots l + 1$$

where l is the "last prime." Consider the number N, Euclid said. It may be prime or it may be composite. In the latter case it can be broken down into prime factors. But then these factors could *not* be any of the primes 2, 3, 5, 7, . . . , 89, 97, . . . , l, as the previous argument has indicated. Hence, since the prime factors or divisors of N are not in the list from 2 to l, they can only be prime numbers beyond l, so that l cannot be the last prime. But N may not be composite. It may be a prime number. But N is obviously larger than l, as its expression above indicates. Then, if N is a prime, it is a prime greater than l. In this way, Euclid provided a *reductio ad absurdum* for the hypothesis that some prime number is the last on the list. Since there is no last prime, the number of primes must be infinite, and Euclid had established his theorem.

Let us continue with another of Euclid's famous number-theory propositions, the one called the *fundamental theorem of arithmetic*. It states that *every integer greater than 1 can be factored into a product of primes in only one way.*

It may seem obvious that if one factors 10,500 into $2 \cdot 2 \cdot 3 \cdot 5 \cdot 5 \cdot 5 \cdot 7$, there is no other way to effect a breakdown into primes. But in modern algebra there are systems (integral domains—see Chapter 4) whose elements are like the integers because they obey the same fundamental arithmetic laws. Nevertheless, such systems may lack the unique factorization property. Euclid revealed the profundity of his thought by realizing that the characteristic in question is not an obvious one but a very special attribute that must be demonstrated.

We shall not immediately consider an integral domain but, for a simple example, shall take the semigroup $\{S, \bullet\}$ where S is the set of positive even integers, $\{2, 4, 6, 8, . . .\}$, and $\bullet$ is ordinary multiplication (hence *associative*). Multiplication is truly a binary operation on S because the product of any two elements in S is an element of S. Now consider the factorization of the numbers of S into smaller numbers of S. We exclude statements like $6 = 2 \cdot 3$, $14 = 2 \cdot 7$, etc. since 3 and 7 are *not* elements of the set S. Let us follow the example of Professor Ivan Niven[*] and call a number in the set S a *pseudoprime* if it cannot be factored into two or more smaller numbers of the aggregate. Then we can obtain a set of pseudoprimes, $\{2, 6, 10, 14, 18, 22, 26, 30, 34, 38, 42, 46, \ldots\}$. All other numbers of the original aggregate S can be factored into pseudoprimes, but there are cases where this factorization is *not* unique, for example, $60 = 2 \cdot 30$ or $60 = 6 \cdot 10$, and $132 = 2 \cdot 66$ or $132 = 6 \cdot 22$.

Euclid's interest in prime numbers was emulated by mathematicians and amateurs alike throughout the ages. What has been sought and never found is a mathematical *formula* for *all* prime numbers. Thus $f(n) = n^2 - n + 41$ will lead to a prime if any of the integers $1, 2, 3, \ldots, 39, 40$ is substituted for n. But if $n = 41$, a composite number results, since $41^2 - 41 + 41 = 41^2$. Another formula, $f(n) = n^2 - 79n + 1601$, yields primes when any natural number less than 80 is substituted for n.

It was inevitable that Fermat, considered by many the greatest arithmetician in history, would seek a formula to yield prime numbers. He conjectured that

$$F_n = 2^{2^n} + 1$$

would produce *only* primes for $n = 0, 1, 2, 3, \ldots$. It is true that the first five of these *Fermat numbers* are primes. Thus there are the five *Fermat primes*,

$$F_0 = 2^{2^0} + 1 = 2^1 + 1 = 3$$
$$F_1 = 2^{2^1} + 1 = 2^2 + 1 = 5$$
$$F_2 = 2^{2^2} + 1 = 2^4 + 1 = 17$$
$$F_3 = 2^{2^3} + 1 = 2^8 + 1 = 257$$
$$F_4 = 2^{2^4} + 1 = 2^{16} + 1 = 65,537$$

But Fermat's hunch was ultimately proved to be erroneous. In 1732 Euler showed that $F_5 = 2^{32} + 1$ is *composite*, with 641 as a divisor. As time passed, F_n was shown to be composite for fifteen other values of n and, to date, no Fermat primes other than the classic five have been revealed. Even with electronic computers, the task of investigating new

* I. Niven, "The Concept of Number," in *Insights into Modern Mathematics*, Twenty-Third Yearbook, National Council of Teachers of Mathematics, Washington, D.C. (1957) pp. 7–35.

Fermat numbers is formidable because of their size. Among the most recent to be proved composite, there are F_{36}, which contains more than 20,000,000,000,000 digits, and F_{73}, which is so enormous that, if its digits were typed on a tape, that tape could be wound around the equator some 60,000,000,000 times!

Fermat primes intrigued Gauss, who was able to apply them, surprisingly, to an age-old problem of Euclidean *geometry*—the question of just which regular (equilateral and equiangular) polygons are constructible with straight-edge and compasses. Euclid's Book IV discusses constructions for regular polygons of 3, 4, 5, and 15 sides. The reader doubtless carried out some of those constructions at school by the method of dividing a circle into a number of equal parts and then joining the points of division. Having constructed 4 equal arcs, it is possible to bisect each of these to obtain 8 equal arcs whose chords form a regular octagon. By bisecting arcs again and again, a regular polygon of 16 or 32 or 64, etc., sides can be constructed. Thus Euclid's Book IV implies the constructibility, with straight-edge and compasses, of regular polygons of $2^k \cdot 3$, $2^k \cdot 4$, $2^k \cdot 5$, $2^k \cdot 15$ sides where $k = 0, 1, 2, 3, \ldots$. Not until the day of Gauss, however, was it known that there are other regular polygons which are constructible by means of those limited tools which Plato had prescribed as a proper discipline for geometry.

A month before his nineteenth birthday Gauss established the fact that a regular polygon of 17 sides can be constructed with straight-edge and compasses alone. This discovery is said to have swayed young Gauss in favor of a career in mathematics rather than in languages and philology. He extended his theorem by proving that Platonic constructibility is possible whenever n, the number of sides of a regular polygon, is a *Fermat prime* or, more generally, when $n = 2^k p_1 p_2 \cdots p_r$, where $p_1 p_2, \ldots, p_r$ are *different* Fermat primes. This general theorem implies, for example, the constructibility of regular polygons of 257, 65537, $2^k \cdot 3 \cdot 17 \cdot 257$, $2^k \cdot 3 \cdot 5 \cdot 17 \cdot 65537$, etc. sides.

Although there is no single formula for all primes, the use of Eratosthenes' sieve leads to a rather involved rule for the *number of primes* up to a certain point in the natural number scale. Thus we know that there are 50,847,478 primes below 1,000,000,000 and the use of the newest electronic computers will probably provide more data of the same sort.

There are factor tables available for researchers and amateurs. Some of these were ground out "by hand" before the era of mechanical calculators, and there are many stories about those who were willing to undertake the taxing arithmetic computations involved. One of these was the German calculating prodigy Zacharias Dase (1824–1861), whose feats of mental computation surpassed all those of other arithmetical prodigies known up to his time. Dase enjoyed the calculation of logarithmic, trigonometric, and other tables which he prepared in his leisure time. The compilation of factors of numbers starting with 7,000,000 was a volunteer activity to which he gave the last few years of his short life.

After the noted French mathematician Émile Borel had advanced certain statistical hypotheses concerning what the proportion of primes should be when exceedingly high integers are reached, a young Bulgarian student named Sougarev prepared enormous statistical tabulations of facts about primes between 2,000,000 and 2,100,000 in order to test the Borelian thesis. Sougarev did this during the years 1937–1939 to pass the time while he was an invalid in various hospitals in France.

Neither Dase nor Sougarev can be called mathematicians, but the best available factor tables are those prepared by a leading American number-theorist, Derrick Norman Lehmer (1867–1938), whose son, Derrick Henry Lehmer, has followed in his father's footsteps by making discoveries in higher arithmetic and applying them to the facilitation of computations and tabulations connected with primes and other number-theoretic issues.

History tells us that Dase was dull and unintelligent except for his computational ability. Sougarev is not at all known in the world of mathematics. The elder Lehmer, however, who was as fascinated by the factorization of numbers as those two amateurs, was an entirely different type of computer, more closely akin to Euclid and Eratosthenes. Like the latter, Lehmer was versatile, interested in poetry and music as well as mathematics. He edited and contributed to a literary periodical. He composed two operas and a number of songs based on legends and musical themes of Indians of the western United States.

In our present scientific era, the various tabulations of both Lehmers are considered invaluable for researchers throughout the world, and here again history offers a contrast. In 1776, that all-important date for Americans, the

Austrian government published a factor table that had been prepared by a Viennese school-teacher, Anton Felkel. This was a remarkable compilation of factors of numbers up to 408,000, but it is not surprising that it was not a best seller. Austrian government authorities, however, appear to have expected wide sales, and when only a small number of subscriptions were received, all the remaining copies of Felkel's tables were declared to be "scrap paper" to be used in preparing cartridges for the war against Turkey. Even more ill-starred, from the point of view of usefulness, is the factor table of J. P. Kulick (1793–1863) which was once in the hands of the Vienna Academy, but has *never* been published. Kulick, a Prague professor, devoted twenty years to preparing the factors of numbers up to 100,000,000. (The Lehmer tables extend to 10,000,000.)

To return to Euclid's theory of primes, no real progress beyond the Alexandrian's ideas was made until the 1850 research of the noted Russian mathematician Pafnuti Lvovich Tchebycheff (1821–1894), whom the British algebraist James Joseph Sylvester (1814–1897), called "the greatest mathematician of this (nineteenth) century or any other age." Sylvester, who obtained a refinement of one of Tchebycheff's number-theoretic approximations, exerted a tremendous influence on American mathematics through his activities from 1877 to 1883. During that period he was professor of mathematics at Johns Hopkins University, and founded (1878) the *American Journal of Mathematics*, the first scholarly mathematical publication in the United States. He also wrote poetry, which he erroneously judged to be of the same high quality as his mathematical discoveries, and was generally given to a poetic style of expression, *vide* his description of Tchebycheff's contribution to the theory of prime numbers: "He was the only man ever able to cope with the refractory character and erratic flow of prime numbers and to confine the stream of their progression within algebraic limits, building up, if I may so say, banks on either side which that stream, devious and irregular as are its windings, can never overflow." The precise nature of Tchebycheff's discovery will be explained below.

The Russian mathematician had been elected to membership in the Royal Society of London and, whenever he visited England to attend Society meetings, he also conferred with Sylvester on research problems, in particular those associated with *applied mathematics*. The two mathematicians would meet at Lincoln's Inn Fields to talk about "linkages" (mechanical devices for drawing straight lines). "His special object," wrote Sylvester, "was to obtain sight of some of the old machines of Watt. . . . He found that the intuitive mechanical sagacity of Watt had anticipated his own mathematical deductions. Tchebycheff has found the best form of 3-bar motion, of which Watt's parallel motion is only a special case, and has arrived at more accurate results than Watt's, with a more compact arrangement, and, in some cases, more convenient of application."

But Tchebycheff is doubtless better known to students of mathematics today as the founder of the highly creative Russian school of probability theory. There is the fundamental "Tchebycheff inequality," for example, which generalizes "Bernoulli's theorem" and leads directly to the important "law of large numbers."

In spite of the important research of Tchebycheff and his followers, a precise formula for all primes was not found. Then Borel and other mathematicians decided to use a statistical approach. The most remarkable result of this type had preceded Borel's efforts. The *prime number theorem* was proved in 1896 by the French mathematician Jacques Hadamard, (1865–1963) and the Belgian Charles J. de la Vallée Poussin (1866–1962). There are many tales of the genius of Hadamard. Among these is the fact that he achieved the highest score ever obtained in the entrance examination to the *École Polytechnique*, France's greatest school of science and, in Hadamard's youth, the foremost world institution of its type. Simplifications and modifications of the proof of the famous theorem were provided by the German Edmund Landau (1877–1938) and others. Then, in 1932, Norbert Wiener deduced a much simpler proof from certain of his own discoveries which G. H. Hardy named "Tauberian theorems" (after the German analyst Tauber). Perhaps the most elementary demonstration to date is the 1949 proof of Atle Selberg, professor at the Institute for Advanced Study. These proofs are called "elementary" in a special technical sense; their content is exceedingly difficult.

The prime number theorem derives from a conjecture of Gauss. He evidently arrived at it empirically by making an actual count in a table of primes. At any rate, logarithmic tables which he used as a lad of fourteen have been found, with a complete statement of the theorem, written in his hand, as a marginal note. The theorem provides a *formula* giving an approximation to the proportion or density of primes among the integers, and indicates that the approximation must become better and better, the greater the number of integers considered. For example, it is known that there are 50,847,478 primes among the first 1,000,000,000 integers. The prime number theorem gives the estimate 48,254,942, an error of only 5 per cent. We do *not* know how many primes there are in still larger intervals but the Hadamard-De la Vallé Poussin theorem proves that for all practical purposes there will be almost no error in the formula after a while. This remarkable prime number theorem states that the proportion or density of primes among the first *n* integers when *n* is large, is approximately equal to $1/\ln n$ where $\ln n$ signifies the natural logarithm of *n* (Chapter 22).

To return to Tchebycheff once more, the nature of his contribution is more readily understood if the prime number theorem is stated in the alternative form: If $P(n)$ is the number of primes equal to or less than the integer *n*, then the ratio of $P(n)$ to $n/\ln n$ approaches the number 1 as a *limit*, as *n* gets larger and larger. The Russian was unable to establish the existence of this limit, but he did show that, for sufficiently large values of *n*, the ratio in the theorem lies between two positive constants, *a* and *A*. These constants are Sylvester's "banks on either side which that stream . . . can never overflow." He himself subsequently brought these "banks" closer together, thus improving Tchebycheff's approximation. But ultimately it was seen that such techniques would not establish the prime number theorem. Hence Hadamard and De la Vallée Poussin resorted to other methods, namely, those of modern *analysis*.

If Gauss initiated the drive for a proof of the great theorem, one must again go back to antiquity for origins, since it was Euclid who first sought a formulation of the primes. His *Elements*, moreover, contained the germ of most of the still unresolved problems of number theory. Although answers are not yet available, these challenging puzzles have served an important purpose in stimulating the creation of an enormous amount of new mathematics through the centuries. One of these problems grew out of the last theorem of the ninth book of the *Elements*, which states: If $2^n - 1$ is a prime, then $2^{n-1}(2^n - 1)$ is equal to the sum of its proper divisors. (A proper divisor is any factor other than the number itself.)

Euclid was able to give a simple proof of this theorem by making it dependent on a fact known to the Pythagoreans, and to the Babylonians before them, namely, that

$$1 + 2 + 2^2 + 2^3 + \cdots + 2^{k-1} = 2^k - 1$$

The reader can derive this rule by applying the formula for the sum of a geometric progression, or he can use "mathematical induction" on the particular observations

$$1 + 2 = 3 = 2^2 - 1$$
$$1 + 2 + 2^2 = 7 = 2^3 - 1$$
$$1 + 2 + 2^2 + 2^3 = 15 = 2^4 - 1$$

where the sum of *two* terms is 1 less than the *second* power of 2, the sum of *three* terms is 1 less than the *third* power of 2, etc.

In Euclid's theorem, one is given that $2^n - 1 = p$, a *prime*, and must prove that $2^{n-1}p$ is equal to the sum of its proper divisors. Now the sum of the proper divisors is

$$1 + 2 + 2^2 + \cdots + 2^{n-2} + 2^{n-1}$$
$$+ p(1 + 2 + 2^2 + \cdots + 2^{n-2})$$

If we use the formula of the previous paragraph, the sum becomes

$$2^n - 1 + p(2^{n-1} - 1)$$

or, since $2^n - 1 = p$,

$$p + p(2^{n-1} - 1) = p + 2^{n-1}p - p = 2^{n-1}p$$

where $2^{n-1}p$ is the desired result.

If $n = 2$, then $2^n - 1 = 2^2 - 1 = 3$, which is a *prime*. Therefore $2^{n-1}(2^n - 1) = 2^1(2^2 - 1) = 2 \cdot 3 = 6$. The fact that $6 = 1 + 2 + 3$ is in agreement with Euclid's theorem.

The Pythagoreans or other early Greek mathematicians had provided the name *perfect* for numbers like 6 that are equal to the sum of all proper divisors. The brotherhood immediately invested perfect numbers with mystic qualities, and other religious groups followed suit. It came to be said that God created the universe in six days because 6 is a perfect number. Alcuin of York (735–804), who established a school at Charlemagne's court, taught that the human race is imperfect because it is descended from the *eight* souls of Noah's ark, and 8 is *imperfect* since it is not equal to the sum of its proper factors, $1 + 2 + 4$.

To obtain examples of perfection, the reader may substitute $n = 3$ and $n = 5$ in Euclid's formula. This will yield the perfect numbers $28 = 1 + 2 + 4 + 7 + 14$ and $496 = 1 + 2 + 4 + 8 + 16 + 31 + 62 + 124 + 248$. (We note that for $n = 4$, $2^n - 1 = 15$, which is *composite*. Hence Euclid's theorem does not apply to this case.) Perfection is very hard to find since, even with the aid of today's digital computers, Euclid's formula has not yielded too many examples of perfect numbers. The twenty-second perfect number in order of size was given computer verification not long ago. That number, corresponding to $n = 9941$, is the perfect number $2^{9940}(2^{9941} - 1)$. It contains 5985 digits! Still more recently (1963) the twenty-third perfect number was found.

Now all the perfect numbers which computers have checked are *even*. Euler proved in fact that Euclid's formula will include *all* even perfect numbers. These facts suggest that, possibly, an odd number cannot be perfect. But no rigorous proof has been found for this conjecture. Hence, although it is known that there is no odd perfect number less than 10,000,000,000, there is the famous unsolved problem of number theory: Can a perfect number be odd or must *all* perfect numbers be even?

The condition for Euclid's formula to yield a perfect number is that $2^n - 1$ be *prime*. Hence the search for *primes* of the form $2^n - 1$ is a problem in itself. The first person to devote himself to that question was Father Marin Mersenne (1588–1648), a close friend of Descartes. Mersenne wrote on a variety of other mathematical subjects as well, and carried on a scientific correspondence with Fermat, Pascal, and all the leading mathematicians of his day. He transmitted the letters of each one to all the others, thus performing single-handedly the sort of service rendered by scholarly journals today.

It is easy to show (Mersenne did so) that if $2^n - 1$ is to be a prime, then n must be a prime. The converse theorem is false, for if, for example, $n = 11$ (a prime), $2^{11} - 1 = 2047 = 23 \cdot 89$ is composite. Knowing this fact, Mersenne proceeded to examine successive numbers, $M_p = 2^p - 1$ where p is a prime, that is, $p = 2, 3, 5, 7, 11, 13, 17, \ldots$. He worked steadfastly until he reached the prime $p = 257$. Then in 1644 he published a list of *eleven* values of p, which he claimed to be the *only* primes up to $p = 257$ for which M_p is a prime.

But Mersenne erred in two respects. He omitted three values of p (less than 257) for which $M_p = 2^p - 1$ is actually prime. On the other hand, he listed M_{67} and M_{257} as primes when, in fact, they are composite. The following story will reveal why one must forgive Mersenne and all those *human* computers who operated before the era of electronic brains. When, in 1903, M_{67} was first proved composite by Frank Nelson Cole (1861–1927), a leading American algebraist, he confided to a friend that it had required "three years of Sundays" to discover that

$$2^{67} - 1 = (193,707,721)(761,838,257,287)$$

In 1931 D. H. Lehmer proved, by theoretical methods, that M_{257} must be composite, but his proof, unlike Cole's, did not produce a pair of numerical factors.

Today we can assert correctly that, among the 55 prime numbers between 2 and 257 inclusive, there are 12 primes, namely,

$$p = 2, 3, 5, 7, 13, 17, 19, 31, 61, 89, 107, 127$$

for which $M_p = 2^p - 1$ is a prime. Such numbers are called *Mersenne primes* and when multiplied by 2^{p-1}, yield perfect numbers. The numbers not on Mersenne's original list are M_{61}, M_{89}, M_{107}. They were not revealed as primes until the years 1883, 1911, and 1914, respectively. The first Mersenne prime for which $p > 257$ is M_{521}, discovered in 1952, more than three centuries after the good friar published his numerical results.

Most number-theoretic issues had their origins in antiquity, as we have seen, with Euclid, the Hellenic mathematician who provided two important sources of inspiration—namely, proofs for certain crucial theorems, and concepts leading to problems that are still unsolved. The story of Euclid's influence must be repeated in relation to the problem of finding all "Pythagorean triples," that is, all sets of natural numbers that satisfy

$$x^2 + y^2 = z^2$$

and hence can be sides of a right triangle. There are tabulations of such triples in Babylonian cuneiform tablets predating Pythagoras by a thousand years. Pythagoras himself did not solve the problem, in the sense of obtaining a formula for all triples, but, in Neugebauer's opinion, the cuneiform documents give indirect evidence that the Babylonians did find a general formula. By Euclid's time the problem was completely solved, and in Book X of the *Elements* there is a geometric wording of the formula

$$x = 2uv$$

$$y = u^2 - v^2$$

$$z = u^2 + v^2$$

where u is a natural number greater than v, u and v have no common factor and one of them is odd, the other even. Thus if $u = 3$, $v = 2$, then $x = 12$, $y = 5$, $z = 13$. If $u = 4$, $v = 1$, then $x = 8$, $y = 15$, $z = 17$. If $u = 5$, $v = 2$, the triple is $\{20, 21, 29\}$.

Strictly speaking, the above formula provides only *primitive* Pythagorean triples, those having no common factor. Every primitive triple leads to an infinite number of other triples that are multiples of the primitive set. Thus from 5, 12, 13 one obtains 10, 24, 26, and 50, 120, 130, etc. Substituting the various triples in $x^2 + y^2 = z^2$ leads to an infinite number of different squares which are equal to the sum of other squares, that is, an infinite number of right triangles with integral sides.

Reflecting on the plethora of integral solutions of $x^2 + y^2 = z^2$, Fermat went on to investigate the possibility of such solutions for $x^3 + y^3 = z^3$, $x^4 + y^4 = z^4$, ..., $x^n + y^n = z^n$, where n is any integer greater than 2. Then, in a marginal note opposite a discussion of Pythagorean triples in his copy of Bachet's *Diophantus*, Fermat made an entry that is as famous in the history of mathematics as, say, the French Revolution in the history of modern man. Fermat wrote: "By contrast it is impossible to separate a cube into two cubes, a fourth power into two fourth powers, or in general any power above the second into two powers of the same degree. I have found a truly marvelous proof of this theorem but this margin is too narrow to contain it."

If only Fermat had published that marvelous proof! But from his day up to the present time, the greatest mathematical minds have attempted and have failed to produce a demonstration of what has come to be known as *Fermat's Last Theorem:* There is no solution in natural numbers of the equation $x^n + y^n = z^n$ if n is an integer greater than 2.

It would be more accurate to describe Fermat's theorem as a *conjecture* since it has never been proved, that is, demonstrated for *all* natural numbers in the aggregate, $\{3, 4, 5, 6,$

7, . . .}. Proofs have been given, however, for many special values of n in that set. Thus it is fairly easy to show, for example, that $x^4 + y^4 = z^4$ has no positive integral solutions (Fermat himself did so). This implies that $x^n + y^n = z^n$ has no such solutions if n is any higher power of 2, that is, if $n = 8$ or 16 or 32 or 64, etc. To see why, consider, for example, $x^8 + y^8 = z^8$, which is the same as $(x^2)^4 + (y^2)^4 = (z^2)^4$ or $a^4 + b^4 = c^4$, if one substitutes $a = x^2$, $b = y^2$, $c = z^2$. Then if there were a triple of natural numbers, $\{x, y, z\}$ satisfying $x^8 + y^8 = z^8$, the squares of these integers could satisfy $a^4 + b^4 = c^4$, which is impossible because Fermat's theorem is true for $n = 4$.

To prove Fermat's theorem for all other cases where $n > 4$ it suffices to demonstrate it where n is any odd prime, that is, any prime greater than 2. For then if n were composite, say, $n = 3099$, one could say that $x^{3099} + y^{3099} = z^{3099}$ or $(x^{1033})^3 + (y^{1033})^3 = (z^{1033})^3$ cannot possibly have a solution in natural numbers because then $a^3 + b^3 = c^3$ (where $a = x^{1033}$, $b = y^{1033}$, $c = z^{1033}$) would have such a solution, which cannot be, once Fermat's theorem is established for odd primes, including $n = 3$.

Although no solution has ever been given for all odd primes, Euler did prove Fermat's theorem for the special prime, $n = 3$. About 1825, proofs for $n = 5$ were given by Legendre and P. G. Lejeune-Dirichlet (1805–1859), working independently. Some fifteen years later, Gabriel Lamé (1795–1870), who was as distinguished in the higher arithmetic as he was in analysis, geometry, and mathematical physics, gave a proof for $n = 7$. Sophie Germain, whom we have already named as one of the few women mathematicians of all time, proved that if the integral solutions x, y, z are restricted to those which are prime to one another and to the exponent n, then it is impossible to solve $x^n + y^n = z^n$ if n is any prime less than 100. In 1908, the American algebraist Leonard Eugene Dickson (1874–1954) extended Germain's theorem to all primes less than 7000, and in more recent times Barkley Rosser extended the upper limit to 41,000,000. Then Emma Lehmer and Derrick H. Lehmer gave a further extension to primes less than 253,747,889. If, in addition to the above restriction on the integers x, y, z, the prime n must be of a certain special type, recent research establishes Fermat's theorem for all such primes less than $2^{3617} - 1$, a number of 1089 digits.

There would perhaps be no point in continuing the list of

great names associated with proofs of special cases of Fermat's Last Theorem if one did not at the same time indicate how attempts to prove the elusive theorem gave rise to some of the most potent concepts of modern mathematics. Thus Ernst Kummer (1810–1893)—like many amateurs and some leading mathematicians, such as Cauchy—thought, at first, that he had arrived at a demonstration. But he discovered he had made the error of assuming that Euclid's fundamental theorem of arithmetic holds for entities that generalize the integers, in other words, that those entities have a unique factorization into "pseudoprimes" (page 196). Hence he next created *ideal numbers* such that composite numbers of the new species do satisfy unique factorization into "prime" ideal numbers. Kummer's ideal numbers led to Dedekind's concept of an *ideal,* a notion we have mentioned previously (Chapter 4). An ideal is *not* a number but a set of numbers qualifying as a special kind of subring (Vol. I, page 128) of a ring. The choice of "ideal" as the name of such a system was an intuitive anticipation of things to come, for, in the hands of later algebraists, in particular, Emmy Noether, the notion was to be revealed as one of the most beautiful and most fruitful in modern algebra.

But the magnificent conception which Kummer launched did *not* enable him to arrive at a proof of Fermat's Last Theorem. However, the theory of ideal numbers made it possible for him to establish certain general conditions under which $x^n + y^n = z^n$ would be unsolvable by means of integers. Kummer's conditions were basic in all subsequent investigations of the problem up to those of the American number theorist H. S. Vandiver, the foremost living authority on Fermat's Last Theorem. His extensions of the Kummer criteria and the creation of further conditions of his own are the basis of recent numerical results that extend the upper boundary of primes for which Fermat's theorem holds. Nevertheless all Vandiver's evidence does *not* constitute proof, and the theorem remains an unsolved problem, the most puzzling challenge in the higher arithmetic.

Mathematicians are still hopeful about obtaining a proof, and logicians have come forth with "metamathematical" theorems offering the possibility that Fermat's Last Theorem is an *undecidable* proposition, one which cannot be proved to be either true or false. Such a state of affairs is likely to destroy a layman's faith in the utter power of mathematical reasoning! At any rate, it could not have been considered by the German professor Paul Wolfskehl, who, in 1908, left 100,000 marks to be awarded to the first person who would give a complete proof of Fermat's Last Theorem. The bequest encouraged countless amateurs to devise ingenious but erroneous proofs. The years have been rolling by since 1908 without any discovery of a proof, but what a handsome prize the Wolfskehl Fund might have become, with all the accumulated compound interest, if World War I had not put an end to the value of the mark!

It was Euclid's formula for Pythagorean triples, we recall, that was the point of departure for Fermat's problem. But now we must go on to details of the mathematical contributions of later number theorists. After Euclid and Fermat, the next major contributors were Euler and Legendre. Then there were Gauss and Riemann, whose influence on number theory was as important as that on differential geometry (and hence on relativity). Each number-theorist in our sequence of great names inspired all his successors. In fact, there is a story which illustrates both Legendre's effect on Riemann and the latter's genius. As a student at the *gymnasium*, the boy Riemann borrowed from the school library Legendre's *Théorie des Nombres*, a scholarly work of 859 pages. When he returned it in less than a week, his mathematics teacher inquired, "How did you like it?" Riemann responded, "That was a marvelous book. I mastered it completely." This was no idle boast, for when, some months later, examiners quizzed the youth in some detail on the contents of the "marvelous book," he answered perfectly.

Let us now illustrate some of Gauss's number-theoretic ideas. We have already spoken of "clock arithmetic" (Chapter 16) which will now be dignified by Gauss's concept of *congruence*. By his definition, two integers are said to be *congruent* with respect to a positive integral *modulus m* if they leave the same remainder when divided by m or, equivalently, if the difference of the integers is exactly divisible by m. Thus, if 7 is selected as the modulus, 37 is congruent to 16, and 5 is congruent to 19. If 3 is selected as the modulus, 85 is congruent to 4. The symbol $\equiv$ is used for "is congruent to," and the above statements are written as

$$37 \equiv 16 \ (\text{mod } 7)$$

$$5 \equiv 19 \ (\text{mod } 7)$$

$$85 \equiv 4 \ (\text{mod } 3)$$

Once more, the fundamental question of arithmetic divisibility is at issue. One advantage of Gauss's concept and symbolism is that congruence statements can be manipulated in a manner somewhat analogous to the technique used in solving algebraic equations. Thus congruence statements, like equations, can be added and multiplied, providing the modulus remains the same throughout such manipulations. It is easy to prove algebraically that this is so. Thus, let us show that if

$$a \equiv b \pmod{m}$$

and

$$c \equiv d \pmod{m}$$

then

$$a + c \equiv b + d \pmod{m}$$

and

$$ac \equiv bd \pmod{m}$$

By Gauss's definition, the given facts are

$$a - b = km$$
$$c - d = lm$$

Since *equations* may be added,

$$(a + c) - (b + d) = (k + l)m$$

and hence

$$a + c \equiv b + d \pmod{m}$$

The given equations may also be written in the form

$$a = b + km$$
$$c = d + lm$$

Since these equations may be multiplied,

$$\begin{aligned}
ac &= (b + km)(d + lm) \\
&= bd + blm + dkm + klm \\
&= bd + (bl + dk + kl)m
\end{aligned}$$

Hence $ac - bd = (bl + dk + kl)m$ and therefore

$$ac \equiv bd \pmod{m}$$

To give a few examples of how Gauss's congruences can be used to reveal divisibility properties, one can provide proofs for rules that are sometimes given in elementary arithmetic without any indication as to *why* they are valid. Thus there is the theorem that a number is divisible by 3 or 9 if and only if the sum of its digits is divisible by 3 or 9. For example 7,104,288,015 is seen to be divisible by 9 (and *a fortiori!* by 3) because the sum of its digits is 36. The proof of the theorem will now be given. In Chapter 1 we saw that any positive integer N expressed in the decimal system has the form

$$N = a_0 + a_1 \cdot 10 + a_2 \cdot 10^2 + \cdots + a_n \cdot 10^n$$

Now, multiplying the congruence $10 \equiv 1$ (mod 3 or mod 9) by itself repeatedly, one obtains

$$10^2 \equiv 1 \text{ (mod 3 or mod 9)}$$
$$10^3 \equiv 1 \text{ (mod 3 or mod 9)}$$
$$\cdot \quad \cdot \quad \cdot$$
$$10^n \equiv 1 \text{ (mod 3 or mod 9)}$$

Therefore

$$a_1 \cdot 10 \equiv a_1$$
$$a_2 \cdot 10^2 \equiv a_2$$
$$a_3 \cdot 10^3 \equiv a_3$$
$$\cdot \quad \cdot \quad \cdot$$
$$a_n \cdot 10^n \equiv a_n$$

and then $N = a_0 + a_1 \cdot 10 + a_2 \cdot 10^2 + \cdots + a_n \cdot 10^n \equiv a_0 + a_1 + a_2 + \cdots + a_n$ or

$$N \equiv a_0 + a_1 + a_2 + \cdots + a_n \text{ (mod 3 or mod 9)}$$

which means that $N = a_0 + a_1 + a_2 + \cdots + a_n + 3k$ (or $9l$)

Thus the right member (and hence N) is divisible by 3 (or 9) if and only if $a_0 + a_1 + \cdots + a_n$ is so divisible.

In a similar way, a rule for testing divisibility by 11 can be derived. Thus

$$10 \equiv -1 \text{ (mod 11)}$$

because

$$10 - (-1) = 10 + 1 = 11 \text{ (which is divisible by 11)}$$

Multiplying

$$10 \equiv -1 \text{ (mod 11)}$$

by itself repeatedly yields

$$10^2 \equiv +1 \pmod{11}$$
$$10^3 \equiv -1 \pmod{11}$$
$$10^4 \equiv +1 \pmod{11}$$
etc.

Therefore, multiplying these congruence statements by $a_1, a_2, \ldots,$ a_n, and adding the results to $a_0 \equiv a_0$ yields

$$N \equiv a_0 - a_1 + a_2 - a_3 + a^4 - a^5 + \cdots \pmod{11}$$

that is,

$$N = a_0 - a_1 + a_2 - a_3 + a^4 - a^5 + \cdots + 11k$$

Hence an integer is divisible by 11 if and only if the sum of its digits with signs alternately plus and minus is divisible by 11. For example, 91,720,453,803 is seen to be divisible by 11 in accordance with this rule.

Although congruences for a fixed modulus may be added, subtracted, and multiplied, they do not obey all the laws which hold for equations. Thus there is the cancellation law for equations: If $ca = cb$, where $c \neq 0$, then $a = b$. This law does *not* transfer to all congruences, $ca \equiv cb$. Thus although $26 \equiv 8 \pmod 6$, that is, $2 \cdot 13 \equiv 2 \cdot 4 \pmod 6$, it is *not* true that $13 \equiv 4 \pmod 6$, since $13 - 4 = 9$, which is *not* a multiple of 6. There is, however, a modified cancellation law for congruences: If c is prime to the modulus m, the $ca \equiv cb$ implies $a \equiv b$.

Again, although a *linear equation* with integral coefficients always has a unique rational solution, a linear congruence may have no integral solution whatsoever or, at the other extreme, may have two or more noncongruent solutions. For example, let us show that $2x \equiv 1 \pmod 4$ has no integral roots. Now any integer will be congruent modulo 4 to a remainder or "residue" in the set $\{0, 1, 2, 3\}$, and hence we need only consider these four numbers as possible roots. Substituting them in the term $2x$, we have $2 \cdot 0 = 0, 2 \cdot 1 = 2$, $2 \cdot 2 = 4$, which is congruent to 0 $\pmod 4$, $2 \cdot 3 = 6$, which is congruent to 2 $\pmod 4$. No one of these results is congruent to 1, as required. Therefore the given congruence has *no* integral solutions.

But let us next consider the linear congruence $3x \equiv 6$ $\pmod{12}$, and seek integral solutions among the residues

$\{0, 1, 2, 3, \ldots, 11\}$. We find the solutions $x = 2$, $x = 6$, $x = 10$, which check because $3 \cdot 2 = 6$, $3 \cdot 6 = 18 \equiv 6$ (mod 12), $3 \cdot 10 = 30 \equiv 6$ (mod 12).

Is there any type of linear congruence that has one and only one solution (modulo m) and is therefore truly analogous to a linear equation? The answer is affirmative for a linear congruence where the modulus and the coefficient of x have no common divisor except 1, that is, are relatively prime. There is a theorem indicating that $ax \equiv b$ (mod m), where a and m are relatively prime, has a unique solution (mod m). For example, in $2x \equiv 1$ (mod 9), 2 and 9 are relatively prime. This congruence has the unique solution $x = 5$ (mod 9), as the reader can check by substituting $x = 0$, 1, 2, $\ldots$, 8 in the formula for the congruence.

An important special case of the above theorem occurs when the modulus m is a prime. In that case, all integers not divisible by m (not congruent to zero) are relatively prime to m and hence, if used as values of a in $ax \equiv b$ (mod m), will lead to a unique solution of that congruence. Hence there is the theorem: If p is a prime, and if $a \not\equiv 0$ (mod p), then $ax \equiv b$ (mod p) has a solution that is unique, modulo p. Thus changing to a *prime* modulus in each of the original examples above, we find that $2x \equiv 1$ (mod 5) and $3x \equiv 6$ (mod 11) have the unique solutions $x = 3$ (mod 5) and $x = 2$ (mod 11), respectively.

If we consider polynomial congruences of higher degree, we surely cannot expect theorems about algebraic equations to carry over, since roots of congruences must be integers. But if, guided by the results with linear equations, we insist on a *prime modulus*, then there is an analogue for the *corollary* to Gauss's *fundamental theorem of algebra* (Chapter 4). That corollary states: A polynomial equation of the nth degree (with coefficients in the complex domain) has at most n roots in the complex domain. The analogous theorem for congruences is due to Lagrange and can be stated as follows: If the modulus is a *prime p*, then a polynomial congruence of the nth degree has at most n roots among the integers $\{0, 1, 2, \ldots, p - 1\}$.

The fundamental theorem for congruences indicates that a congruence of higher degree may have *no* integral roots whatsover even though the modulus is prime. Also, if $p < n$, the congruence has, of necessity, fewer than n integral roots in the set $\{0, 1, 2, \ldots, p - 1\}$. Thus, as an example of a quadratic congruence, there is

$$x^2 \equiv 1 \pmod 3$$

which has two roots, the maximum number possible, in the set $\{0, 1, 2\}$, namely, $x = 1$ and $x = 2$. Again, there is the cubic congruence

$$x^3 + x^2 \equiv 1 \pmod 5$$

which has the unique solution $x = 3$ in the set $\{0, 1, 2, 3, 4\}$. And finally there is

$$x^4 \equiv 2 \pmod 5$$

with *no* solutions in the set $\{0, 1, 2, \ldots, 4\}$.

Returning to the congruence $x^2 \equiv 1 \pmod 3$, which had the maximum number of solutions possible, we might try to generalize that happy result in a number of ways. For example, if we observe that the degree of the congruence is 1 less than the prime modulus, we might next examine $x^4 \equiv 1 \pmod 5$, $x^6 \equiv 1 \pmod 7$, $x^{10} \equiv 1 \pmod{11}$, etc. In the first of these congruences, $x = 1, 2, 3, 4$ are *all* roots because $1^4 = 1$, $2^4 = 16 \equiv 1 \pmod 5$, $3^4 = 81 \equiv 1 \pmod 5$, $4^4 = 256 \equiv 1 \pmod 5$. In the case of $x^6 \equiv 1 \pmod 7$, the solutions $\pmod 7$ are the residues in the set $\{1, 2, 3, 4, 5, 6\}$ because $1^6 = 1$, $2^6 = 64 \equiv 1 \pmod 7$, $3^6 = 729 \equiv 1 \pmod 7$, $4^6 = 4096 \equiv 1 \pmod 7$, $5^6 = 15625 \equiv 1 \pmod 7$, $6^6 = 46656 \equiv 1 \pmod 7$. We leave to the reader the task of proving that the first ten natural numbers are solutions of $x^{10} \equiv 1 \pmod{11}$.

The above numerical examples all suggest Fermat's "little theorem": If p is a prime, then the first $p - 1$ natural numbers are the solutions, modulo p, of the congruence $x^{p-1} \equiv 1 \pmod p$.

The theorem in question may be described as "little" in comparison with Fermat's more famous theorems, but his "small" result is truly remarkable because there is nothing analogous to it in the classic theory of polynomial equations. What the "little theorem" tells us is that in *every* system $\{S, \otimes\}$ where $\otimes$ is multiplication modulo p, a prime, and $S = \{1, \ldots, p - 1\}$, the non-zero residues modulo p, *every* number of the system (which is readily shown to be an abelian group) is a root of the congruence $x^{p-1} \equiv 1 \pmod p$. This signifies that *all* integers except those divisible by p are roots of the congruence.

Alternative statements of Fermat's theorem point up its potential applications to problems of divisibility. Thus one can subtract $1 \equiv 1 \pmod{p}$ from the congruence $x^{p-1} \equiv 1 \pmod{p}$ to obtain $x^{p-1} - 1 \equiv 0 \pmod{p}$ and one can then multiply by $x \equiv x \pmod{p}$, where $x \not\equiv 0$, to yield the result $x^p - x \equiv 0 \pmod{p}$. Then Fermat's theorem implies: If p is a prime and x is any integer such that $x \not\equiv 0 \pmod{p}$, then $x^{p-1} - 1$ and $x^p - x$ are exactly divisible by p.

As early as 500 b.c. the Chinese were aware of one divisibility fact included in Fermat's theorem, for their manuscripts asserted that $2^p - 2$ is divisible by p when p is a prime. Thus $2^{11} - 2 = 2046$ is divisible by 11, which can readily be checked, and $2^{9941} - 2$ is divisible by the prime 9941, a fact which no one would care to verify "by hand."

But Fermat's theorem implies an infinite number of other divisibility statements. For example, $3^{9941} - 3$, $4^{9941} - 4$, $5^{9941} - 5, \ldots,$ $9940^{9941} - 9940$ must all be divisible by 9941, and $2^{65537} - 2$, $3^{65537} - 3, \ldots,$ $65536^{65537} - 65536$ are all divisible by the Fermat prime 65537.

Although $2^n - 2$ must be divisible by n if n is a prime number, the early Chinese (and even, much later, the great Leibniz) erred in conjecturing that the converse statement would be true. They believed that if $2^n - 2$ is divisible by n, then n would, of necessity, be prime, so that the divisibility property could then be used as a test of primality. The conjecture was discovered to be false only in 1819, when it was shown that $2^{341} - 2$ is exactly divisible by $341 = 11 \cdot 31$, a *composite* number. Subsequently it was found that $2^n - 2$ is divisible by n for an infinite number of other composite values of n.

We have discussed the general *linear* congruence and one special type of *binomial* congruence, $x^{p-1} \equiv 1 \pmod{p}$ where p is a prime. Theory shows that the question of solving any *quadratic congruence*, $Ax^2 + Bx + C \equiv 0 \pmod{m}$, can be reduced to a matter of solving *linear* congruences and *binomial quadratic* congruences. Therefore it is not surprising that in the initial sections of the great *Disquisitiones Arithmeticae* Gauss gave a complete and elegant treatment of the binomial quadratic congruence $x^2 \equiv a \pmod{m}$. Its theory is much more difficult than that for the binomial equation $x^2 = a$, which has, immediately, the roots $x = +\sqrt{a}$ and $x = -\sqrt{a}$. In connection with binomial quadratic congruences, Gauss proved (when he was only nineteen years of age) a fact that Euler and Legendre had observed but were unable to demonstrate rigorously. This was the law of *quadratic reciprocity*, one of the most famous theorems in all of number theory. It states that if p and q are different prime numbers other than 2, then

$$x^2 \equiv q \pmod{p} \qquad \text{and} \qquad x^2 \equiv p \pmod{q}$$

are *both* solvable, or *both* unsolvable, unless *both* p and q are congruent to 3 (mod 4), that is, leave the remainder 3 when divided by 4, in which case one of the congruences is solvable and the other is not.

Some numerical examples will clarify the meaning of this law. Observe first that if any integer is divided by 4, the possible remainders are {0, 1, 2, 3,}. But since the moduli in the reciprocity law must be *odd* primes, the remainders from division by 4 cannot be 0 or 2 since the former remainder would imply that the modulus is exactly divisible by 4 and the latter would make it divisible by 2. Hence 1 and 3 are the only possible remainders in connection with the reciprocity theorem. Let us then take $p = 5$, $q = 11$. These moduli leave the remainders 1 and 3, respectively, when divided by 4. Hence, by the reciprocity law, *both* or *neither* of the following must be solvable:

$$x^2 \equiv 11 \pmod{5} \qquad \text{and} \qquad x^2 \equiv 5 \pmod{11}$$

Since $11 \equiv 1 \pmod{5}$, the first congruence can also be expressed as $x^2 \equiv 1 \pmod{5}$. This congruence and $x^2 \equiv 5 \pmod{11}$ are *both* solvable, the former being satisfied by $x = 1$ and $x = 4$, the latter by $x = 4$ and $x = 7$. Again, take $p = 5$, $q = 13$, both of which leave the remainder 1 when divided by 4. Once more, both or neither of the following should be solvable:

$$x^2 \equiv 13 \pmod{5}, \text{ that is, } x^2 \equiv 3 \pmod{5} \quad \text{and} \quad x^2 \equiv 5 \pmod{13}$$

Here *neither* is solvable, as the reader can check by substituting $x = 0, 1, 2, 3, 4$ successively in the first, and $x = 0, 1, 2, 3, \ldots, 12$ in the second.

The second case of the quadratic reciprocity law is illustrated when $p = 7$ and $q = 3$, since *both* these moduli leave a remainder of 3 when divided by 4. We can see by substituting $x = 0, 1, 2, \ldots, 6$ that

$$x^2 \equiv 3 \pmod{7}$$

is not solvable, whereas

$$x^2 \equiv 7 \pmod{3}, \text{ that is, } x^2 \equiv 1 \pmod{3}$$

is solvable, having the roots $x = 1$ and $x = 2$.

The theory of numbers is a vast domain, and hence we can consider only certain selected aspects of the subject. Thus we have discussed, in the main, the elementary classic treatment of the divisibility and primality of integers. But we have mentioned that Tchebycheff, Hadamard, De la Vallée Poussin, Landau, Wiener, Hardy, and all the latter-day number theorists used *analysis*, the mathematics of the *continuum*, in order to shed light on the *discrete* set of integers. This is just one more of the paradoxes of the higher arithmetic! We cannot go deeply into the subject of *analytic number theory*, but even a superficial discussion will indicate that the concepts and tools are of a type that would appear (except to a mathematical genius) exceedingly unlikely to reveal properties of the numbers of everyday arithmetic.

To begin with, we shall go back to the ideas of the mathematician who represented "analysis incarnate," namely, Leonhard Euler. Among other infinite series he considered, there was the series

$$1 + \frac{1}{2} + \frac{1}{3} + \frac{1}{4} + \cdots + \frac{1}{n} + \cdots$$

He proved that this series is *divergent*. The reader can show, as follows, that the sum in question cannot be defined because its value would have to exceed that of any set of half-dollars, however large their number. Thus we shall group the terms of the series as follows in order to indicate that the sum of each subset is equal to or greater than 1/2 (a half-dollar). Thus we have

$$\underbrace{\frac{1}{2}}_{} + \underbrace{\frac{1}{2}}_{} + \underbrace{\frac{1}{2}}_{} + \underbrace{\frac{1}{3} + \frac{1}{4}}_{} + \underbrace{\frac{1}{5} + \frac{1}{6} + \frac{1}{7} + \frac{1}{8}}_{} + \underbrace{\frac{1}{9} + \frac{1}{10} + \cdots + \frac{1}{16}}_{}$$

$$+ \underbrace{\frac{1}{17} + \frac{1}{18} + \cdots + \frac{1}{32}}_{} + \cdots$$

To see why this is so, let us examine the set $\{1/3 + 1/4\}$. There $1/3 > 1/4$ and hence $1/3 + 1/4 > 1/4 + 1/4$, that is, $1/3 + 1/4 > 1/2$. In the same way, each of the first three fractions in the sum, $1/5 + 1/6 + 1/7 + 1/8$, is greater than $1/8$, and hence the total is greater than $4/8$. Similarly, the next collection of numbers in the above series has a sum exceeding $8/16$, etc., and the group after that has a total greater than $16/32$, etc. The next group (not printed) would contain 32 fractions ending with $1/64$, and its sum would exceed $32/64$, etc. Thus, if one continued the series to the point where there were 2,000,000,000 such groups, each one of which (except for the first three) totals more than $1/2$, then the grand total would be greater than 1,000,000,000, and far, far greater sums could be obtained by continuing the series. Therefore it is meaningless to speak of a definite, finite sum for the entire infinite series.

But Euler went farther. He showed that if the series is modified slightly by raising the denominators of the fractions to a power greater than one, then the series "converges," that is, has a sum (Chapter 22). Thus

$$1 + \frac{1}{2^{1.1}} + \frac{1}{3^{1.1}} + \cdots + \frac{1}{n^{1.1}} + \cdots$$

$$1 + \frac{1}{2^2} + \frac{1}{3^2} + \cdots + \frac{1}{n^2} + \cdots$$

$$1 + \frac{1}{2^3} + \frac{1}{3^0} + \cdots + \frac{1}{n^3} + \cdots$$

all have finite sums, and hence all are *convergent* series. Euler incorporated all convergent series of this type into a single function, namely,

$$\zeta(s) = 1 + \frac{1}{2^s} + \frac{1}{3^s} + \cdots + \frac{1}{n^s} + \cdots$$

where s is any real number such that $s > 1$, and ζ is the Greek letter zeta, so that $\zeta(s)$ is read as "zeta of s."

Euler developed properties of the function $\zeta(s)$ and related them to the theory of primes. But the importance of the function in analytic number theory occurs through a generalization which Riemann made in an epochal memoir published in 1859. In that paper, Riemann considered the meaning of

$$\zeta(s) = 1 + \frac{1}{2^s} + \frac{1}{3^s} + \cdots + \frac{1}{n^s} + \cdots$$

when the exponent s is a *complex variable*, $x + iy$, where x and y are real numbers. To a general reader who is not a specialist in mathematics, formal symbols like 2^{5-4i} or 3^{-1+i} will surely seem puzzling. But a complex "power" of a natural number is meaningful in the branch of analysis called "theory of functions of a complex variable," a subject founded by Riemann and analysts who were his contemporaries. The facts of the matter are that, for convergence of the above series when the variable s is complex, that is, when $s = x + iy$, it is necessary to impose the restriction $x > 1$. In other words, if the complex numbers $x + iy$ are represented as number pairs (x, y) and plotted as points in the XY-plane, only points to the right of the line $x = 1$ are permissible if $\zeta(s)$ is to converge. But Riemann extended the domain of the complex function $\zeta(s)$. Using a method that is termed "analytic continuation," he assigned values to $\zeta(s)$ for $s = x + iy$ and $x \leqq 1$, that is, for points of the XY-plane on or to the left of the line $x = 1$. [Only one point had to be excluded from the domain, namely, $(1, 0)$.]

The complex function $\zeta(s)$, defined as we have just explained, is known as the *Riemann zeta-function*. Its properties were applied by Riemann, Hadamard, and most modern researchers on the distribution of primes. In his memoir of 1859, Riemann asked: For what values of s will $\zeta(s) = 0$? He *conjectured* that all values of $s = x + iy$ for which $\zeta(s) = 0$ and x lies between 0 and 1 would be of the form $\frac{1}{2} + iy$. This is the "Riemann hypothesis," one of the famous unsolved problems of mathematics. In 1914 Godfrey Harold Hardy made considerable progress with this difficult problem, but neither he nor anyone else has obtained a proof up to the present time.

Some of the great analytic number-theorists after Riemann treated his conjecture as a postulate and, on assuming its truth, were able to deduce some remarkable theorems of "additive number theory," a subject which treats the decomposition of natural numbers into sums of primes or the expression of integers in other interesting forms. All such theorems are conjectures, since they are based on a conjecture.

But the Russian I. M. Vinogradov and his disciples initiated a new type of analytic methodology. They applied it to providing substantial backing for another famous conjecture about primes, the hypothesis which the Russian C. Goldbach (1690–1764) confided to Euler in 1742. Goldbach had observed for many special cases that an even number greater than 2 is the sum of two primes. Thus $4 = 2 + 2$, $6 = 3 + 3$, $8 = 3 + 5$, $10 = 5 + 5$, $12 = 5 + 7$, ..., $100 = 3 + 97$, $102 = 5 + 97$, ... Goldbach conjectured that *every* even number is the sum of two primes but was unable to *prove* it. However, about 1937, Vinogradov was able to establish that every "sufficiently large" even number is the sum of *at most four* primes. This result, called the Vinogradov-Goldbach theorem, seems to "approximate" the truth of Goldbach's conjecture.

Since the theory of the zeta-function, the analytic maneuverings of Hardy, and the "trigonometric sums" of Vinogradov would all take us far beyond the scope of the present book, we cannot discuss them. But because analytic number theory is related to the theory of functions of a complex variable, we now offer a capsule introduction to the elements of that subject. In truth it is *not* a difficult branch of analysis and has a special beauty of its own, as well as important physical applications. Today an engineer will study its elementary aspects and a Cambridge don will develop its purest, most advanced issues. Its origins must be credited to Gauss, Cauchy, Riemann, and Weierstrass. The subject matter of "complex variable theory" consists of the analytic geometry, the differential and integral calculus, and the general infinite processes associated with functions where independent and dependent variables are complex.

Let us begin with the Cartesian geometry of such functions. We know that $y = x^2$, where x and y are *real* variables, has a parabola as its graph. But what is the picture of $w = z^2$ where w and z are complex variables, that is, where $z = x + iy$ and $w = u + iv$, x, y, u, v being real variables?

In ordinary Cartesian graphs, there is an X-axis of *real* numbers and a Y-axis of *real* numbers. Then the domain of $w = z^2$, that is, the set of values which z may assume, will be located in the XY-plane. But if z may have any complex values whatsoever, its domain will be the *entire* XY-plane. In order to provide a graphic picture of the range, a second plane is needed, in which there are *real* U and V axes, and the range is the set of points in this plane representing the values assumed by $w = u + iv$. The function $w = z^2$ may also be expressed as

$$u + iv = (x + iy)^2$$

or

$$u + iv = x^2 + 2ixy - y^2$$

Since the real and imaginary parts of each member of this equation must be respectively equal,

$$u = x^2 - y^2$$

and

$$v = 2xy$$

These equations represent a *mapping* of the *points* of the XY-plane into those of the UV-plane since, corresponding to each point (x, y), there is defined a unique point (u, v).

In the UV-plane (Figure 21.1a) the equations of the "streets," or lines parallel to the V-axis, are $u = 1$, $u = 2$, $u = 3$, etc., and the equations of the "avenues," or lines parallel to the U-axis, are $v = 1$, $v = 2$, $v = 3$, etc. Substituting these values of u and v in the pair of equations above, one obtains the *hyperbolas* $x^2 - y^2 = 1$, $x^2 - y^2 = 2$, $x^2 - y^2 = 3$, etc., and $2xy = 1$, $2xy = 2$, $2xy = 3$, so that as another *geometric* interpretation of the complex function $w = z^2$ there is the *correspondence* between the meshwork of hyperbolas (Figure 21.1b) and the rectangular network of straight lines. It can be proved that the *mapping* of the hyperbolas onto the straight lines is *conformal*, that is, *angles* are *invariant* under the mapping (providing the origin $x = 0$, $y = 0$ is excluded from the domain of the function). The perpendicu-

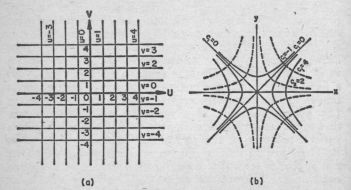

(a)   (b)

Figure 21.1   The complex function $w = z^2$ as a conformal mapping. The lines $u = c_1$, $v = c_2$ correspond to the hyperbolas $x^2 - y^2 = c_1$, $2xy = c_2$, respectively.

larity of the straight lines corresponds to the orthogonality of the two systems of hyperbolas.

After the above example of the analytic geometry of complex functions, let us illustrate the calculus of such functions. Thus from experience with real functions, one might conjecture that for $w = z^2$ the derivative $dw/dz = 2z$. Such an assertion would be a mere formalism, since there is no meaning involved until an exact *definition* of the derivative of a complex function has been furnished. This definition is strictly analogous to that in the case where y is a real function of x and

$$\frac{dy}{dx} = \text{limit } \frac{\Delta y}{\Delta x}$$

as Δx approaches zero, *providing* such a limit exists (Chapter 22). Then if w and z are complex variables, and w is a function of z,

$$\frac{dw}{dz} = \text{limit } \frac{\Delta w}{\Delta z}$$

as Δz approaches zero, providing such a limit exists.

It looks as if, after all, the differential calculus of complex functions must be much the same as the elementary calculus of real functions. But a remarkable new feature is concealed in the clause "as Δz approaches zero." The *geometric* interpretation of $\Delta y/\Delta x$ for a real function is the slope of a secant to the curve representing the function, and "Δx approaches zero" is associated with the fact that a variable point of the curve approaches coincidence with the fixed point as the secant approaches the tangent (Vol. I, page 267) to the curve at point P. Now "Δz approaches zero" means that a variable point in the XY-plane approaches coincidence with a fixed point, and if the complex function is continuous, a similar motion toward coincidence occurs in the UV-plane (Δw approaches zero). However, there is *not* a unique motion toward coincidence analogous to the real case where a variable point moves along a real curve toward a fixed point P. There are an infinite number of paths along which Δz can approach zero, that is, which will produce the desired coincidence. The question arises: Will the limit of $\Delta w/\Delta z$ have the *same* value regardless of how $\Delta z \to 0$? It seems natural that the path of approach might influence the final result, and this is actually the case. It is only when the limit exists, and is the *same* for every path of approach, that the complex function is said to have a derivative at the point in question.

If the path of approach is along the X-axis, then $\Delta z = \Delta x$ and

$$\frac{\Delta w}{\Delta z} = \frac{\Delta u + i\Delta v}{\Delta x} = \frac{\Delta u}{\Delta x} + i\frac{\Delta v}{\Delta x}$$

If, on the other hand, the path of approach is along the Y-axis where $z = x + iy$ becomes $z = 0 + iy$, then $\Delta z = i\Delta y$ and

$$\frac{\Delta w}{\Delta z} = \frac{\Delta u}{i\Delta y} + \frac{\Delta v}{\Delta y} = -i\frac{\Delta u}{\Delta y} + \frac{\Delta v}{\Delta y}$$

If limits exist for both paths of approach, and if these limits have the same value, then

$$\frac{\partial u}{\partial x} + i\frac{\partial v}{\partial x} = -i\frac{\partial u}{\partial y} + \frac{\partial v}{\partial y}$$

Equating real and imaginary parts of the left and right members, one arrives at the *Cauchy-Riemann* differential equations, which pervade the theory of functions of a complex variable, namely,

$$\frac{\partial u}{\partial x} = \frac{\partial v}{\partial y} \quad \text{and} \quad \frac{\partial v}{\partial x} = -\frac{\partial u}{\partial y}$$

If a function has a derivative at a point, then these equations must be satisfied at that point. Conversely, if these equations are satisfied and if the partial derivatives are continuous, then $f(z)$ has a derivative. If the Cauchy-Riemann equations are satisfied throughout some region of the XY-plane, then $f(z)$ is said to be *analytic* in that region. What happens when the fundamental equations are *not* satisfied? There may be *singular points* at which this occurs, and this requires special study. But there may be failure of the Cauchy-Riemann conditions in general. Then the function is *non-analytic*. This may occur because the derivative is not uniquely defined for all the different paths along which Δz may approach 0. Then in contrast to being *monogenic*, the function is *polygenic*.

If, in addition to the conditions satisfied above, the functions $u(x, y)$ and $v(x, y)$ have continuous partial derivatives of the second order, then (Chapter 9)

$$\frac{\partial^2 u}{\partial x \partial y} = \frac{\partial^2 u}{\partial y \partial x} \quad \text{and} \quad \frac{\partial^2 v}{\partial x \partial y} = \frac{\partial^2 v}{\partial y \partial x}$$

Differentiating the first Cauchy-Riemann equation with respect to x and the second with respect to y so that

$$\frac{\partial^2 u}{\partial x^2} = + \frac{\partial^2 v}{\partial x \partial y}$$

$$\frac{\partial^2 v}{\partial y \partial x} = - \frac{\partial^2 u}{\partial y^2}$$

one obtains

$$\frac{\partial^2 u}{\partial x^2} = - \frac{\partial^2 u}{\partial y^2}$$

or

$$\frac{\partial^2 u}{\partial w^2} + \frac{\partial^2 u}{\partial y^2} = 0$$

This means that $u(x, y)$ is a solution of Laplace's equation (Chapter 9) and, in a similiar fashion, it can be shown that $v(x, y)$ satisfies the same equation. Thus the theory of functions of a complex variable is another field in which partial differential equations, the Cauchy-Riemann set and the equation of Laplace, play a basic role.

To understand the integral calculus of complex functions, the reader would need a more profound understanding of certain ways in which the Cauchy-Mengoli integral (Chapter 27) can be generalized. The more important aspects of that question will be treated in later chapters. Here we might remark that whereas the Cauchy-Mengoli integral

$$\int_a^b f(x)\,dx$$

represents the limit of a sum where a typical term can be taken as $f(x_t)\,\Delta x$, where x_t is a point on an interval or segment of the X-axis from a to b, it is possible to form a definite integral where $f(x)$ varies along a curve. Such an interpretation is possible for the complex integral

$$\int_C f(z)\,dz$$

Then the fundamental proposition about complex integrals is the *Cauchy integral theorem*, which establishes the fact that if $f(z)$ is differentiable at all points in a certain region of the plane and C is a closed curve (like a circle or ellipse or some oval) in that region, then

$$\int_C f(z)\,dz = 0$$

From this theorem various Cauchy integral formulas are derived, and these are associated with the development of complex functions into infinite series in z. It turns out that if $f(z)$ is differentiable at all points on a circle C with center at $(0, 0)$, then

$$f(z) = a_0 + a_1 z + a_2 z^2 + \cdots + a_n z^n + \cdots$$

(where the coefficients are complex numbers determined by the Cauchy integral formulas) is a series that converges for all values of $z = x + iy$, corresponding to points (x, y) within the circle C.

If, as in the case of a real variable, a function $f(z)$ is defined to be *analytic* (in a region) provided that it can be expressed as a power series convergent in the region, then by virtue of the Cauchy formulas, one can say that for *complex functions*, a *differentiable* function is an *analytic* function. One cannot make a similar assertion for real functions.

Although the discussion of the last few pages takes us past the kindergarten stage of the theory of functions of a complex variable, it cannot transport us to such summits as the Riemann zeta-function. Since all the material was motivated by the *analytic* theory of numbers, it seems fitting to end with the human story of the mathematician who, probably more than any other during the twentieth century, helped to foster analytic methods for the resolution of the discrete problems of the higher arithmetic. That man was Godfrey Harold Hardy (1877–1947). For some facts about his life, personality, and general contributions to mathematics, we shall now quote one of his great successors, Professor E. C. Titchmarsh of Cambridge University.* Then we shall follow with the story of the Hindu number-theory genius,

* Royal Society of London, *Obituary Notices of Fellows*, Vol. 6, No. 18 (November 1949), pp. 446 ff.

Srinivasa Ramanujan (1887–1920), who, through Hardy's efforts, became known to the mathematical world and was enabled to leave a remarkable arithmetical legacy to posterity.

Godfrey Harold Hardy was born on 7 February 1877, at Cranleigh, Surrey. He was the only son of Isaac Hardy, Art Master, Bursar and House Master of the preparatory branch of Cranleigh School. His mother, Sophia Hardy, had been Senior Mistress at the Lincoln Training College. Both parents were extremely able people and mathematically minded, but want of funds had prevented them from having a university training.

The future professor's interest in numbers showed itself early. By the time he was two years old he had persuaded his parents to show him how to write down numbers up to millions. When he was taken to church he occupied the time in factorizing the numbers of the hymns, and all through his life he amused himself by playing about with the numbers of railway carriages, taxi-cabs and the like.

As soon as he was old enough G. H. went to Cranleigh School, and by the time he was twelve he had passed his first public examination with distinctions in mathematics, Latin and drawing. His mind was turned in the direction of Cambridge by a curious incident, which he has related in *A Mathematician's Apology*. He happened to read a highly coloured novel of Cambridge life called *A Fellow of Trinity*, by "Alan St Aubin" (Mrs Frances Marshall), and was fired with the ambition to become, like its hero, a fellow of Trinity. He went up to Trinity College, Cambridge, as an entrance scholar in 1896.

Hardy was fourth wrangler in 1898. He took Part II of the Tripos in 1900, being placed in the first division of the first class, Jeans being then below him in the second division of the first class. In the same year he was elected to a Prize Fellowship at Trinity, and his early ambition was thus fulfilled. Hardy and Jeans, in that order, were awarded Smith's Prizes in 1901.

His life's work of research had now begun, his first paper apparently being that in the *Messenger of Mathematics*, Vol. 29, 1900. It is about the evaluation of some definite integrals, a subject which turned out to be one of his permanent minor interests, and on which he was still writing in the last year of his life.

In 1906, when his Prize Fellowship was due to expire, he was put on the Trinity staff as lecturer in mathematics, a position he continued to hold until 1919. This meant that he had to give six lectures a week. He usually gave two courses, one on elementary analysis and the other on the theory of functions. The former included such topics as the implicit function theorem, the theory of unicursal curves and the integration of functions of one variable. This was doubtless the origin of his first Cambridge tract, *The Integration of Functions of a Single Variable*. This work is so well known now that it is often forgotten that its systematization was due to Hardy. He also sometimes took small informal classes on elementary subjects, but he was never a "tutor" in the Oxford sense.

In 1908 Hardy made a contribution to genetics which seems to be little known by mathematicians, but which has found its way into textbooks as "Hardy's Law." There had been some debate about the proportions in which dominant and recessive Mendelian characters would be transmitted in a large mixed population. The point was settled by Hardy in a letter to *Science*. It involves only some simple algebra, and no doubt he attached little weight to it. As it happens, the law is of central importance in the study of Rh-blood-groups and the treatment of haemolytic disease of the newborn. In the *Apology* Hardy wrote, "I have never done anything 'useful.' No discovery of mine has made, or is likely to make, directly or indirectly, for good or ill, the least difference to the amenity of the world." It seems that there was at least one exception to this statement.

He was elected a Fellow of the Royal Society in 1910, and in 1914 the University of Cambridge recognized his reputation for research, already worldwide, by giving him the honorary title of Cayley Lecturer.

To this period belongs his well-known book *A Course of Pure Mathematics*, first published in 1908, which has since gone through numerous editions and been translated into several languages. The standard of mathematical rigour in England at that time was not high, and Hardy set himself to give the ordinary student a course in which elementary analysis was for the first time done properly. *A Course of Pure Mathematics* is hardly a *Cours d'Analyse* in the sense of the great French treatises, but so far as it goes it serves a similar purpose. It is to Hardy and his book that the outlook of present-day English analysts is very largely due.

Another turning point in Hardy's career was reached about 1912, when he began his long collaboration with J. E. Littlewood. There have been other pairs of mathematicians, such as Phragmén and Lindelöf, or Whittaker and Watson, who have joined forces for a particular object, but there is no other case of such a long and fruitful partnership. They wrote nearly a hundred papers together, besides (with G. Pólya) the book *Inequalities*.

Soon afterwards came his equally successful collaboration with the Indian mathematician Ramanujan, though this was cut short six years later by Ramanujan's early death. An account of this association is given by Hardy in the introductions to Ramanujan's collected works and to the book *Ramanujan*. In a letter to Hardy in 1913, Ramanujan sent specimens of his work, which showed that he was a mathematician of the first rank. He came to England in 1914 and remained until 1919. He was largely self-taught, with no knowledge of modern rigour, but his "profound and invincible originality" called out Hardy's equal but quite different powers. Hardy said, "I owe more to him than to any one else in the world with one exception, and my association with him is the one romantic incident in my life."

Hardy was a disciple of Bertrand Russell, not only in his interest in mathematical philosophy, but in his political views. He sympathized with Russell's anti-war attitude, though he did not go to the lengths which brought Russell into collision with the authorities. In a little book *Bertrand Russell and Trinity*, which he had printed for private circulation in 1942, Hardy has described the Russell case and the storms that raged over it in Trinity. It was an unhappy time for those concerned, and one may think that it all would have been better forgotten. It must have been with some relief that, in 1919, he heard of his election to the Savilian Chair of Geometry at Oxford, and migrated to New College.

In the informality and friendliness of New College Hardy always felt completely at home. He was an entertaining talker on a great variety of subjects, and one sometimes noticed every one in common room waiting to see what he was going to talk about. Conversation was one of the games which he loved to play. He played several games well, particularly real tennis, but his great passion was for cricket. A vivid account of Hardy's affection for cricket and his life in his later Cambridge years is given by C. P. Snow, in an article entitled "A mathematician and cricket," in *The Saturday Book, 8th Year*.

In *A Mathematician's Apology* Hardy is at some pains to show that [pure] mathematics is useless, or at any rate harmless. He says, "It is true that there are branches of applied mathematics, such as ballistics and aerodynamics, which have been developed deliberately for war . . . but none of them has any claim to ranks as 'real'. They are indeed repulsively ugly and intolerably dull; even Littlewood could not make ballistics respectable, and if he could not, who can?" His views on this subject were obviously coloured by his hatred of war, but in any case his whole instinct was for the purest of mathematics.

Nevertheless, he was a Fellow of the Royal Astronomical Society, which he joined in 1918 in order that he might attend the meetings at which the theory of relativity was debated by Eddington and Jeans. He even once, in 1930, took part in a debate on stellar structure, which involved R. H. Fowler's work on Emden's and allied differential equations. On this he made the characteristic remark that Fowler's work, being pure mathematics, would still be of interest long after all the physical theories, which had been discussed had become obsolete. This prophecy has since been very largely fulfilled.

His likes and dislikes, or rather enthusiasms and hates, can be listed as follows:

Enthusiasms
    (i) Cricket and all forms of ball games.
    (ii) America, though perhaps he only came into contact with the pleasanter side of it.

(iii) Scandinavia, its people and its food.

(iv) Detective stories.

(v) Good literature, English and French, especially history and biography.

(vi) Walking and mild climbing, especially in Scotland and Switzerland.

(vii) Conversation.

(viii) Odd little paper games, such as making teams of famous people whose names began with certain combinations of letters or who were connected with certain countries, towns or colleges. These were played for hours in hotels or on walks.

(ix) Female emancipation and the higher education of women (though he opposed the granting of full membership of the university to Oxford women).

(x) *The Times* cross-word puzzles.

(xi) The sun.

(xii) Meticulous orderliness, in everything but dress. He had a large library and there were piles of papers all about his rooms, but he knew where everything was and the exact position of each book in the shelves.

(xiii) Cats of all ages and types.

Hates

(i) Blood sports of all kinds, war, cruelty of all kinds, concentration camps and other emanations of totalitarian governments.

(ii) Mechanical gadgets; he would never use a watch or a fountain pen, and the telephone only under compulsion. He corresponded chiefly by prepaid telegrams and post cards.

(iii) Looking-glasses; he had none in his rooms, and in hotels the first thing he did in his room was to cover them over with bath-towels.

(iv) Orthodox religion, though he had several clerical friends.

(v) The English climate, except during a hot summer.

(vi) Dogs.

(vii) Mutton—a relic of his Winchester days, when they had by statute to eat it five days a week.

(viii) Politicians as a class.

(ix) Any kind of sham, especially mental sham.

In 1928–1929 he was Visiting Professor at Princeton and at the California Institute of Technology, O. Veblen coming to Oxford in his place. In 1931 Hardy returned to Cambridge to accept the Sadleirian chair of Pure Mathematics.

Perhaps the most memorable feature of this period was the Littlewood-Hardy seminar or "conversation class." This was a model of what such a thing should be. Mathematicians of all nationalities and ages were encouraged to hold forth on their own work, and the whole thing was conducted with a delightful informality that gave ample scope for free discussion after each paper. The topics dealt with were very varied, and the audience was always amazed by the sure instinct with which Hardy put his finger on the central point and started the discussion with some illuminating comment, even when the subject seemed remote from his own interests.

He also lectured on the calculus of variations, a subject to which he had been drawn by his work on inequalities.

After his return to Cambridge he was elected to an honorary fellowship at New College. He held honorary degrees from Athens, Harvard, Manchester, Sofia, Birmingham, Edinburgh, Marburg and Oslo. He was awarded a Royal Medal of the Royal Society in 1920, its Sylvester Medal in 1940 and the Copley Medal in 1947. He was President of Section A of the British Association at its Hull meeting in 1922, and of the National Union of Scientific Workers in 1924–1926. He was an honorary member of many of the leading foreign scientific academies.

Some months before his death he was elected "associé étranger" of the Paris Academy of Sciences, a particular honour, since there are only ten of these from all nations and scientific subjects. He retired from the Sadleirian chair in 1942, and died on 1 December 1947, the day on which the Copley Medal was due to be presented to him.

For the biography of the mathematician who furnished the "one romantic incident" in Hardy's life, there is the statement of Professor Robert D. Carmichael, one of whose numerous mathematical specialities is number theory.*

During our generation no more romantic personality than that of Srinivasa Ramanujan has moved across the field of mathematical interest. Indeed it is true that there have been few individuals in human history and in all fields of intellectual endeavor who draw our interest more surely than Ramanujan or who have excited more fully a certain peculiar admiration for their genius and their achievements under adverse conditions. There is nothing particularly noteworthy about Ramanujan's ancestry to account for his great gifts. His father and paternal grandfather were petty accountants in Kumbakonam, an important town in the Tanjore district in India. His mother was a woman of strong common sense. For some time after marriage she was without children. Her father prayed to a famous local goddess to bless his daughter with children; and shortly afterwards Ramanujan, her eldest child, was born.

His school and college education were meager and somewhat

* Robert D. Carmichael, "Some Recent Researches in the Theory of Numbers," *American Mathematical Monthly*, Vol. 39, No. 3 (March 1932), pp. 139 ff.

irregular. On January 16, 1913, at 25 years of age, he wrote to G. H. Hardy a letter containing the following words:

"I have had no University education but I have undergone the ordinary school course. After leaving school I have been employing the spare time at my disposal to work at Mathematics. I have not trodden through the conventional regular course which is followed in a University course, but I am striking out a new path for myself."

On February 27 of the same year he wrote to Hardy as follows:

"I have found a friend in you who views my labours sympathetically. This is already some encouragement to me to proceed. . . . I find in many a place in your letter rigorous proofs are required and you ask me to communicate the methods of proof. . . . The sum of an infinite number of terms of the series $1 + 2 + 3 + 4 + . . . = -1/12$ under my theory. If I tell you this you will at once point out to me the lunatic asylum as my goal. . . . What I tell you is this. Verify the results I give and if they agree with your results . . . you should at least grant that there may be some truths in my fundamental basis. . . . To preserve my brains I want food and this is now my first consideration. Any sympathetic letter from you will be helpful to me here to get a scholarship either from the University or from Government. . . ."

These passages from Ramanujan's letters will give a faint indication of the human side of a correspondence which stands as a remarkable one in the history of our science. Along with the letters numerous astonishing mathematical results were communicated by Ramanujan to Hardy. Many of these were right; not a few were wrong; even the errors themselves were sometimes brilliant. The association thus opened up with Hardy became one of the prime factors in the life of Ramanujan. He went to England in 1914.

Hardy has put on record the fact that his appearance set a great puzzle for solution. What was to be done in teaching such an intellect the spirit and methods of modern mathematics? In some directions his knowledge was profound. In others his limitations were quite startling. He could work out modular equations and theorems of complex multiplication, to orders unheard of. His mastery of continued fractions was remarkable. He had found for himself properties of the Zeta-function and applied them to many famous problems in the analytic theory of numbers. Yet he had never heard of a doubly periodic function or of Cauchy's theorem (the most fundamental fact of complex variable theory). Indeed, he had but the vaguest idea of a function of a complex variable. His conception of mathematical proof was quite inadequate. His results, new or old, right or wrong, had been obtained by argument, intuition, induction, mingled in a way which he himself could not coherently describe. Many of his proofs were invalid. Not a few of his results were false. His approximations were not as close as he supposed. But, notwithstanding the fact that he had never seen a French or German book and that his command of English was meager, he had conceived for himself and had treated in an astonishing way problems to which for a hundred years some of the finest intellects in Europe had given their attention without having reached a complete solution. That such an untrained mind made mistakes in dealing with such questions is not remarkable. What is astonishing is that it ever occurred to him to treat these problems at all.

In a few years after reaching England Ramanujan had a fair knowledge of the theory of functions and the analytic theory of numbers. He had learned to know when he had proved a theorem and when he had not. And his flow of original ideas kept up without abatement during this period of acquisition.

In the spring of 1917 he began to show evidence of being unwell. He went to a Nursing Home at Cambridge early in the summer of 1917 and was never afterwards out of bed for long at a time. He died April 26, 1920, a little more than seven years after writing his initial letter to Hardy, the event which brought him for the first time into touch with modern mathematical ideas. During this brief interval, about one-third of which was spent in bed on account of illness, he added to the achievements made unaided during the first years of his life a body of contributions which is sure to exert a marked influence on the development of certain chapters of mathematics, indeed has already exerted such an influence.

Under the title *Collooted Papers of Srinivasa Ramanujan* there has been brought together in a single volume everything published by Ramanujan with the exception of a few solutions of questions proposed by other mathematicians and answered by him in the *Journal of the Indian Mathematical Society*. He left behind him a large mass of unpublished material in note-books now famous, and these have been edited and published.

Although complex variable theory led Hardy and Ramanujan to discoveries which the former liked to describe as useless, another part of modern analysis was designed to cope with one of the most constant and pressing of human issues, the need to be thrifty. It appeared to scientists that nature also observed frugality, and the physical principles involved were expressed in analytic language. Because the analysis of the late nineteenth century did not suffice for this purpose, new analytic concepts had to be created and, as we shall see in the next chapter, the results were notions as "pure" and abstract as those employed by Hardy and all the analytic number-theorists.

Chapter 22

The Reformation of Analysis

One reason for the present primary position of pure mathematical theories is that time and again in mathematical history logical crises have arisen from failure to purify fundamental notions completely, that is, to divorce ideas from their origins in the world of reality. In this respect, calculus was no exception. In the long period of its development from Archimedes to Newton and Leibniz, basic conceptions were related to physical situations and procedures were derived by intuitive arguments. Kepler measured an area swept out by the *motion* of a (celestial) point on a physical "continuous curve." Newton's derivative was a "fluxion of a fluent," usually illustrated by an instantaneous velocity or acceleration. Again, the derivative was visualized as the limit of the slope of a variable secant as one point of a *curve* moves to coincidence with another. Thus, definitions were dependent on the meaning of "motion" and "continuous curve." That our intuitions about motion will produce logical paradoxes was indicated by Zeno of Elea about 450 B.C. (Chapter 24). But even earlier, the Pythagoreans had become aware of the great danger of putting one's faith in intuition.

The "common sense" view of a line segment will never suggest its possible incommensurability, and by the end of the nineteenth century there were a number of examples of how our perception of motion along ordinary paths may lead to faulty mathematical judgments. Surely no one (except a modern mathematician) would ever expect a continuous line or curve to lack a definite direction (that is, a tangent) at each and every one of its points, and thereby make the geometric definition of the derivative as the slope of a

tangent fall apart. Nor would one think it possible for a
curve to fill an *area* completely. Yet Giuseppe Peano (1858–
1932) showed that both these things can happen. To obtain
a *Peano curve* (Figure 22.1), let a square be divided into
four equal squares numbered 0, 1, 2, 3, counterclockwise,
starting at the bottom left-hand corner. Now divide each of
these squares into four equal squares, and run around the 0
square clockwise, ending opposite a square of 1; pass into the
square of 1, and round 1 counterclockwise into 2, and so on.
Carry the division further, stage by stage *forever*, running
continuously round the squares, starting always at the bottom left-hand corner, running counterclockwise round the
first newly divided square after an odd number of divisions
and clockwise after an even number, and alternating passages round the squares indicated in the diagram. At each
stage of the process there is ambiguity of direction at each
"corner" of the path because there the curve has two per-

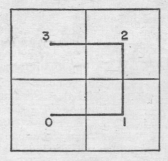
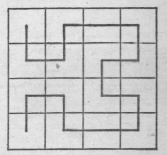

Figure 22.1   Construction of the Peano curve

pendicular directions. As the process continues there are
more and more corners, closer together, so that ultimately
the points of ambiguity are all points of the path.

In an address* to the American Mathematical Society at
the turn of the century, James Pierpont (1866–1938), professor at Yale and a leading analyst of his day named *eight*
properties which we automatically assign to a curve on the
basis of geometric intuition. He demolished each of these in
turn by the production of monstrosities indicating that intuition is erroneous. Two of Pierpont's eight points have
been illustrated by the Peano curve. He stated further that
our most firmly rooted intuitive notion of a curve, the one
often used as a definition, is that it can be generated by the
motion of a point. Here, he said, two ideas are essential,
namely that motion is continuous and that at each instant it
has a definite direction and speed. Now, as we have seen,
direction and speed are obtained from the *derivatives* dy/dx
and ds/dt. But suppose that the curve "generated by the motion of a point" is like the four-leaved rose (Figure 7.21).
What happens when the moving point reaches the origin?
There is no unique answer since there are apparently eight
different paths possible. Suppose the path of a moving point
to be the continuous curve of Figure 22.2 whose equation is

$$y = 0 \quad \text{for} \quad x = 0$$
$$y = x \sin \frac{1}{x} \quad \text{for} \quad x \neq 0$$

That curve lies between two straight lines each making an
angle of 45° with the X-axis, and oscillates with indefinitely
increasing frequency (and *change of direction*) as it approaches the origin. The result is that at the origin *no* direction (tangent) can be specified. We ask: How does the
point move as it passes through the origin? Or if it is to
start at the origin and is to proceed to right or left, in what
direction should it move?

After indicating other fallacious notions, Pierpont emphasized that any definition that is to serve as a basis for *rigorous* deduction must be an idealization of physical experience
and can only correspond approximately to hazy intuitive
notions. He prescribed that the definitions of analysis be

---

* See James Pierpont, "On the Arithmetization of Mathematics," *Bulletin
of the American Mathematical Society,* Vol. 5 (May 1899), p. 398.

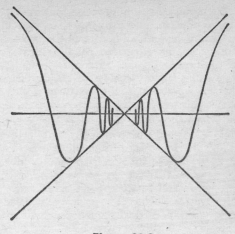

Figure 22.2

framed by using the "epsilon, delta" (ϵ, δ) criterion of Augustin-Louis Cauchy (1789–1857) and Karl Wilhelm Theodor Weierstrass (1815–1897).

It is the purpose of this chapter to explain the nature of this criterion, and to reveal how the two mathematicians named by Pierpont succeeded in banishing "monsters" by making analysis more rigorous. Pierpont stated that the "ϵ, δ" definitions make it possible to reason with absolute precision, and nevertheless arrive at deductions in accord with the evidence of our intuition. It is the custom to say. that Weierstrass "arithmetized" analysis, by which is meant that he replaced definitions and proofs based on geometric pictures or sensory observations by concepts expressed in terms of *real numbers*. To obtain a rigorous formulation of limits, continuity, and the like, Weierstrass was forced to create his own special theory of irrational numbers.

In analysis, the fundamental concept is that of *limit*, and it is to Cauchy that we owe the first rigorous definition. We have seen that integral calculus defines lengths, areas, volumes as the *limiting* values (when such exist) of certain approximating sums, and that the *derivative*, the basic notion of differential calculus, is likewise a limit. Up to this point we have handled the fundamental concepts of calculus in an informal, intuitive fashion, in much the same spirit as the founders of the subject. But even a layman today should be made aware of the extreme lack of rigor in the reasoning of Newton and Leibniz. We must then reexamine our previous arguments and present a more tenable treatment of limits, one that will not produce "monsters."

We have associated calculus concepts with approximative processes. In such estimation, if a first result seems too crude, there is an attempt to improve it, and if a second approximation does not satisfy standards of precision, there is a third, and so on. We shall now suppose that we are dealing with techniques of estimation that are not hit-or-miss, but possess a definite formula or algorithm that will always provide a *better* approximation than some approximation previously made, so that successive estimates will provide a sequence of better and better approximations to the "ideal" measurement we are seeking. Thus, for our present purposes, let us consider a hypothetical sequence in which successive estimates are

$$\frac{1}{2}, \frac{2}{3}, \frac{3}{4}, \frac{4}{5}, \frac{5}{6}, \frac{6}{7}, \frac{7}{8}, \frac{8}{9}, \dots$$

Suppose that some new light on the situation indicates that all further estimates will be governed by the law $n/(n+1)$, where n is the integer giving the position of the estimate in the above sequence. Thus the next estimate would be the *ninth*, and since $n = 9$, this approximation would equal 9/10, and if we continued approximating, the millionth result would be 1,000,000/1,000,001. This millionth estimate may satisfy our standard of precision, and we can then use it as an approximation to the measurement we are seeking, or we may assert that for all practical purposes, 1,000,000/1,000,001 is so close to 1 in value that we may as well assert that the entity in question measures 1 unit. Our conviction that this is a good thing to do is strengthened if we reexamine the sequence. We see that the fractions constantly increase in size, so that approximations after 1,000,000/1,000,001 will be larger, but never quite 1, since the denominator exceeds the numerator. Yet the difference from 1 will diminish if we continue the sequence of approximations. Algebraically, this difference for the nth term is

$$1 - \frac{n}{n+1} = \frac{n+1-n}{n+1} = \frac{1}{n+1}.$$

If $n = 1,000,000,000,000$, the difference will be about 0.000,000,000,001, which is exceedingly slight. The sum total of all these numerical facts is implied in the statement that 1 is the *limit* of the sequence whose law is $n/(n + 1)$.

About standards of precision, we shall say that any set of numbers approximates a particular number c within a *standard* ϵ (where ϵ is a positive number), if the numerical difference between c and every number of the set is less than ϵ. Thus the set $\{2, 9, 3, 8, 4, 7, 5\}$ aproximates the number 6 within the *standard* 5. But this is not the smallest standard, since the set also approximates 6 within the standard 4.1 or 4.01 or 4.001. Again, the sequence whose law is $n/(n + 1)$ approximates 1 within the standard 0.6 because all terms of the sequence differ from 1 by less than 0.6. But here we could also say the sequence approximates 1 within the standard 0.51 and also within the even finer standard 0.50001. The reader will readily see that the set of terms $n/(n + 1)$ for which n is greater than a million approximates 1 within the standard 0.000,001 or an even smaller standard, since, for example, if $n = 1,000,000$, then $1,000,000/1,000,001$ differs from 1 by $1/1,000,001$, which is less than our standard, and successive terms will differ from 1 by even less.

Now we are ready for the *definition:* The sequence of real numbers $\{a_1, a_2, a_3, \ldots, a_n, \ldots\}$ is said to have the *limit* L if, corresponding to each (positive) standard of approximation ϵ, however small, a term a_m of the series can be found so that all succeeding terms approximate L within the standard ϵ.

To clarify this definition, consider the sequence

$$1\frac{2}{3}, 1\frac{8}{9}, 1\frac{26}{27}, 1\frac{80}{81}, \cdots$$

whose law formation is

$$a_n = 2 - \frac{1}{3^n}$$

This means that the *first* term is found by subtracting $1/3^1$ from 2, the second by subtracting $1/3^2$ from 2, the third by subtracting $1/3^3$ from 2, etc. Then the eighth term will be

$$a_8 = 2 - \frac{1}{3^8} = 1\frac{6560}{6561}$$

By inspection, we might say that 2 is the *limit* of the sequence. But taking the formal requirement of the definition, suppose that we assign the standard $\epsilon = 0.01$, what selection must we make for m so that all terms subsequent to a_m should differ from 2 by less than 0.01? If we examine the first four terms of the sequence, no one of them will come within the standard. But the fifth term is $2 - 1/3^5$, which differs from 2 by $1/3^5$ or about 0.004. Therefore we select $m = 4$. Then a_5 differs from 2 by less than 0.01, and subsequent terms differ from 2 by $1/3^6$, $1/3^7$, $1/3^8$, ... which are all smaller than $1/3^5$. Then *a fortiori* they will differ from 2 by less than 0.01.

Now suppose that someone assigns the standard $\epsilon = 0.0001$. Then we find that we can choose $m = 8$, since $a_9 = 2 - 1/3^9$ differs from 2 by $1/3^9$, or by 0.00005, approximately, and subsequent terms of the sequence differ from 2 by still less.

No matter how small the value assigned to the positive number ϵ, a value of m can be selected so that $1/3^{m+1}$ will be smaller than ϵ and therefore $a_{m+1} = 2 - 1/3^{m+1}$ will differ from 2 by less than ϵ, and for terms after a_{m+1} the difference will be even less.

This seems like a lengthy argument to establish a fact which is "intuitively" obvious, but we have indicated at some length that modern mathematics demands the arithmetization of analysis lest various "monsters" develop from intuitive reasoning. In each of the following sequences, arithmetic proof can be given to indicate the existence or nonexistence of a limit:

Sequence	Law for a_n
(1) $1, \dfrac{1}{2}, \dfrac{1}{3}, \dfrac{1}{4}, \dfrac{1}{5}, \dfrac{1}{6}, \cdots$	$\dfrac{1}{n}$
(2) $1, \dfrac{1}{4}, \dfrac{1}{3}, \dfrac{1}{8}, \dfrac{1}{5}, \dfrac{1}{12}, \cdots$	$\dfrac{1}{n}$ (if n is odd)
	$\dfrac{1}{2n}$ (if n is even)
(3) $1, -\dfrac{1}{2}, \dfrac{1}{3}, -\dfrac{1}{4}, \dfrac{1}{5}, -\dfrac{1}{6}, \cdots$	$\dfrac{1}{n}$ (if n is odd)
	$-\dfrac{1}{n}$ (if n is even)

(4) 4, 4, 4, 4, 4, 4, ...   4

(5) 2, 4, 8, 16, 32, 64, ... 2^n

(6) −2, 2, −2, 2, −2, 2, ...   −2 (if n is odd)

                                                2 (if n is even)

We remark that it is essential to know the law of formation of a sequence if one wishes to draw conclusions about terms beyond those specifically listed. On intelligence tests a type of question frequently asked calls for the next term of a sequence like

$$1, \frac{1}{4}, \frac{1}{9}, \ldots$$

The answer given in the key is 1/16. But we claim that 1/22 would also be a correct response. No law of formation is stated in the test, and therefore there is no reason to assume that $a_n = 1/n^2$. Why not, then, use

$$a_n = \frac{1}{n^3 - 5n^2 + 11n - 6}$$

since it fits the three terms given? To show this, let

$$n = 1 \qquad a_1 = \frac{1}{1 - 5 + 11 - 6} = 1$$

$$n = 2 \qquad a_2 = \frac{1}{8 - 20 + 22 - 6} = \frac{1}{4}$$

$$n = 3 \qquad a_3 = \frac{1}{27 - 45 + 33 - 6} = \frac{1}{9}$$

Then if our alternative law of formation is used, for

$$n = 4 \qquad a_4 = \frac{1}{64 - 80 + 44 - 6} = \frac{1}{22}$$

Why is it not *more* intelligent to select a less obvious formula that is possible on the evidence of a_1, a_2, a_3? We could furnish many other alternatives in addition to the above.

To return to the six sequences whose law of formation we

have listed definitely, it seems evident that a limit exists in the first three instances and that this limit is *zero* in each case. The sequences differ, however, in appearance and in formula for a_n. If we wish to provide this fact with empirical meaning, we may think that three different approximative procedures are used for the measurement of the *same* entity. As for the proofs that zero is the limit in the sequences (1), (2), (3), above, they rest on the fact that if *any* positive value is assigned to ϵ, then m can be selected in each case so that $1/m$, $1/2m$, $-1/m$ will each differ from zero by less than the value of ϵ. Then a_m and *a fortiori* all terms after a_m will approximate zero within the standard ϵ.

The limit of the fourth of the illustrative sequences is 4 since, however small a positive value of ϵ is assigned, we can select $m = 1$, $a_m = 4$ and all subsequent terms are also 4, and therefore the difference from 4 is equal to zero, which is definitely less than ϵ. The sequence in question illustrates the theorem: The *limit* of a constant sequence is the constant itself.

Lest we think that every sequence has a limit, there are (5) and (6) above. In sequence (5) the terms just grow larger and larger without any upper bound. If we have the feeling that the terms will never exceed 1,000,000,000,000, say, all we need do is compute a_{40}. To approximate its value we can readily compute $2^{10} = 1024$, which exceeds 1000. Then $2^{40} = (2^{10})^4$ and so will exceed $(1000)^4$, which is the figure named above. Then the fortieth term and every term thereafter will exceed this huge number. If we name any figure, however large, 2^m will exceed it for some value of m. Then it is hopeless to seek any number as a possible limit, that is, a number to which all terms of the sequence after a certain one will be very close. It might seem that there could be no empirical counterpart for such a sequence, but we can imagine that cells in some malignant growth double in number repeatedly at regular short intervals of time. In mathematics, if not in life, this process could continue indefinitely, and the number of cells would exceed all bounds.

Sequence (6) fails to have a limit by virtue of oscillation. The terms are alternately very close to -2 and 2—in fact, they coincide with these numbers—but the terms after a particular one are not *all* close to -2, or *all* close to 2, or close to any other number. Then if we think of -2 as a possible limit we *cannot* choose m so that a_m and all subsequent terms differ from -2 by an amount $\epsilon = 0.01$, say, and the same difficulty exists if we think of 2 as a possible limit. For a physical suggestion of this sequence, we can picture a clock pendulum (that never slows down). The numbers describing the succession of its extreme left and extreme right positions would form an oscillatory sequence like (6) above.

As one more illustration we adduce one of the most important sequences in mathematics:

$$2^1, \left(1\frac{1}{2}\right)^2, \left(1\frac{1}{3}\right)^3, \left(1\frac{1}{4}\right)^4, \left(1\frac{1}{5}\right)^5, \left(1\frac{1}{6}\right)^6, \ldots$$

with the law of formation

$$a_n = \left(1 + \frac{1}{n}\right)^n$$

To reveal that this law applies we rewrite the above terms of the sequence as

$$\left(1 + \frac{1}{1}\right)^1, \left(1 + \frac{1}{2}\right)^2, \left(1 + \frac{1}{3}\right)^3, \left(1 + \frac{1}{4}\right)^4,$$
$$\left(1 + \frac{1}{5}\right)^5, \left(1 + \frac{1}{6}\right)^6, \ldots$$

The sequence has a limit, but it is difficult to establish this fact by using the definition of a limit, and it becomes advisable instead to use a special theorem on limits.

As a preliminary, we recall that sequence (5) above failed to approach a limit because a_n increased *without bound*. But let us picture a different type of increasing sequence. Let us say that a child has just learned to walk and the maximum distance he can proceed without falling is 9 feet. The proud parents take movies of Baby's first steps and project them. Then one slow-motion sequence might show the child at the following distances (in feet) from the starting point

$$1, 1\frac{1}{2}, 2, 2\frac{1}{2}, 3, 3\frac{1}{2}, 4, 4\frac{1}{2}, 4\frac{3}{4}, 4\frac{7}{8}, 4\frac{15}{16}, \ldots$$

Here the terms increase steadily, but the situation is not the same as in (5) above, because there is an upper bound. Baby cannot advance beyond 9 feet. The sequence is empirical and we cannot give a definite rule of formation, but if we examine the last few terms listed, it appears that Baby is beginning to totter, and will soon reach his "limit" somewhere in the neighborhood of 5 feet. The picture suggests the following theorem for sequences: If the terms of a sequence increase steadily, but are less than some real number A, then the sequence has a limit, and this limit is either A or a number smaller than A.

Now, returning to the important sequence $a_n = (1 + 1/n)^n$, the approximate values of the first few terms are 2.00, 2.25, 2.37, 2.44, 2.49, ... Use of a table or computing machine or logarithms will yield the approximations

$$a_{100} = (1.01)^{100} = 2.705$$
$$a_{1000} = (1.001)^{1000} = 2.717$$

We assert, and it can actually be proved, that the terms of the sequence increase steadily, but that after a while the steps, like Baby's, become very tiny. We observe that between the hundredth and thousandth term, the "distance" progressed is only about 0.012. If we go beyond the thousandth term, the steps become even smaller, and the progress above 2.717 is infinitesimal. For example, the ten-thousandth term is 2.718, which makes the progress after 9000 steps only about 0.001. It would appear safe to name 3 as an upper bound beyond which the terms cannot go. Then, according to the theorem, the sequence has a limit, and this limit is either 3 or a number smaller than 3. Since the ten-thousandth term (to four decimal places) is 2.7183 (approximately), the limit lies between this number and 3.

It can be proved that this limiting number is irrational, but the proof is not as simple as that for $\sqrt{2}$. Moreover, the limit is not a run-of-the-mill irrational, expressible as a square root, cube root, or root of any order. Nor is it a finite combination of such roots. But before we say more about this particular limiting number, let us call it by its traditional name. The symbol e is customarily used for the *limit* of the sequence whose law is $(1 + 1/n)^n$, and since it is a difficult irrational but, like π, a very important one, we emphasize that $e = 2.7183$ is merely an approximation to its value. To continue the story of e from the *pure* mathematician's point of view, it is not only an irrational without a *finite* expression in terms of roots, but it is not even possible to write an algebraic equation (with integer coefficients) of any degree—millionth, trillionth, etc.—that has e as one solution. For this reason e is called a *transcendental* number, in the sense that it *transcends* classic algebra. This remarkable fact was proved in 1873 by the French mathematician Charles Hermite (1822–1905). Although the Babylonians and other peoples of antiquity had good rational approximations to π, its "utter irrationality" was not established until 1882, when the German C. L. F. Lindemann (1852–1939) proved that π, like e, is transcendental. But ignorance of the ultimate character of π did not interfere with its usefulness for some 3500 years prior to the demonstration of its "nonalgebraic" nature. The transcendental character of both e and π is a *theoretical* issue whose primary interest lies in the domains of philosophy and abstract mathematics.

The transcendental e is much younger than π; it made its first appearance in the seventeenth century not long after the Scotsman John Napier (1550–1617) formulated his concept of logarithms. A modification of the Napierian system led to *natural logarithms*. They are exponents of the base e, that is,

$$x = \text{natural logarithm of } y$$

usually symbolized by

$$x = \ln y \quad \text{or} \quad y = e^x$$

Natural logarithms are the simplest for calculus and modern analysis in general. That the term "natural" is appropriate can be illustrated by their appearance in various laws of growth and decay. For example, bacteria in a certain culture may grow (approximately) according to the law

$$A = A_0 e^{0.8t} \quad \text{or} \quad t = 1.25 \ln \frac{A}{A_0}$$

where A_0 and A are the initial number of bacteria and the number at time t, respectively. Again, an *approximate* formula for the decay of a certain radioactive substance might be

$$A = A_0 e^{-0.0004t} \quad \text{or} \quad t = 2500 \ln \frac{A_0}{A}$$

where A_0 and A are the initial amount and the amount left after t years, respectively. Suppose that we wish to find the half-life of the substance, that is, the time in which it will decay to half the original amount. At that time $A_0/A =$

2. Then from the formula, $t = 2500 \ln 2$; if we reveal that the approximate value of the natural logarithm of 2 is equal to 0.69, then $t = 1725$ years *approximately*.

Let us now indicate one application of limits which has been anticipated in earlier chapters—namely, the matter of finding the sum of an infinite series. Thus we used an algebraic trick (Chapter 2) to show how a repeating decimal can be converted into a common fraction. Such a procedure will indicate, for example, that $0.3333 \ldots = 1/3$. But instead, we can consider $0.3333 \ldots$ as equivalent to the infinite series,

$$0.3 + 0.03 + 0.003 + 0.0003 + \ldots$$

and can inquire whether or not that series has a finite sum.

In connection with the present discussion we shall associate an appropriate *sequence* with a series, and if that sequence has a *limit*, we shall say that the series is *convergent* and the limit is its *sum*. Thus, in any infinite series, we shall choose the sequence $S_1, S_2, S_3, S_4, \ldots, S_n, \ldots$ where the S's are the sums corresponding to 1, 2, 3, 4, $\ldots$, n terms, respectively.

Before studying the sequence corresponding to the above series, we observe that it belongs to a type described as a *geometric progression*, where the ratio of each term (after the first) to its predecessor is a constant. Thus, in the series under consideration, $0.03/0.3 = 0.003/0.03 = 0.0003/0.003 = 0.1$, and the reader will observe that the "common ratio" in the following geometric progression is 2:

$$1 + 2 + 4 + 8 + \cdots + 2^{n-1} + \cdots$$

Now in elementary algebra it is proved that S_n, the sum of the first n terms of a geometric progression, that is, the nth term of its *associated sequence* is,

$$S_n = \frac{a_1 - a_1 r^n}{1 - r}$$

where a_1 is the first term of the progression and r is the common ratio. Hence, in the sequence corresponding to the repeating decimal,

$$S_n = \frac{0.3 - 0.3(0.1)^n}{1 - 0.1} = \frac{0.3 - 0.3(0.1)^n}{0.9}$$

In other words,

$$S_n = \frac{1}{3} - \frac{1}{3}(0.1)^n$$

Thus S_n approximates $1/3$ closely for large values of n; in fact, S_n differs from $1/3$ by the amount, $1/3(0.1)^n$, which can be made arbitrarily small. For example, if we choose the standard of approximation, $\epsilon = 0.000,001$, it would suffice to choose $n = 6$, for then

$$\frac{1}{3}(0.1)^6 = \frac{0.000,001}{3} = \frac{\epsilon}{3}$$

which is surely less than the standard ϵ. However small ϵ is chosen, it will be possible to find an m such that S_m approximates $1/3$ within the specified standard. Therefore the sequence has the *limit* $1/3$, or the series has the *sum* $1/3$, and this is the value of $0.3333. \ldots$

Applying the geometric progression formula once again, we find that for the sequence associated with the series

$$1 + 2 + 4 + 8 + \cdots + 2^n + \cdots$$

$$S_n = \frac{1 - 1(2)^n}{1 - 2} = \frac{2^n - 1}{2 - 1} = 2^n - 1$$

As n grows greater and greater, 2^n increases beyond all bounds. For example, if $n = 20$, 2^n is greater than $1,000,000$ and $S_n = 2^n - 1$ is almost as huge. Thus S_n has no limit, and in that case the series is said to *diverge*. The present example resembles that of the harmonic series illustrated in the previous chapter.

Infinite series need not be geometric progressions. Consider the infinite series:

$$1 - \frac{1}{2} + \frac{1}{2} - \frac{1}{3} + \frac{1}{3} - \frac{1}{4} + \frac{1}{4} - \frac{1}{5} + \cdots \text{forever}$$

where the general term is $1/n$ for n odd, $-1/n$ for n even. The sum of the terms listed is

$$1 - \frac{1}{5} = \frac{4}{5}$$

since all the terms balance except the first and last. If we take an odd number of terms of this series, even as many as

1,000,001, S_n, the sum of n terms, will obviously be 1. If we go out to $-1/1,000,000$, S_n will be

$$1 - \frac{1}{1,000,000} = 0.999999$$

We see that no matter how far out we go, the sums S_n are alternately 1 and numbers closer and closer to 1. Therefore, this infinite series converges and its sum is said to be 1.

Consider the infinite series

$$1 + 1 - 1 - 1 + 1 + 1 - 1 - 1 + \cdots$$

Notice that the sums will fluctuate taking the values 1, 2, 1, 0 no matter how far out in the series we go. Therefore, the sums do not get close and remain close to any single number, that is, S_n does not have a limit. The series is *divergent*, and there is no meaning to the term sum as applied to it.

To come back to the concept of a *limit*, we have treated only the case of the limit of a sequence. To allude to terminology we have used earlier, this is the *discrete* case of a limit, because a sequence is a *function* whose *domain* is the set of natural numbers ordered according to size, $\{1, 2, 3, \ldots, n, \ldots\}$. The *range*, that is, the set of corresponding functional values, listed in the corresponding order, is $\{a_1, a_2, a_3, \ldots, a_n, \ldots\}$, the ordered set which is a *sequence*. The limit of a sequence is then the limit of a *special* type of *function*, one with a discrete domain.

But what about a function with a "continuous" domain like the real number continuum or an interval on the real number line? If we reexamine our previous discussion of the calculus, we find that, in the main, this was the type of function occurring in the limiting processes we used. We shall now proceed to an elementary example, but before doing so, we state once and for all that every function mentioned in an illustration or definition will be assumed to have the real number continuum or one of its subsets (made up of one or more "continuous" intervals) as its domain.

Let us then consider the function defined by $y = f(x)$ where

$$(x) = \frac{2x^2 - 2x}{x - 1} \qquad \text{for } x \neq 1$$

(We have excluded $x = 1$ from the domain because it would lead to a zero denominator, and division by zero is impossible.) If then we draw the Cartesian graph of $y = f(x)$, we obtain a straight line with a puncture at the point $(1, 2)$ (Figure 22.3).

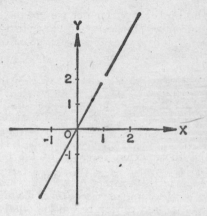

Figure 22.3

The graph shows that for values of x slightly smaller or slightly larger than 1, the corresponding values of y or $f(x)$ are close to 2, and $f(x)$ approximates 2 within smaller and smaller standards as x is taken closer to the value 1. This would seem to justify the statement that "the limit of f at 1 is equal to 2," symbolized by

$$\lim_1 f = 2$$

Perhaps the following alternative wording and symbolism will hold more appeal: The limit of $f(x)$ as x "approaches" 1 is equal to 2, or

$$\lim_{x \to 1} f(x) = 2$$

The reason this statement is considered less rigorous than the other is that the term "approaches" has an intuitive connotation associating it with motion, and if there is anything rigor must prevent, it is one of the monstrous paradoxes brought on by our ideas of physical motion.

To return to our example, we can justify the same limiting value of the function by means of an algebraic argument. Now

$$f(x) = \frac{2x^2 - 2x}{x - 1} = \frac{2x(x - 1)}{(x - 1)} = 2x \qquad \text{for } x \neq 1$$

Just as long as we do not take $x = 1$, we may substitute any other values of x in

$$f(x) = 2x$$

Taking values close to 1, say $x = 0.9$ and $x = 1.1$, we obtain $f(0.9) = 1.8$ and $f(1.1) = 2.2$, which are values close to 2. If x approximates 1 more closely, $f(x)$ will approximate 2 more closely. Thus for $x = 0.99$ and $x = 1.01$, we have $f(0.99) = 1.98$ and $f(1.01) = 2.02$. We could continue to select better and better approximations of 1 as values of x and then the corresponding values of $f(x)$ would be better and better approximations of 2, and this justifies our conclusion that $\lim_{1} f = 2$. We observe that although $\lim_{1} f$ is defined and equal to 2, the symbol $f(1)$ is meaningless because $x = 1$ does *not* belong to the domain of the function.

Our illustration suggests the formal definition: The function f is said to have the limit L at a if and only if, for every positive real number ϵ (however small), a positive number δ (depending on ϵ) can be found such that for all values of x except $x = a$ in the interval $(a - \delta, a + \delta)$, the set of corresponding values, $f(x)$, approximate L within the standard ϵ.

For a more compact wording of this definition we introduce the term *absolute value* of a real number, which signifies its magnitude regardless of sign (direction). Thus, the absolute value of -5 is 5, symbolized as

$$|-5| = 5$$

Similarly we see that $|+2| = 2$, $|-0.01| = 0.01$, $|3.4 - 3| = 0.4$, $|2.6 - 3| = 0.4$, etc. The last two of these examples show that 3.4 and 2.6 are equally good approximations of 3.

Now we can abbreviate our definition as follows:

$$\lim_{a} f = L$$

if and only if, for every positive ϵ (however small), a positive δ (depending on ϵ) can be found such that

$$|f(x) - L| < \epsilon$$

for all $x \neq a$ satisfying the inequality

$$|x - a| < \delta$$

Let us apply the formal definition to the problem of finding $\lim_0 f$ where f is defined by

$$f(x) = \frac{x^3 + 5x}{x} \qquad \text{for } x \neq 0$$

We can guess the value of $\lim_0 f$ and then give formal proof. We see that

$$\text{for } x \neq 0, \qquad f(x) = \frac{x(x^2 + 5)}{x} = x^2 + 5$$

Hence, for values of x close to 0, $f(x)$ will be close to 5. Therefore we guess that $\lim_0 f = 5$. For *proof* we must show that if a positive ϵ is given, a positive δ (depending on ϵ) can be found such that

$$|f(x) - 5| < \epsilon$$

for all $x \neq 0$ satisfying the inequality

$$|x - 0| < \delta$$

or

$$|x| < \delta$$

To set about finding δ in terms of ϵ, we observe that if $x \neq 0$, we can substitute $x^2 + 5$ for $f(x)$ in the first inequality above, and that requirement becomes

$$|x^2 + 5 - 5| < \epsilon$$

or

$$|x^2| < \epsilon$$

which is satisfied if $|x| < \sqrt{\epsilon}$, an inequality of the same form as $|x| < \delta$. Therefore, if we choose $\delta = \sqrt{\epsilon}$, the conditions of the definition are satisfied. To clarify this point, suppose that the assigned standard of approximation is $\epsilon = 0.25$. Then $\sqrt{\epsilon} = 0.5$, and

$$|f(x) - 5| < 0.25$$

that is,

$$|x^2 + 5 - 5| < 0.25 \text{ or } |x^2| < 0.25$$

for all $x \neq 0$ satisfying the inequality $|x| < 0.5$. Perhaps the original wording of the definition will lend further clarification. Hence we say, alternatively, that $\lim_0 f = 5$ because for all x except $x = 0$ in the interval $(0 - 0.5, 0 + 0.5)$, that is, $(-0.5, 0.5)$, the set of corresponding values, $f(x)$, approximates 5 within the standard 0.25.

Let us choose our next illustration from the calculus. If $s = 16t^2$ is given as the distance formula for a falling body, and we require the *derivative* or *instantaneous velocity* at the time $t = 2$, we must find the *limit* of the average velocity as t "approaches" 2. To find this limit, we first formulate the average velocity during the interval between $t = 2$ and $t = 2 + h$ where $|h|$ is a small positive number. If h itself is positive, we have an interval just after $t = 2$ seconds. If h is negative, we have an interval just before $t = 2$. From the tabulation,

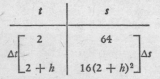

we find that $\Delta s = 16(4 + 4h + h^2) - 64 = 64h + 16h^2$, and $\Delta t = h$ so that the average velocity is

$$\frac{\Delta s}{\Delta t} = \frac{64h + 16h^2}{h} = 64 + 16h \qquad \text{if } h \neq 0$$

Thus, in common usage, the average velocity would be described as f, a "function of h" whose domain is a *continuum*. By definition, the *derivative* or *instantaneous velocity* we are seeking is $\lim_0 f$, or $\lim_{h \to 0} f(h)$ which is read as "the *limit* of $f(h)$ as h approaches 0." Since $f(h) = 64 + 16h$, we see that as $|h|$ gets smaller and smaller or closer to 0, $f(h)$ gets closer to 64. Hence our intuition tells us that the limit is equal to 64. To establish it rigorously, we must show that given any standard ϵ, we can determine δ so that

$$|f(h) - 64| < \epsilon$$

for all $h \neq 0$ satisfying the inequality

$$|h - 0| < \delta, \qquad \text{that is,} \qquad |h| < \delta$$

Substituting $64 + 16h$ for $f(h)$ in the first inequality above expresses that condition as

$$|64 + 16h - 64| < \epsilon \quad \text{or} \quad |16h| < \epsilon$$

which will be satisfied if

$$|h| < \frac{\epsilon}{16}$$

This inequality is of the same form as $|h| < \delta$ above. Hence we can meet the requirements of the definition by selecting $\delta = \epsilon/16$.

To indicate the "common sense" of the rigorous proof, suppose that the standard assigned is $\epsilon = 0.16$. We choose $\delta = 0.01$ and must show that

$$|f(h) - 64| < 0.16$$

for all $h \neq 0$ satisfying the inequality

$$|h| < 0.01$$

But, as indicated above, $|f(h) - 64| = |16h|$. Now if $|h| < 0.01$, $|16h| < 0.16$ and we have proved our point.

Since some of our examples of the hazards of intuition were associated with the meaning of a continuous curve or a continuous motion, let us now identify both these ideas with the continuity of a function, and provide an "ϵ, δ" definition for that concept. Perhaps counterexamples can be of some help in suggesting a definition of continuity. For instance, examination of the punctured line of Figure 22.3 would reveal a discontinuity of the line or the corresponding function at $x = 1$. In fact, with $f(x)$ as defined for the graph, $f(1)$ was a meaningless symbol. This suggests that if a function f defined by $y = f(x)$ is to be continuous at $x = a$, then $f(a)$ must be defined, that is, a must belong to the domain of the function. But that is not enough. If we continue our study of Figure 22.3, we see that the discontinuity at $x = 1$ would not be removed merely by defining $f(1)$. For if we define $f(1) = 4$, the graph would then consist of the punctured line and the single lonely point $(1,4)$ "vertically" above the puncture. To fill the gap we would have not only to give meaning to $f(1)$ but also to choose $f(1) = 2$, the constant which we proved to be $\lim_{1} f$.

Our illustration shows that for continuity of a function at $x = a$, $f(a)$ must be defined and also it must be true that $f(a) = \lim_{a} f$. But there is one final issue: Is it possible that $\lim_{a} f$ does not exist? That is the difficulty at the "jumps" in the "step function" pictured in

Figure 14.10. There, if a jump occurs at $x = a$, the functional value $f(a)$ is defined. (It corresponds to the height of the upper step.) But $\lim_a f$ does *not* exist because, while $f(x) \rightarrow f(a)$ as x approaches a *from the right*, $f(x)$ approaches a lower value than $f(a)$ as x approaches *a from the left*.

In the hyperbola of Figure 7.17 (which Omar Khayyám used in his solution of a cubic equation), there is a discontinuity at $x = 0$. We can consider it to be produced by two types of failure. In the first place, $f(0)$ is not defined. The reader can examine the effect of choosing $f(0) = 20$ or $f(0) = -10$, etc. and plotting in the graph of Figure 7.17 the corresponding points, $(0, 20)$ or $(0, -10)$, etc. No matter what real number he might assign to $f(0)$, the point $(0, f(0))$ would be an isolated point and would not serve the purpose of making the left branch of the hyperbola continuous with the right. In the present case, if x approaches 0 from the right, $f(x)$ gets larger and larger and never remains close to any constant value. As x approaches 0 from the left, $f(x)$ takes values like -100, -1000, $-1,000,000$, etc. These numbers represent greater and greater "debts," as it were, so that $f(x)$ gets smaller and smaller as x approaches 0 from the left, but $f(x)$ never remains close to any constant value. Hence there are neither right nor left limits for f and $\lim_0 f$ does *not* exist.

Our illustrations suggest the following definition: The function f is *continuous* at a if and only if (1) a belongs to the domain of f, that is, $f(a)$ is defined, (2) $\lim_a f$ exists, and (3) $f(a) = \lim_a f$. Or we can express this definition in ϵ, δ form by stating: A function f is continuous at a if and only if $f(a)$ is defined and if, corresponding to every positive number ϵ (however small), a positive number δ depending on ϵ) can be found such that

$$|f(x) - f(a)| < \epsilon$$

for all x satisfying the inequality

$$|x - a| < \delta$$

Figure 22.4 shows that the continuity of a graph or function at a or at the point $(a, b = f(a))$ signifies that, for each pair of horizontal lines, one at a distance ϵ above, the other at the same distance below (a, b) there is a pair of vertical lines, one at a distance δ to the right, the other at the same distance to the left of (a, b) such that every point of the graph between the vertical lines is also between the

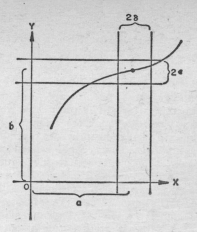

Figure 22.4

horizontal lines. In Figure 22.5 there is a jump discontinuity at (a, b), and no pair of vertical lines can be found so that the property just described is fulfilled.

The rigorization of analysis was begun in 1821 when Cauchy gave the "ϵ, δ" definition of limit and then defined continuity, derivative, and integral in terms of his limit concept. The further arithmetization of analysis was carried out,

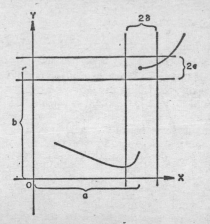

Figure 22.5

in the main, by Weierstrass, and was inspired by the various analytic "freaks" he and other analysts were able to derive from intuitive notions. With Weierstrass the "ϵ, δ" technique became the basic language of modern analysis.

The nonspecialist, however, rarely acquires any fondness for the Cauchy-Weierstrass formal procedures, chiefly because determining δ in terms of ϵ does, in instances less elementary than those we have illustrated, require considerable ingenuity and algebraic skill. The layman has a leaning toward intuitive formulation, however faulty, and an "ϵ, δ" proof may seem an esoteric technique introduced to handle the calculus of exceptional, abnormal functions, produced *ad hoc* by pure mathematicians. But a brontosaurus is no anomaly in a Paleozoic age, and epsilons and deltas, far from being exceptional, populate modern analysis and actually prevent the multiplication of logical "monsters." Some readers may feel that treating them in general works or in elementary texts is part of the "new mathematics" movement, but this is not the case. The author's high school mathematics teacher and lifelong inspiration, John A. Swenson, presented the Cauchy conception of a limit to high school students, and dealt with it in textbooks written years ago.*

Leaving for later consideration the details of how analysis progressed after its arithmetization, we conclude our chapter with biographies, personal and mathematical, of the two mathematicians who rigorized analysis.

Augustin-Louis Cauchy can be cited both for the quantity and for the quality of his mathematical output. He produced almost eight hundred papers, which filled twenty-four large quarto volumes. These memoirs presented his rigorization of analysis, his pioneer work in the theory of finite groups, his contributions to differential equations and functions of a complex variable, and his applied mathematical discoveries— in mechanics and astronomy. Cauchy accomplished all of this in spite of such handicaps as physical frailty and the hazards of the period of political unrest in which he lived.

His place and date of birth are equally famous—Paris, 1789. During his childhood, French schools were closed, and Augustin, the eldest of six children, was educated by his father, as were all the other children. This had definite ad-

* See, for example, John A. Swenson, *Integrated Mathematics,* Book V, Edwards Bros., Ann Arbor, 1937.

vantages. In the first place, Cauchy senior removed his family from Paris in order to escape the Terror, and they settled in the village of Arcueil. The great Laplace, who was a friendly neighbor at Arcueil, soon discovered Augustin's remarkable mathematical talent, and encouraged him, in fact, to follow a career in pure mathematics rather than in engineering, which, for practical reasons, was the boy's first choice.

A second advantage that accrued from schooling with Cauchy père was that Augustin-Louis' intellectual development extended to literary as well as scientific areas. In later life he thought nothing of shaping his addresses before learned academies in the form of (lengthy) poems. He was a remarkable linguist, mastering not only the classical, but also the Semitic and modern languages. When he taught in Italy and Austria, he had no difficulty in lecturing in Italian and German. Also, unlike many great mathematicians, who affect weakness in computation, Cauchy was a lightning calculator, able to defeat the arithmetic prodigy Mandeux.

After the early education at home, Cauchy attended two of France's great schools, the École Polytechnique and the École des Ponts et Chaussées. Having acquired an engineering degree from the latter, he served as a civil engineer from 1808 to 1813, first assisting with the construction of the Ourcq canal and then with the Cherbourg dike. Then, at age twenty-four, he decided to follow Laplace's advice, and renounced engineering in favor of pure mathematical research. Within a couple of years he was appointed to a chair in analysis and mechanics at the École Polytechnique, where he taught until 1830. It was in the lectures at the Polytechnique that he began the rigorization of analysis.

By the time he was twenty-seven, in 1816, Cauchy had made many brilliant contributions to various branches of mathematics and was recognized as one of the leading mathematicians in Europe. He was therefore worthy of admission to membership in the great Académie des Sciences. There were no vacancies, however, and here some ugly politics came into play. Gaspard Monge (1746–1818), the great geometer whose name is associated with the creation of that *descriptive geometry* which is so useful in mechanical drawing, had been a close friend to Napoleon. Lazare Carnot (1753–1823), disciple of Monge and father of Sadi Carnot (1796–1832) who became truly renowned in the history of science, had opposed Napoleon. In 1816 both Monge and

Carnot were purged from the Académie and Cauchy was assigned by royal decree although he had not been elected by the members of the Académie. This created an enormous scandal in scientific circles and Cauchy became very unpopular.

In 1830 the tables were turned; Louis-Philippe came to power and Cauchy, as a loyal Bourbon, refused to swear allegiance to the new government. He went into voluntary exile and accepted a professorship in mathematical physics at the University of Turin. In 1833 the deposed King Charles X, living in exile in Prague, summoned Cauchy to tutor his grandson, the thirteen-year-old Duke of Bordeaux. For five years the great analyst served as a sort of baby-sitter to the pampered youth, and Charles made him a baron for this martyrdom. Finally, in desperation, Cauchy escaped to Paris by saying he had to attend the celebration of his parents' golden wedding anniversary. Once back in France, he was permitted to resume his post at the Académie, but when he was unanimously elected to the Collège de France, he refused the proffered chair because it involved the taking of an oath of allegiance.

The Bureau des Longitudes saw fit to place him "temporarily" without making an issue of loyalty. For four years Cauchy was able to carry on important work at the Bureau and make his own major contributions to mathematical astronomy. In 1843 the government stepped in and decided to replace Cauchy, since his position was only "temporary." Cauchy then addressed a brilliant literary open letter to the people, stating his case and the ethical principles he felt were involved. From this time on, French scholars, who on the whole disagreed with Cauchy's political views, came to see him in a different light—as an eccentric, perhaps, but also as a man of principle, willing to suffer to uphold what he believed to be right.

In 1848 Louis-Philippe was ousted, and oaths of allegiance were abolished. Napoleon III restored them in 1852, but he took a liberal attitude which exempted Cauchy, who was able therefore to live the remaining five years of his life in security, lecturing at the Sorbonne and continuing his endless researches in every area of mathematics and mathematical physics.

On the German front, the battle for rigorization was waged by Weierstrass. He was born at Ostenfelde in the district of Münster in 1815 just about the time of Napoleon's Waterloo and Cauchy's appointment to a professorship at the École Polytechnique. Whereas Cauchy brought sounder logical methods into analysis almost casually, that is, without any formal declaration or manifesto, Weierstrass, with German thoroughness, carried on an intellectual campaign to indicate the mathematical disasters inherent in failing to rigorize analysis.

It would be hard to conceive of a confirmed bachelor and an ardent advocate of extreme mathematical rigor as a romantic figure. Nevertheless one cannot give Weierstrass' biography without describing his role as teacher and sponsor of a great and beautiful woman mathematician, Sonya Kovalevsky (1850–1891). The Russian girl was Weierstrass' favorite pupil, and in one of her discoveries she was associated with that other advocate of rigor, Cauchy. The first basic proposition in the theory of partial differential equations is the Cauchy-Kovalevsky theorem.

Whereas Cauchy had been favored by an understanding and loving father who was able to direct his education properly, Weierstrass was hindered by a domineering parent, a customs officer who failed to recognize his son's mathematical genius and tried to force him into the rigid mold of the civil service. Karl had been an excellent student at the *gymnasium* (secondary school) and at the end of each term had received all the prizes, six or seven, except the award for good penmanship. Ironically, teaching calligraphy was to be one phase of his earning his bread and butter later on. While he was at the *gymnasium* it was ham and butter that were a source of income, for, at age fifteen he started to do the accounting for a female merchant who dealt in these commodities.

He attended the University of Bonn, where his father sent him for the purpose of studying accounting, commerce, and law. But Karl spent all his time there in fencing and enjoying the *gemütlichkeit* of the beer halls. When he returned home in 1839 without a diploma, one can imagine what his father's reaction was. Next, young Weierstrass decided to prepare himself for a career in teaching and entered the Academy of Münster, which was near his home. This was a fortunate step, for there he encountered an able and inspiring mathematics professor, Christoph Gudermann (1798–1852), who aroused his interest in the newly created *elliptic functions* of Abel and Jacobi. Gudermann confided his own ideas to his pupil and told him that he had striven fruitlessly for years to use *power series* (infinite series involving variables) to represent elliptic functions. Where his teacher failed Weierstrass succeeded, and such series are the keynote to all his subsequent analytic discoveries.

From 1841 to 1854, or almost until the age of forty, Weierstrass taught school and simultaneously carried on remarkable mathematical research without ever offering any of it for publication or discussing it with another living soul. The one exception was his *Abelian Integrals,* a memoir that appeared in the catalogue of studies for 1848–1849 of the Royal Catholic Gymnasium at Braunsberg. This article was completely unintelligible to the students, parents, and teachers who read the catalogue, but their only reaction was "That's math. What do you expect?" What no one expected or suspected was that Weierstrass' article contained epochal discoveries.

In 1854 Weierstrass decided to submit a memoir on *Abelian Functions* to the *Journal für die reine und angewandte Mathematik* (usually called Crelle's Journal, after the name of the founder, A. L. Crelle [1780–1855]). This periodical was one of the two (the other was the Frenchman Liouville's Journal) scholarly mathematical publications on the continent. The research paper of the obscure secondary school teacher created a furor in scientific circles. The University of Koenigsberg conferred an honorary doctorate on Weierstrass, and the Ministry of Education gave him a year's leave with pay so that he could continue his research. Then he became a professor at the Royal Polytechnic School in Berlin, and eventually at the University of Berlin, where, from 1864 to 1897, he carried on those investigations for which he was recognized as the leading world figure in the field of analysis.

When he first met Sonya Kovalevsky he was in his middle fifties and she was twenty. She had enjoyed the very advantages he had lacked in his own youth, in particular, prosperous and kindly parents. She was the daughter of a Russian general, Ivan Sergyevitch Krukovsky. The family circle and friends, among whom the writer Dostoevsky was included, are pictured charmingly in Sonya Kovalevsky's own literary account of her childhood, *The Sisters Rajevsky.* Sonya and her sister Anyuta were part of a young people's movement to promote the emancipation of women in Russia. It was customary for one of the girls to contract a marriage of convenience to enable her to leave the country and study at a foreign university. Then her whole retinue of friends could also escape—on the pretext of visiting the "married" friend in France or Germany. At eighteen Sonya contracted just such a nominal marriage with Vladimir Kovalevsky.

Vladimir escorted her to Heidelberg, where she studied mathematics and he geology. He soon left for Jena and she for Berlin, where she was befriended by Weierstrass. Since Sonya, as a woman, could not be admitted to university lectures, Weierstrass gave her sets of notes on his lectures, directed her reading, held conferences with her, and provided critical appraisals of her original mathematical efforts. Because his academic schedule was a very crowded one, the supervision of Sonya's mathematical education, was an added burden. To make this task easier, Weierstrass' sisters invited Sonya to the family home on Sundays, and following a lengthy afternoon mathematical discussion between teacher and pupil, the entire family would meet for Sunday night supper. It is recorded that Weierstrass' sisters, who were little interested in mathematics, nevertheless derived great pleasure from Sonya's company and the regular Sunday evening get-togethers.

Sonya worked diligently at mathematical studies for a full four years and finally was awarded a doctorate in 1874 at the University of Göttingen (*in absentia*, because she was a woman). In spite of this degree, and Weierstrass' letters of recommendation, she was unable to obtain an academic position anywhere in Europe. For this reason she returned to her family in Russia. Very soon she became involved in the gay social whirl at St. Petersburg. When Tchebycheff, the leading Russian mathematician of the day, paid a visit to Berlin, Weierstrass had news of Sonya's activities, and was keenly disappointed to hear of her apparent frivolity. He wrote a letter in which he reproached her gently, but in no uncertain terms. His scolding had little effect for some time, but after a lapse of several years, she returned to mathematics. She wrote to Weierstrass to ask for assistance and information on technical problems, and once again he supervised her research, this time from afar, by means of regular correspondence.

In the interim, Sonya had met Vladimir Kovalevsky again; this time he wooed and won her in earnest, and they lived happily together. Their first and only child, a daughter, Foufie, was born in 1878. Vladimir became professor of paleontology at the University of Moscow, and all went well until he became involved in shady speculations that eventually resulted in his disgrace and suicide.

Sonya found herself once more in a foreign country, this time on no intellectual lark, but faced with a serious problem—that of earning a living for herself and her little daughter. Once again Weierstrass came to her assistance. Through Mittag-Leffler, another of Weierstrass' distinguished students, she secured a position as lecturer at the University of Stockholm. The advanced attitude of the Swedish toward women worked to her advantage. In 1889 Mittag-Leffler succeeded in obtaining a life professorship for her.

During her years in Stockholm Sonya Kovalevsky did her best work. Weierstrass, always her friend, continued his inspirational mathematical correspondence with her; the great teacher once again advised from afar when he could not be present in person. His distinguished pupil wrote a paper on the refraction of light in a crystalline medium, and followed this with the memoir that won the Prix Bordin of the French Academy, namely, *On the Rotation of a Solid Body about a Fixed Point*. The judges considered this paper so exceptional that they raised the prize from 3000 to 5000 francs, a large sum of money in those days.

Two years later (1891) there was an epidemic of influenza in Stockholm and Sonya succumbed to it. She died at the age of forty-one. Weierstrass survived her by half a dozen years. His life span was double hers, for he died peacefully in Berlin in his eighty-second year. Although he is renowned in mathematical history mainly for his role as a very great analyst, nevertheless, in the opinion of some, he made a comparable contribution in helping Sonya Kovalevsky to become one of the foremost women mathematicians of all time.

Chapter 23

Royal Roads to Functional Analysis

It should have become increasingly clear that the function concept is a thread which runs through all of mathematics. At different points of our story we have in fact discussed propositional functions, logical functions, real functions, complex functions, analytic functions, set functions, payoff functions, decision functions, frequency (density) functions, distribution functions, the Riemann zeta-function, etc. All these and still other kinds of functions which have played a role in our development show the advantage of *pure* (abstract) theories of functions (and relations) where the domain and range need not be number sets but may be aggregates of arbitrary nature. Such generality would permit the domain, in special instances, to be a *set of functions*, and the range to be a set of numbers. In the present chapter we shall see how the ideas of the great Italian mathematician Vito Volterra (1860–1940) led him to a study of such "functions of other functions," as he called them. Jacques Hadamard (Chapter 21) named them *functionals*, and Paul Lévy gave the name *functional analysis* to the study of analytical properties of functionals.

But the Volterra-Hadamard-Lévy "royal road" is a modern, abstract, advanced one. Therefore let us begin by indicating how, early in mathematical history, issues in the physical world motivated the construction of paths which converged to larger routes that ultimately flowed into the broad highway of functional analysis.

According to legend, the first "royal road" in the direction of functional analysis was blazed by Queen Dido about 800 B.C. In Vergil's *Aeneid* there is a reference to the story in question. Dido, fleeing from the Phoenician city of Tyre ruled by King Pygmalion, her tyrannical brother, and arriving at the site that was to become Carthage, sought to purchase land from the natives. They asserted that they would sell only as much ground as she could surround with a bull's hide. She accepted the terms and made the most of them by cutting a bull's hide into narrow strips which she pieced together to form a single, very long strip. Then, by sheer intuition, she reasoned that the *maximum* area could be encompassed by shaping the strip into the circumference of a circle. A rigorous mathematical proof that Dido made the optimum choice was not achieved until the nineteenth century. But today we speak of the general *problem of Dido,* namely, the question of finding what closed curve of specified length will enclose a maximum area.

A slight modification of an example already considered (Chapter 8) will solve Dido's problem for a special case. Suppose then that we ask: What are the dimensions of the *rectangle* of maximum area that has a perimeter of 40 ft. (or, more generally, of $4a$ linear units, where $a > 0$)? If we represent the unknown width by x, then two sides of the rectangle will have length x, and $40 - 2x$ (more generally, $4a - 2x$) will be left for the two remaining sides. Hence each will measure $20 - x$ (or, in the general case, $2a - x$). Hence the area will be

$$y = x(20 - x) \quad \text{or} \quad y = x(2a - x)$$

that is,

$$y = 20x - x^2 \quad \text{or} \quad y = 2ax - x^2$$

As we have indicated earlier, the graph of such a formula is a quadratic parabola with a highest point corresponding to the maximum value of y, the area. Instead of reading the coordinates of the maximum point from a graph, it is more convenient to apply the fact that the slope of the tangent is zero at the maximum point. Thus

$$\frac{dy}{dx} = 20 - 2x \quad \text{or} \quad \frac{dy}{dx} = 2a - 2x$$

$$20 - 2x = 0 \quad \text{or} \quad 2a - 2x = 0$$
$$x = 10 \qquad\qquad x = a$$
$$20 - x = 10 \qquad\qquad 2a - x = a$$

The dimensions would be 10 ft. by 10 ft. (a by a), and the maximum area would be 100 sq. ft. (a^2). Thus the *rectangle of maximum area for a given perimeter is a square*.

Dido's problem is described as *isoperimetric*. The story of her ingenuity may be fictional, but it is *true* that Pappus of Alexandria (*ca*. 300 A.D.) considered isoperimetric problems in Book V of his greatest work, the *Mathematical Collection*. Not only did he treat the areas of figures with the same perimeter, but also the volumes of solids bounded by the same surface area. At one point Pappus proved that the honeybee's choice of a *regular hexagonal* cell makes possible the storage of a *maximum* amount of honey with a *minimum* use of wax.

Today mathematicians tend to apply the adjective "isoperimetric" to any problem in which an extremum, that is, a maximum or a minimum, is to be determined subject to one or more *constraints*. As an example of such constraints, we have just required (1) that a figure be a rectangle and (2) that it have a perimeter of 40 ft. Loosely speaking, even a game-theory issue where a player seeks to maximize or minimize a payoff $E(x_1, x_2, \ldots, x_n)$ is "isoperimetric," with constraints requiring $x_1 \geq 0$, $x_2 \geq 0$, $\ldots$, $x_n \geq 0$, and $x_1 + x_2 + \cdots + x_n = 1$.

But our ultimate objective is to discuss *functionals*. Hence let us illustrate such functions in connection with Dido's problem. In the special case with the constraints (1) and (2) of the previous paragraph, the *area* of the rectangle is a function of its boundary, or if we use another of Volterra's descriptive phrases, the area is a "function of a line." One can picture (Figure 23.1) a few of the infinite variety

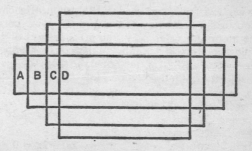

Figure 23.1

of rectangles possible under restriction (2). Three of the rectangles in the diagram enclose a smaller area than that bounded by the square of the same perimeter. But our emphasis is on the fact that a functional, one of Volterra's "functions of lines," is involved. Some of the ordered pairs belonging to the functional appear in the diagram and can be tabulated as follows.

Boundary Line	A	B	C	D (square)
Area Enclosed	51	75	96	100

Strictly analogous to Dido's problem is the matter of finding the form which will give the greatest volume within a fixed surface area. The solution to this problem is a *sphere*, and again a proof would involve consideration of a functional. If one selects an area of 150 sq. in., one can picture it as belonging to a cube whose edge is 5 in., or to a box with dimensions 7½, 5, 3 (measured in inches), or as belonging to some polyhedron in the form of a crystal or to some oval surface, or, in fact, to an infinite variety of different surfaces. The volumes of the above cube and box are 125 and 112.5 cubic inches, respectively, so that there is more volume for the *same* surface area in the former case. Using the formulas $S = 4\pi r^2$ and $V = 4/3\pi r^3$, the reader can verify that a sphere with radius 3.46 in. (approximately) will have a surface area of about 150 sq. in. and a volume of about 173 cu. in., so that the content enclosed by the same area is far greater than in the two instances above. This does *not* prove, however, that 173 cu. in. is the greatest volume which 150 sq. in. can enclose. Cartesian geometry will furnish equations or functions for the different closed surfaces having an area of 150 sq. in. As such functions vary, so will the volume enclosed, and to each function there will correspond a unique volume; or the volume is a function of a function, that is, it is a *functional*.

In Hellenic antiquity, Dido (according to legend) and Pappus, in actual fact, were not alone in applying functionals to geometric and physical problems involving maxima and minima. Heron of Alexandria postulated a minimum principle for optics more than two centuries prior to Pappus' isoperimetric theorems. To give a popular version of a major question in Heron's *Catoptrica* (*ca.* 60 A.D.), let us suppose that A and B in Figure 23.2a are two houses and

that line CD is a straight river bank. A boy living in house
A is to proceed to the river to fill a pail of water. Then he
is to bring the full pail to his neighbor in house B. What
point on the bank will enable the boy to walk the minimum distance? The reader may try to· solve this problem
by trial, but it is not difficult to prove, by elementary geometry, that if the boy walks to a point E such that angle
α = angle β (Figure 23.2a), the path AEB is the shortest
possible. The proof is suggested by Figure 23.2b, where the
allegedly optimal path AEB is equal in length to the straight
line segment FEB. In the diagram, the dotted line AHB
represents any other path the boy might choose. Now the
path AHB has the same length as FHB, and FHB is longer

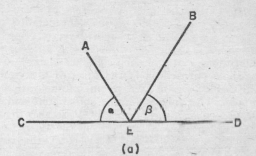

(a)

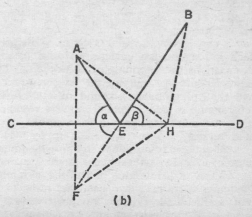

(b)

Figure 23.2.

than *FEB* because the straight line segment is the shortest distance between two points.

Suppose that in Figure 23.2*a*, *CD* represents a *mirror*. Then, according to Heron's assumption, a ray of light starting at *A* and reaching point *B* after reflection in the mirror must follow the shortest route, namely *AEB* in Figure 23.2*a*, where angle α = angle β. Hence Heron asserted as the law of reflection of light: *The angle of incidence is equal to the angle of reflection.*

Heron's assumption of a *minimal* path is correct for a straight mirror, but if the reflecting surface should be curved as in Figure 23.3, it is still true that the angle of incidence equals the angle of reflection. However, the path followed is *maximal*. Figure 23.3 suggests that the actual

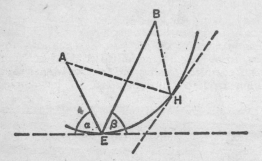

Figure 23.3   Reflection from a concave mirror

path *AEB* is longer than any neighboring path such as *AHB*. In the general case, the equal angles α and β are those between the light rays and the tangent to the curved mirror, and for all mirrors, straight or curved, the path formed by incident and reflected rays is always an *extremum*, that is, a local maximum or minimum. The matter we wish to emphasize is that our diagrams involve a *functional*, where the length of any (hypothetical) path is a function of the path, as that hypothetical path is varied.

The problems of Dido, Heron, and Pappus illustrate a type of law or general principle that was to dominate latter-day physics and applied mathematics. Hellenic thinkers were geometers, and hence the extrema they considered were lengths, areas, and volumes. But the forefathers of modern mathematics dealt with maxima and minima of various other physical entities. In 1662 Fermat generalized Heron's postulate by assuming a principle of *least time* for all of optics. Later there were physical principles which made extrema of energy, "action," entropy, separation in the space-time of relativity. In probability and statistics there were "least squares" and maximum likelihood. *Minimax* principles, as we have seen, are basic in modern game theory, statistical decision, and mathematical economics. In fact, scientific models through the centuries appear to have been formulated as one long "game against nature" (Chapter 12). In actuality, it is not a case of nature's behavior, but rather of man's tendency to project his own characteristics and thus to see principles of thrift in nature's organization of the universe. In some instances it has become apparent that nature will not be disciplined into conformity with the parsimony prescribed by man. Nevertheless the numerous precepts of economy have been a means of unifying whole branches of science, linking past developments to further progress, furnishing orientation to students of science who might go completely astray in reading learned treatises or consulting modern "introductions" to new branches of science.

We have illustrated that differential calculus will handle some types of extrema. The more advanced species gave rise to the *calculus of variations*, a highly technical subject which can nevertheless be described as a generalization of the treatment of maxima and minima in the elementary calculus. In his *Methodus inveniendi lineas curvas minimive proprietate gaudentes* (1744), Euler explained and extended maximinimal notions of Newton, the Bernoullis, Maupertuis. His 1753 *Dissertatio de principio minimae actionis* associates him with Lagrange as co-inventor of the calculus of variations.

Since the methodology of that subject is specialized and intricate, we shall not develop it but shall point out only those features that form the background for functional analysis. Moreover, some of the more technical aspects of applying minimax principles were treated at length in our discussion of statistical decision, and hence it would seem advisable to go beyond such ideas rather than to present more of the same. But even with our ultimate objective in view, we must indicate the nature of a typical problem in the calculus of variations.

The first challenging variational issue was formulated in 1696 by Jean Bernoulli (1667–1748), younger brother of Jacques Bernoulli, whose important contributions to probability have already been noted. The younger Bernoulli posed the problem of determining the shape of the most thrilling slide, that is, the path of fastest descent or *brachistochrone*. (In Greek *brachys* means short, *chronos* signifies time.) To state the problem exactly, suppose that one is given two points not in the same vertical line. How can one select from all the many curves joining the points that one along which the time taken by a particle to slide without friction under the action of gravity from the higher to the lower point will be a *minimum?* In Figure 23.4 we have

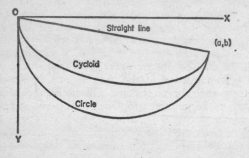

Figure 23.4   Brachistochrone problem

indicated only three of the infinite variety of possible paths, namely, a *straight line,* an arc of a *circle,* and an arc of a *cycloid* (Chapter 8). A race among three steel ball bearings, say, rolling down *smooth* inclines with the three shapes of Figure 23.4 would (in theory) always result in victory for the object on the cycloidal path. This would be the case even if there were hundreds or thousands of other paths (elliptic, parabolic, cubic, sinusoidal, etc.) in the competition. We must now give some idea of what Bernoulli had to do in order to *prove* that the cycloid is the brachistochrone.

In Figure 23.4 we have selected the origin as the higher of the two points to be joined. Hence its coordinates are $(0, 0)$. Let us call the coordinates of the lower point (a, b), and consider an arbitrary curve through the two points, namely $y = f(x)$. Since the two points are on the curve, we must have $f(0) = 0$, $f(a) = b$. Elementary mechanics and the facts of the calculus indicate that, when a definite function $y = f(x)$ is specified, the time of descent is equal to the definite integral (Vol. I, page 288).

$$T = \int_0^a \sqrt{\frac{1 + (y')^2}{2gy}} \, dx$$

where y' represents the derivative of the function $y = f(x)$, and $g = 32$ (approximately) is the acceleration due to gravity.

As the function $y = f(x)$ is varied, the time T varies and the left member of the above formula becomes $T(y)$. *Time* is a function of the function y, that is, time is a *functional* dependent on the different expressions for $y = f(x)$ [and hence for $y' = f(x)$] substituted in the definite integral according to whether the two points are joined by a straight line segment, a parabolic arc, an elliptic arc, a cycloidal arc, etc. But to each function or curve, $y = f(x)$, there will correspond a unique value of the time T, and hence time is a function of the curve selected. Bernoulli's problem was typical, since the general problem of the calculus of variation takes the form of solving for the unknown function $y = f(x)$ which is to minimize or maximize a functional that is expressed as a definite integral of the form

$$I(y) = \int_0^a F(x, y, y') \, dx$$

But Bernoulli, Euler, and Lagrange did *not* handle such integrals as functionals. Instead they introduced a single numerical *parameter* α by using for $y(x)$ variable curves (functions) which are expressible as a one-parameter family

$$y(x) = Y(x) + \alpha\eta(x)$$

with slope

$$y'(x) = Y'(x) + \alpha\eta'(x)$$

where $Y(x)$ is a particular function or curve which is subjected to continuous variation by changing α continuously. Thus imagine, in a special problem, that the original curve is the parabola $Y(x) = x^2$ and select $\eta(x) = x$, say. Then

$$Y(x) = x^2 + \alpha x$$

a one-parameter family of parabolas with slope formula

$$Y'(x) = 2x + \alpha$$

If these formulas are substituted in the integral above, it will become a function of the numerical variable α. Thus

$$I(\alpha) = \int_0^a F(x, x^2 + \alpha x, 2x + \alpha)\ dx$$

This example suggests the calculus of variation procedure. At any rate, if $I(\alpha)$ is just an ordinary function of a real variable, elementary calculus applies and $I'(\alpha) = 0$ is a necessary condition for a maximum or a minimum. The corresponding values of α can then be substituted to see whether, in a particular problem, the above condition suffices and the geometric or physical entity—length, area, volume, separation, energy, "action"—is actually an extremum for the value (or values) of α obtained.

But our own purpose is to get away from the classic procedure with its reduction to functions of a numerical variable. Instead of forcing problems into the artificial mold of the calculus of elementary functions, there is the alternative of generalizing the meaning of functionality, and this objective leads us to Volterra's work. Although he was not primarily concerned with extrema, nevertheless just such integrals as we have been considering are featured in the questions he raised, and his problems once again call for finding an unknown function which appears under the integral sign.

Volterra's pure mathematical researches were almost always motivated by applications—from mechanics, mathematical physics in general, biology, or economics. Some of the problems drawn from these special fields called for the solution of *integral equations*, and such equations involved functionals. Crudely put, an integral equation is one where the unknown is a function which appears under the integral sign. When we carried out the calculus process of differentiation, we were solving a very elementary integral equation. Instead of being asked to find the derivative of x^4, the question might be put in the form: What function when integrated over the interval $(0, x)$ will give x^4 as answer? In the Leibnizian symbolism, this problem would be written thus:

$$x^4 = \int_0^x f(t)\ dt$$

and would be considered as an *integral equation* of the general type

$$g(x) = \int_0^x f(t)\ dt$$

where $g(x)$ is a given, specified function. This equation, when interpreted, expresses *all* of *differential calculus*, since finding $f(t)$ for any $g(x)$ is identical with finding the derivative of $g(x)$. Thus an entire branch of analysis becomes a mere study of one type of functional, or one kind of integral equation.

But the solution of more general integral equations involves much more than differential calculus. Before proceeding to such issues, we might indicate that the life of the creator of the concept of functional was almost as unusual as his mathematical ideas. The following are biographical details as recorded by one of Volterra's admirers, the mathematical physicist Sir Edmund Whittaker (1873–1956).*

Vito Volterra was born at Ancona on May 3, 1860, the only child of Abramo Volterra and Angelica Almagià. When he was three months old the town was besieged by the Italian army and the infant had a narrow escape from death, his cradle being actually destroyed by a bomb which fell near it.

When he was barely two years old his father died, leaving the mother, now almost penniless, to the care of her brother Alfonso Almagià, an employee of the Banca Nazionale, who took his sister into his house and was like a father to her child. They lived for some time in Terni, then in Turin, and after that in Florence, where Vito passed the greater part of his youth and came to regard himself as a Florentine.

At the age of eleven he began to study Bertrand's *Arithmetic* and Legendre's *Geometry*.† and from this time on his inclination to mathematics and physics became very pronounced. At thirteen, after reading Jules Verne's scientific novel *Around the Moon*, he tried to solve the problem of determining the trajectory of a projectile in the combined gravitational field of the earth and moon: this is essentially the "restricted Problem of Three Bodies," and has been the subject of extensive memoirs by eminent mathematicians both before and after the youthful Volterra's effort: his method was to partition the time into short intervals, in each of which the force could be regarded as constant, so that the trajectory was obtained as a succession of small parabolic arcs. Forty years later, in 1912, he demonstrated this solution in a course of lectures given at the Sorbonne.

*Royal Society of London, *Obituary Notices of Fellows,* Vol. 3, No. 10 (December 1941), pp. 691 ff.

† The standard *liceo* or secondary school mathematics texts in the late nineteenth and early twentieth centuries.

When fourteen he plunged alone, without a teacher, into Joseph Bertrand's *Calcul différentiel;* he does not seem to have had access to any work on the integral calculus at this time, and when he attacked various special problems relating to centres of gravity, he discovered for himself that they could be solved by means of an operation (integration) which was the inverse of differentiation.

His family, whose means were slender, wished him to take up a commercial career, while Vito insisted on his desire to become a man of science. The struggle between vocation and practical necessity became very acute, and the family applied to a distant cousin, who had succeeded in the world, to persuade the boy to accept their views. This man, Edoardo Almagià, who died at the age of eighty in 1921, was one of the most celebrated civil engineers and financiers in Italy in the latter part of the nineteenth century; as a contractor of public works he constructed many important railways and harbours at home and abroad, including the harbours of Alexandria and Port Said in Egypt; the proprietor of vast estates in Tuscany and the Marches, he was renowned for his charities; and it was in the course of excavations at his palace in the Corso Umberto, once the Palazzo Fiano-Ottoboni, that the discovery was made of the sculptures of the Ara Pacis of the Emperor Augustus, which are now among the treasures of the Museo delle Terme in Rome.

His interview with his young relative turned out differently from what the family had expected. Impressed by the boy's sincerity, determination and ability, the older man threw his influence on the side of science, and turned the scale. Professor Roiti offered a nomination as assistant in the Physical Laboratory of the University of Florence, though Vito had not yet begun his studies there; it was accepted, and now the die was cast. The young aspirant entered the Faculty of Natural Sciences at Florence, following the courses in Mineralogy and Geology as well as in Mathematics and Physics. In 1878 he proceeded to the University of Pisa, where he attended the lectures of Dini, Betti and Padova; in 1880 he was admitted to the Scuola Normale Superiore, where he remained for three years; and here, while still a student, he wrote his first original papers. Under the influence of Dini he had become interested in the theory of aggregates and the functions of a real variable, and he gave some examples which showed the inadequacy, under certain circumstances, of Riemann's theory of integration, and adumbrated the developments made long afterwards by Lebesgue.

In 1882 he graduated Doctor of Physics at Pisa, offering a thesis on hydrodynamics in which certain results, actually found earlier by Stokes, were rediscovered independently. Betti at once nominated him as his assistant. In 1883, when only twenty-three years of age, he was promoted to a full professorship of Mechanics in the University of Pisa, which after the death of Betti was exchanged for the Chair of Mathematical Physics. He now set up house in Pisa with his mother, who up to that time had continued to live with her brother. In 1888 he was elected a non-resident member of the Accademia dei Lincei; in 1892 he became professor of mechanics in the University of Turin, and in 1900 he was called to the Chair of Mathematical Physics in Rome, as the successor of Eugenio Beltrami. In July of that year he married Virginia Almagià, one of the daughters of the distinguished relative who had first made it possible for him to follow a scientific career. She had inherited intellectual brilliance from her father, and great beauty from her mother, and as the wife of Vito Volterra took upon herself all the cares which might have distracted her husband from his scientific work, undertaking the education of their children and the administration of all their possessions. Six children were born of the union, of whom four now survive. His mother still lived with them, and died at the age of eighty at the Palazzo Almagià in March 1916.

As a comparatively young man he was appointed by the Government as Chairman of the Polytechnic School at Turin, and Royal Commissioner. The way was open for him to become a great figure in political and administrative life; but he preferred the career of a pure scientist, and took an active part in public affairs on only two occasions—the World War of 1914–1918, and the struggle with Fascism.

In July 1914 he was, according to his custom at that time of year, at his country house at Ariccia, when the war broke out. Almost at once his mind was made up that Italy ought to join the Allies; and in concert with D'Annunzio, Bissolati, Barzilai and others, he organized meetings and propaganda which were crowned with success on the 24th of May in the following year, when Italy entered the war. As a Lieutenant in the Corps of Engineers he enlisted in the army, and, although now over fifty-five years of age, joined the Air Force. For more than two years he lived with youthful enthusiasm in the Italian skies, perfecting a new type of airship and studying the possibility of mounting guns on it. At last he inaugurated the system of firing from an airship, in spite of the general opinion that the airship would be set on fire or explode at the first shot. He also published some mathematical works relating to aerial warfare, and experimented with aeroplanes. At the end of these dangerous enterprises he was mentioned in dispatches, and decorated with the War Cross.

Some days after the capitulation of Gorizia he went to this town while it was still under the fire of Austrian guns, in order to test the Italian instruments for the location of enemy batteries by sound. At the beginning of 1917 he established in Italy the Office for War Inventions, and became its Chairman, making many journeys to France and England in order to promote scientific and technical collaboration among the Allies. He went to Toulon and Harwich in order to study the submarine war, and in May and

October 1917 took part in the London discussions regarding the International Research Committee, to the executive of which he was appointed. He was the first to propose the use of helium as a substitute for hydrogen, and organized its manufacture.

When in 1917 some political parties—especially the Socialists—wanted a separate peace for Italy, he strenuously opposed their proposals; after the disaster of Caporetto, he with Sonnino helped to create the parliamentary *bloc* which was resolved to carry on the war to ultimate victory.

On the conclusion of the Armistice in 1918, Volterra returned to his purely scientific studies and to his teaching work in the University. The most important discoveries of his life after the war were in the field of mathematical biology, and of these we must now give an account.

His discourse at the opening of the academic year following his election to the Roman Chair, shows that already in 1901 he was interested in the biological applications of mathematics. His own researches in this field, stimulated by conversations with the biologist Umberto D'Ancona of the University of Siena, began at the end of 1925; his first and fundamental memoir on the subject appeared soon thereafter, and was followed by several further papers. In the winter of 1928–1929 it was made the subject of a course of lectures delivered by Volterra at the Institut Henri Poincaré in Paris. These lectures, together with a historical and bibliographical chapter compiled by D'Ancona, were published in 1931.

The entities studied in these investigations were *biological associations*, i.e. systems of animal (or plant) populations of different species, living together in competition or alliance in a common environment; and the theory is concerned with the effects of interaction of these populations with one another and the environment as expressed in their numerical variations.

Volterra's scientific activity overflowed in many domains quite outside his more usual fields of research. For instance, the student of topology (Chapter 25) who reads Professor Lefschetz's admirable monograph on *Analysis Situs* (Paris, 1924), finds therein the photographs of a number of ingenious models constructed by Volterra in order to show how two manifolds, defined in very different ways, may nevertheless be homeomorphic (Chapter 25) to each other.

There remains to be told the melancholy story of his later years. In 1922 Fascism seized the reins in Italy. Volterra was one of the very few who recognized from the beginning the danger to freedom of thought, and immediately opposed certain changes in the educational system, which deprived the Italian Middle Schools of their liberty. When the opponents of the Fascist Government in the House of Deputies withdrew altogether from the debates, a small group of Senators, headed by Volterra, Benedetto Croce and Francesco Ruffini, appeared, at great personal risk, at all the Senate meetings and voted steadily in opposition. At that time he was President of the Accademia dei Lincei and generally recognized as the most eminent man of science in Italy.

By 1930 the parliamentary system created by Cavour in the nineteenth century had been completely abolished. Volterra never again entered the Senate House. In 1931, having refused to take the oath of allegiance imposed by the Fascist Government, he was forced to leave the University of Rome, where he had taught for thirty years; and in 1932 he was compelled to resign from all Italian Scientific Academies. From this time forth he lived chiefly abroad, returning occasionally to his country-house in Ariccia. Much of his time was spent in Paris, where he lectured every year at the Institut Henri Poincaré; he also gave lectures in Spain, in Roumania, and in Czechoslovakia. On all these journeys he was accompanied by his wife, who never left him, and learned type-writing in order to copy his papers for him; he was accustomed to say that the signature "V. Volterra" in his later works repre-sented not Vito but Virginia Volterra.

In the autumn of 1938, under German influence, the Italian Government promulgated racial laws, and his two sons were de-prived of their University positions and their civil rights; at their father's suggestion, they left their native country to begin a new life abroad. (One of them, Enrico Giovanni, is Professor of Mathematics at the University of Texas.)

Vito Volterra had a remarkable power of inspiring affection. When in the last months of his life the new laws forbade him to have Italian servants, all of them refused to leave; a maid who had been with him for more than twenty years, and who was forced to leave, died of sorrow a week afterwards.

In December 1938 he was affected by phlebitis: the use of his limbs was never recovered, but his intellectual energy was un-affected, and it was after this that his two last papers were pub-lished by the Edinburgh Mathematical Society and the Pontifical Academy of Sciences respectively. On the morning of 11 October 1940 he died at his house in Rome. In accordance with his wishes, he was buried in the small cemetery of Ariccia, on a little hill, near the country-house which he loved so much and where he had passed the serenest hours of his noble and active life.

To return to the research in integral equations that Vol-terra had begun half a century before the last sad period of his life, we illustrate one type that he considered, namely,

$$g(x) = \int_0^x K(x, t) f(t) \; dt$$

where $g(x)$ and $K(x, t)$ are *known* functions, and $f(t)$ is the unknown function that is to be found. If, for example, the given functions are

$$g(x) = x^4$$
$$K(x, t) = xt$$

then the equation becomes

$$x^4 = \int_0^x xt\, f(t)\ dt$$

By trial, we can obtain the solution

$$f(t) = 3t^2$$

We can see that this will check, since it is true that

$$x^4 = \int_0^x 3xt^2 dt$$

The reader can verify, by using antidifferentiation in place of integration in the right member, that the result is equal to x^4. The antiderivative of $3t^2$ is $t^3 + c$, and since x is treated as a constant in the right member of the equation, the antiderivative of $3xt^2$ is $xt^3 + c$. Following the pattern of Chapter 8, we might imagine the latter expression to be the formula for a growing area, volume, or quantity of work, etc. Let us picture then that an area is involved and that

$$A = xt^3 + c$$

The Leibnitzian symbol $\int_0^x$ would signify that growth starts with $t = 0$ and stops when $t = x$. Substituting the first condition,

$$0 = 0 + c \quad \text{and} \quad c = 0$$

Then substituting $t = x$, the value of t when growth terminates,

$$A = x(x^3) = x^4$$

which is the desired result.

But a general theory of such integral equations would require consideration of whether there are solutions for all selections of $g(x)$ and $K(x, t)$, and if the answer is in the negative, what restrictions must be placed on these two functions in order that solutions may exist. Also, there is the matter of a method other than trial and error for finding a solution when it is known to exist.

A still more difficult type of Volterra equation is

$$g(x) - f(x) = \int_0^x K(x, t) f(t)\ dt$$

where once again $g(x)$ and $K(x, t)$ are given, and $f(t)$ (or $f(x)$, which is essentially the same function) is to be found. If, for example, the given functions are

$$g(x) = x^7 + 5x^3$$
$$K(x, t) = x^2 t$$

then

$$f(t) = 5t^3 \qquad \text{and hence} \qquad f(x) = 5x^3$$

will check in the above integral equation, since it is true that

$$x^7 + 5x^3 - 5x^3 = \int_0^x x^2 t(5t^3)\,dt = \int_0^x 5x^2 t^4 dt$$

Again, using antidifferentiation for the expression under the integral sign, $A = x^2 t^5 + c$. Now the condition, $A = 0$ when $x = 0$, gives $c = 0$. The value of A is required for $t = x$, so that $A = x^2(x^5) = x^7$, the value of the left member.

Instead of studying the general theory, we shall examine integral equations that arise naturally from problems in mathematical physics. Here we wish to point out the connection of integral equations with the concept of *functional*. In both types of integral equation above, the *kernel*, $K(x, t)$, is given and then the value of the integral

$$\int_0^x K(x, t)\,f(t)\,dt$$

depends on the selection of the unknown function $f(t)$. For each permissible selection of $f(t)$ there will be a unique value of the integral, that is, the integral is a function of the function $f(t)$, hence a functional. The second type of Volterra equation illustrated above can also be expressed in the form

$$g(x) = f(x) + \int_0^x K(x, t)\,f(t)\,dt$$

and therefore in this case as well the right member is a functional dependent on f. In both types of equation the problem is to select the independent variable f so that the value of the functional in the right member will be equal to the given function $g(x)$. Therefore the concept involved is just a generalization of algebra with the most elementary type of function. In school algebra pupils are asked: If $y = 8 - 3x$ and $y = 2$, what is the value of x? The integral equation poses a similar problem, namely: Given the value of the dependent variable, find the corresponding value of the independent variable.

Then the reader may not be surprised to learn that Volterra and Hilbert were able to reduce integral equations to algebra of a type that is familiar, namely the solution of a set of linear equations. In school days one learned how to find x and y when, for example,

$$3x + 2y = 7$$
$$2x + 5y = 12$$

and also solved systems of three or more linear equations in three or more unknowns. But the systems derived from integral equations involve an *infinite* number of equations in an infinite number of unknowns. Nevertheless the methodology is not more difficult than in the finite case, but naturally has to be followed up with some consideration of limits, convergence, etc., as is usual in infinite processes.

The general technique of solving such infinite systems was something new in Volterra's day, for although some historians claim that Fourier was the first to solve such an infinite system, it appears that George William Hill (1838–1914) provided the first rigorous solution to receive any publicity. In 1877 he solved an infinite number of linear equations involving an infinite number of unknowns by using the method of "determinants." He did this in connection with research analyzing the motion of the moon's perihelion. Subsequently Hill's method was made rigorous by Poincaré and by the Scandinavian mathematician von Koch (1870–1924). Hill rated high among American scientists of his day; the *Biographical Directory* of such men of science paired him with Simon Newcomb (1835–1909) for first rank among U.S. astronomers, and it classified him as second only to E. H. Moore as a pure mathematician. The ability of all three men was recognized by their mathematical contemporaries, who elected Hill, Newcomb, and Moore as third, fourth and sixth presidents of the American Mathematical Society in 1895, 1897, 1901, respectively.

If integral equations can be converted into Hill sets of linear equations, a converse fact is true. Turning to a physical example, as Volterra always did, one can consider a finite system at first, a system derived from the study of a mechanical configuration in stable equilibrium where very tiny oscillations about the equilibrium state can occur. If the configuration can be determined by 1, 2, 3, 4, . . . , n *generalized coordinates* (angles, distances, areas, etc.), it has 1, 2, 3, 4, . . . , n "degrees of freedom," as physicists say. It can be proved that in this case any tiny oscillation is the resultant of 1, 2, 3, 4, . . . , n simple harmonic vibrations, a situation reminiscent of Fourier's technique (Chapters 7 and 9). To specify a simple harmonic vibration, that is, a sine or cosine function, we must know its amplitude and period. Dynamic theory shows that the necessary facts can be obtained by solving 1, 2, 3, 4, . . . , n linear equations, respectively. To see how this is done, consider the system of two equations in two unknowns illustrated above. If the set of real numbers is the domain of variables x and y, then either trial and error or elementary algebraic techniques lead to the unique solution

$$x = 1 \qquad y = 2$$

Next, try to solve

$$3x + 2y = 7$$
$$6x + 4y = 11$$

and you will readily see that there is no answer because the second equation contradicts the first. An equation consistent with the first equation would be

$$6x + 4y = 14$$

and not

$$6x + 4y = 11$$

But then if we had the system

$$3x + 2y = 7$$
$$6x + 4y = 14$$

where x and y represent real numbers, either equation would be equivalent to the other, so that it is actually a case of one equation in two unknowns, an *indeterminate* problem. Then

$$x = a$$
$$y = \tfrac{1}{2} \ (7 - 3a)$$

where a is any real number.

Thus a system of two linear equations in two unknowns may have no solutions, a unique solution, or an infinite number of solutions. One equation of such a system might be

$$2x + 3y = 0$$

and the other

$$\lambda x - 4y = 0$$

The reader can readily obtain the solution $x = 0$, $y = 0$. The value of the coefficient λ does not matter. But if other solutions for x and y are sought, they can only exist when the two equations reduce to one, that is, when the corresponding coefficients in the two equations are proportional, and

$$\frac{\lambda}{2} = \frac{-4}{3}$$

$$3\lambda = -8$$

$$\lambda = -\frac{8}{3}$$

The second equation now becomes

$$-\frac{8}{3}x - 4y = 0$$

or, multiplying by $-3/4$,

$$2x + 3y = 0$$

which is identical with the first.

Returning now to the tiny oscillations of a mechanical system with two "degrees of freedom," the associated linear equations would look something like

$$(5 - \lambda)x + 2y = 0$$
$$2x + (5 - \lambda)y = 0$$

(where the figures have been selected somewhat unrealistically in order to make the arithmetic easy).

It would be interesting to consider the physical origin of these equations. The mechanical configuration in this case is two-dimensional, and the small oscillations are represented by a plane linear transformation of homogeneous or centered affine type (Chapter 17). Thus if x' and y' are the generalized coordinates after a slight displacement from the state of equilibrium,

$$x' = 5x + 2y$$
$$y' = 2x + 5y$$

To be up to date, such a transformation is now called a *linear operator*.

From a geometric point of view, as Klein described it, one should seek the points, lines, etc., that are unchanged by the affine transformation or operator. If a point is unchanged, its new coordinates are the same as the old and this signifies $x' = x$, $y' = y$ in the above equations. Now, substituting x' for x and y' for y, the solution of the simultaneous equations thus obtained is

$$x = 0$$
$$y = 0$$

This means that the only point unchanged by the operator is the origin.

If any *lines* are to be invariant or unchanged by the operator, this does *not* require that their individual points be unchanged; they may merely be shifted along these lines. For example, if a line like $y = 2x$ (Figure 23.5) were in-

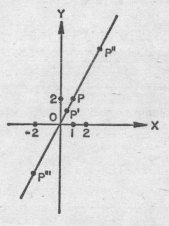

Figure 23.5

variant under homogeneous affine transformation, the point P (1, 2) might shift to P' (½, 1) or to P'' (3, 6) or to P''' (−2, −4). Thus if a point lies on a line through the origin and is to remain on this same line, its coordinates after transformation are equimultiples of its original coordinates, that is, $\lambda x = x'$, $\lambda y = y'$, where λ is some real number. But the linear operator above states that $x' = 5x + 2y$ and $y' = 2x + 5y$. Hence

$$\lambda x = 5x + 2y$$
$$\lambda y = 2x + 5y$$

or

$$(5 - \lambda)x + 2y = 0$$
$$2x + (5 - \lambda)y = 0$$

This is the pair of equations in the illustration with which we started. The origin, that is, $x = 0$, $y = 0$, will satisfy this pair of equations, whatever the value of λ. But if the equations are to be satisfied for other values of x, this can occur, as previously explained, only if the coefficients in the equations are proportional. Therefore

$$\frac{5 - \lambda}{2} = \frac{2}{5 - \lambda}$$

or

$$25 - 10\lambda + \lambda^2 = 4$$
$$\lambda^2 - 10\lambda + 21 = 0$$

and

$$\lambda = 3 \quad \text{or} \quad \lambda = 7$$

If $\lambda = 3$ is substituted in the two linear equations above, they reduce to the same equation,

$$2x + 2y = 0$$

or

$$x + y = 0$$

and the net result is a single indeterminate equation with an infinite number of real solutions,

$$x = a$$
$$y = -a$$

where a is any real number. Geometrically, the above equation, $x + y = 0$, is a straight line, and the solutions represent all its points, some of which are $(0, 0)$, $(1, -1)$, $(2, -2)$, $(-1, 1)$, $(5/3, -5/3)$, $(-2, 2)$, etc. In accordance with our assumption, the linear operator multiplies the coordinates of these points by $\lambda = 3$, Thus, $x + y = 0$, or $y = -x$, is a line that is left invariant by the linear operator, because $(0, 0)$, a point on it, remains fixed, and other points on it are merely shifted along the line when their coordinates are trebled.

For $\lambda = 7$, both equations reduce to

$$x - y = 0$$

and the solutions are

$$x = b$$
$$y = b$$

the set of points of the invariant line $x - y = 0$ or $y = x$. The effect of the linear operator on the individual points of $y = x$ is to leave the origin unchanged and shift the other points by multiplying their coordinates by $\lambda = 7$.

In problems like the above, the two values $\lambda = 3$ and $\lambda = 7$ are usually referred to as *eigenvalues,* from the German *Eigenwerte.* The hybrid term has maintained its own in spite of attempts to use names like *characteristic values* or *proper values.* In the theory of vector spaces the invariant lines are called *eigenvectors.*

In the physical interpretation of the present problem (the tiny oscillations of a mechanical system), an eigenvalue is equal to the square of the period of a harmonic vibration, and there are two component harmonic vibrations with periods $\sqrt{3}$ and $\sqrt{7}$, or frequencies $1/\sqrt{3}$ and $1/\sqrt{7}$. This means that in the first component about 0.6 of a vibration is completed in one second, and in the other component, about 0.4 of a vibration. The sine formulas for the component vibrations are

$$A \sin \frac{2\pi}{\sqrt{3}} t \qquad \text{and} \qquad B \sin \frac{2\pi}{\sqrt{7}} t$$

The invariant lines (eigenvectors), namely, $y = x$ and $y = -x$, are perpendicular, and their inclinations, 45° and 135°, are called the principal directions associated with this mechanical problem.

For the sake of practice, the reader can show that $\lambda = 2$ and $\lambda = 7$ are the eigenvalues of the linear operator

$$x' = 3x - 2y$$
$$y' = -2x + 6y$$

and that the principal directions are given by the (perpendicular) invariant lines, $y = \frac{1}{2}x$ and $y = -2x$.

There are many algebraic issues that may arise in such problems—for example, the matter of *equal* values of λ, or the question of what numerical restrictions the linear operator must obey so that the values of λ should be real and positive (so that the periods, $\sqrt{\lambda}$, may be real), etc. There are also the associations of the algebra with elementary analytic geometry, for example, in the transformation of the equations of a conic section to standard or normal form. Thus, the *matrix* of coefficients in the original linear operator, namely,

$$\begin{pmatrix} 5 & 2 \\ 2 & 5 \end{pmatrix}$$

can be interpreted to apply to the equation of the conic section, $5x^2 + 4xy + 5y^2 = 1$, if we write the left member as the rectangular array

$$\begin{pmatrix} 5x^2 & 2xy \\ 2xy & 5y^2 \end{pmatrix}$$

Here the matrix coefficients make their appearance. Theory shows that a suitable *rotation* (Chapter 17) will transform this equation into

$$3(x')^2 + 7(y')^2 = 1$$

where the *coefficients* are the *eigenvalues*, 3 and 7. This is the equation of an ellipse, with semiaxes (found by substituting $y' = 0$ or $x' = 0$) equal to the "frequencies" $1/\sqrt{3}$ and $1/\sqrt{7}$. Thus the analytic geometry of an ellipse is associated with the above problem in mechanics. Similarly, in association with the practice example suggested for the reader, the conic section

$$3x^2 - 4xy + 6y^2 = 1$$

can be transformed into the ellipse

$$2(x')^2 + 7(y')^2 = 1$$

If a mechanical system has 4, 5, . . . , n degrees of freedom, then a set of 4, 5, . . . , n linear equations will give the solution for its small oscillations. In general there will be 4, 5, . . . , n real, distinct eigenvalues for λ and an equal number of principal directions in an abstract hyperspace of

4, 5, $\cdots$, n dimensions. But other vibrations—those of continuous media like a musical string, a membrane, an elastic solid, the "ether" of classical physics—will have a *countably infinite* (Chapter 24) number of degrees of freedom, and if the procedure for mechanical systems is generalized, there will be an infinite set of linear equations with an infinite number of unknowns. Volterra and Hilbert showed that such an infinite set could be replaced by a single integral equation.

To make this fact seem reasonable, one need only recall the applications of integral calculus where an area is approximated by a sum of rectangles or squares or sectors, and the limit of such a sum, as the number of terms became infinite, defines the area. In this limiting process the sum of an infinite series

$$\Delta t(f_1 + f_2 + f_3 + \cdots + f_n + \cdots)$$

led to the definite integral

$$\int_a^b f(t)\,dt$$

where the domain of $f(t)$ is a *continuum*, the interval of real numbers from a to b. (In what follows we shall adjust linear units so that $a = 0$, $b = 1$.) This suggests that if we had a series, $K_1 f_1 + K_2 f_2 + K_3 f_3 + \cdots + K_n f_n + \cdots$, where the underlying limiting process converges, a replacement by

$$\int_0^1 K(t)\,f(t)\,dt$$

might prove to be valid.

If the issue of vibrations of continuous media is just a matter of extending the linear operator from a finite number n to an infinite number of variables and equations, then the eigenvalues and principal directions (eigenvectors) will be infinite in number and will be obtained by solving

$$\lambda f_1 = K_{11} f_1 + K_{12} f_2 + K_{13} f_3 + \cdots + K_{1n} f_n + \cdots$$
$$\lambda f_2 = K_{21} f_1 + K_{22} f_2 + K_{23} f_3 + \cdots + K_{2n} f_n + \cdots$$
$$\lambda f_3 = K_{31} f_1 + K_{32} f_2 + K_{33} f_3 + \cdots + K_{3n} f_n + \cdots$$
$$\cdot \qquad \cdot \qquad \cdot \qquad \cdot \qquad \cdot$$
$$\cdot \qquad \cdot \qquad \cdot \qquad \cdot \qquad \cdot$$
$$\cdot \qquad \cdot \qquad \cdot \qquad \cdot \qquad \cdot$$
$$\lambda f_m = K_{m1} f_1 + K_{m2} f_2 + K_{m3} f_3 + \cdots + K_{mn} f_n + \cdots$$

where the unknowns are λ, f_1, f_2, f_3, . . . , f_n, . . . and the K's are numerical constants making the infinite series in the above equations *converge* (Chapter 22). Also, because the operator is *symmetric*, the values of the K's must be such that $K_{12} = K_{21}$, $K_{13} = K_{31}$, $K_{23} = K_{32}$, etc. and, in general, $K_{ij} = K_{ji}$.

If we assume the validity of replacement of series by definite integrals, we can substitute

$$\lambda f_1 = \int_0^1 K_1(t)\, f(t)\, dt$$

for the first equation above, and similarly for the other equations—

$$\lambda f_2 = \int_0^1 K_2(t)\, f(t)\, dt$$

$$\lambda f_3 = \int_0^1 K_3(t)\, f(t)\, dt$$

etc. The subscripts 1, 2, 3, in $K_1(t)$, $K_2(t)$, $K_3(t)$, etc., are meant to indicate that these are *different* functions. The reason for this is that the K coefficients in the right member of each linear equation are, in general, different.

If we wish to symbolize the entire set of linear equations by a *single* integral equation, we can do so by introducing another variable in addition to t. The continuous variation in t as it proceeds from 0 to 1 corresponds to the progress from term to term in each of the above series, for example, from $K_{11}f_1$ to $K_{12}f_2$ to $K_{13}f_3$ to $K_{14}f_4$, etc. in the first series. We now introduce an additional continuous variable s (whose domain is also the interval from 0 to 1) to replace the progress from row to row in the set of integral equations above, where K_1 changes to K_2 to K_3, etc., and simultaneously in the *left* member f_1 changes to f_2 to f_3, etc. Then the integral equation corresponding to the entire system is

$$\lambda f(s) = \int_0^1 K(s,\, t)\, f(t)\, dt$$

where λ is a real numerical parameter, and $f(t)$ is an unknown function but $K(s,t)$, the kernel, is a known function. The integral in the right member is called a *linear operator* by analogy with the algebraic situation. The integral equation is classified as linear in type as might be expected from the fact that it is a composite of an infinite set of linear algebraic equations.

Such an infinite set, or else a single linear integral equation, describes the vibrations of a musical string of unit length when a suitable choice is made for the kernel $K(s,t)$. Then the solution is possible only for proper values of λ, that is, for the eigenvalues. It turns out that the eigenvalues are $\lambda = (1/kc)^2$, and hence the periods $\sqrt{\lambda} = 1/kc$, where c is a constant determined by the physical condition of the string and k is any one of the positive integers, 1, 2, 3, ... The corresponding frequencies are kc, and this result indicates the basic *law* of musical *harmony*, namely, that a musical tone is composed of a fundamental note and overtones whose *frequencies* (kc) are all integral multiples of the fundamental frequency (c). As in the case of the elementary linear operators, the eigenvalues will now be substituted either in the set of linear equations or in the corresponding integral equation. Then the solutions obtained are

$$f(t) = \sin k\pi t \qquad \text{or its equivalent,} \qquad f(s) = \sin k\pi s$$

where k is one of the positive integers, 1, 2, 3, ...

After later developments in the theory and application of integral equations, due mainly to the Swedish mathematician Ivar Fredholm (1866–1927), optical rather than acoustical vocabulary came into vogue, and the set of values for λ was referred to as the *spectrum* of eigenvalues. (A strict analogy with a *frequency* spectrum would use $1/\sqrt{\lambda}$.) It was Hilbert who established the general *spectral theory of symmetric linear operators*. Prior to this particular research it required mathematics of the greatest difficulty to attack even the simplest problems in the field, and therefore Hilbert's methods were an enormous contribution to mathematics and theoretical physics.

The term "linear operator" has been applied to the right member of

$$\lambda f(s) = \int_0^1 K(s, t)\, f(t)\, dt$$

by analogy with the corresponding set of linear algebraic equations. But such a set of equations can also be considered as representing a *transformation* (in the special case considered, a homogeneous affine transformation). Then the right member of the integral equation is described as an *integral transform*, and $\lambda f(s)$ is called the transform of $f(t)$ by the kernel $K(s,t)$. In the above integral equation the transform is equal to a numerical multiple of the function $f(t)$ (or $f(s)$, which is the same function).

Integral transforms take a more general form in modern applied mathematics. If $f(t)$ and the kernel $K(s, t)$, are known functions, then the transform of $f(t)$ in some interval (a, b) may be found, namely,

$$\int_a^b K(s, t) \, f(t) dt$$

In general, the transform is *not* a mere numerical multiple of $f(t)$, but is some entirely different function, $g(s)$, that is,

$$g(s) = \int_a^b K(s, t) \, f(t) dt$$

Often, in applied mathematics, $K(s,t)$ and $g(s)$ are known functions, and $f(t)$ is unknown. In this case one must solve an integral equation to find $f(t)$.

There are a number of different types of integral transform which are of enormous importance in facilitating solution of differential equations and boundary value problems (mathematical physics), as well as in other areas of applied mathematics, for example, mathematical statistics. In particular, there is the *Laplace transform*

$$g(s) = \int_0^\infty e^{-st} f(t) dt$$

where the kernel is always e^{-st}, and $f(t)$ and $g(s)$ vary with the problem to be solved. The symbol ∞ makes the integral "improper." What that means is that $\int_0^A$ must be found and then one must see whether the result has a limit as A gets larger and larger. If a limit exists, it is the value of $g(s)$.

There is a *Fourier transform* which generalizes that of Laplace, and there are still other integral transforms. Laplace was aware of the need to "invert" his transform, that is, to find $f(t)$, given $g(s)$, and Fourier actually did invert his more general transform, although he did not conceive of his procedure in terms of an integral equation. But he did accomplish what was equivalent to such a solution and thus, in a sense, was the first mathematician in history to accomplish the solution of an integral equation.

Now to return to the general question of *functional analysis*, one must point to a very significant concept that developed in relation to Hilbert's contributions to that sub-

ject. This was the idea of *Hilbert space*, the infinite analogue of a *Euclidean space* of 1 or 2 or 3 or . . . *n* dimensions.

We shall approach the concept of Hilbert space through
some very elementary considerations. Thus the function expressed by the equation $y = x^2$ can be represented by a
plane Cartesian graph in which the *domain* or set of values
of the independent variable x is the real number continuum,
that is, the X-axis, a *Euclidean space* of one dimension. A
function of two numerical variables like $z = x - y^2$ has a
surface as its Cartesian picture if a *Euclidean plane* is its
domain, that is, if its domain is the set of real number pairs
(x, y). Next we can adduce a function like

$$w = x^2 + y^2 - 4z^2$$

which can be named a *hypersurface* because geometric language is a convenience. The domain of this last function is
an ordinary *Euclidean space* (of three dimensions). We can
go on to functions whose domains are Euclidean 4-space,
5-space, etc. so that

$$y = g(x_1, x_2, x_3, \ldots, x_n)$$

represents a function g whose domain is a Euclidean space
with n dimensions, where n is a *finite* positive integer.

The next step would be to consider

$$y = g(x_1, x_2, x_3, x_4, \ldots, x_n, \ldots)$$

where the domain is a space with a *countable* infinity of
dimensions (Chapter 24). Hilbert endowed this sort of abstract space with the type of structure that seemed desirable
for *functional* problems he encountered in his study of the
spectra of linear operators. By a *structure* we mean the fundamental set of *definitions and postulates* that governs the
"points," $(x_1, x_2, x_3, x_4, \ldots, x_n, \ldots)$ of the infinite-dimensional space and from which the theorems of its "geometry"
can be deduced.

Hilbert's constant use of Fourier series in spectral analysis
emphasized in his mind the fact that a function which can
be represented by a Fourier series determines the coefficients
of the terms in such an expansion and conversely, given a
sequence of permissible coefficients, a function is determined.
Acoustically, this signifies that a musical tone can be broken
down into a fundamental note and its overtones, and con-

versely a synthesis of simple harmonic vibrations with specific amplitudes will constitute a musical tone. Thus, Hilbert observed, there is no intrinsic difference between a function capable of Fourier series representation and the infinite sequence of its Fourier coefficients. If we symbolize the sequence by $(x_1, x_2, x_3, x_4, \ldots, x_n, \ldots)$ we can consider it as a "point" of an infinite-dimensional space, named a *Hilbert space*, after its creator. Since a sequence is equivalent to the function it represents, a point in Hilbert space corresponds to both sequence and function, and the Hilbert space can be described as a *function space*, that is, a space whose points are in one-to-one correspondence with the set of all functions of a certain type.

In functional analysis such a space is analogous to the X-axis of plane Cartesian geometry. If one is studying functions of a single numerical variable like $y = x^2$, $y = 3x - 7$, etc., the X-axis contains the domain, the set of values which x may take. But the calculus of variations, integral equations, general spectral analysis, etc., deal with functions of a function f, and if f can be expressed by a Fourier series, then it corresponds to a point $(x_1, x_2, x_3, x_4, \ldots)$ of *Hilbert space*, which is thus the *domain of the functional*. Here there is subtlety similar to the replacement of an infinite set of linear algebraic equations by an integral equation, the former being a discrete aggregate, and the latter containing a function defined on a continuum. In the same way the sequence of coordinates (Fourier coefficients) of a function or point of Hilbert space is discrete, whereas the function it represents has a continuous domain. But it is not such philosophical issues that make Hilbert space mathematically useful. Its applicability derives from the axioms that govern the algebra and the analysis of this space, the basic rules for performing arithmetic operations with the different elements symbolized by $x_1, x_2, x_3, \ldots$), the assignment of a *metric*, that is, a distance formula, etc. In all considerations, matters of convergence—that is, the existence of limits—are involved since the points correspond to *infinite* sequences. We have seen that in Euclidean plane and solid geometry the square of the distance of a point from the origin is represented by $x^2 + y^2$ and $x^2 + y^2 + z^2$, respectively, by virtue of the Pythagorean theorem. If metric properties of Hilbert space are to be analogous to those in Euclidean spaces of finite dimension, then the square of the "distance" of a point from the origin should be

$$x_1^2 + x_2^2 + x_3^2 + x_4^2 + \cdots x_n^2 + \cdots$$

and this infinite series will have meaning only if it *converges*. This fact must be incorporated in the definition of Hilbert space, which is therefore *not* the set of all sequences $(x_1, x_2, x_3, x_4, \cdots)$ but only the set of those sequences for which $x_1^2 + x_2^2 + x_3^2 + x_4^2 + \cdots x_n^2 + \cdots$ *converges*. Thus the sequence $(1, 1, 1, 1, \ldots, 1, \ldots)$ is not a point in Hilbert space since

$$1^2 + 1^2 + 1^2 + 1^2 + \cdots + 1^2 \cdots = 1 + 1 + 1 + 1 + \cdots$$
$$+ 1 + \cdots$$

does not converge, because the sum of the first n terms is n, which does not approach a limit but merely gets larger and larger with increasing values of n.

Hilbert space is only one type of generalized space. The great Polish mathematician Stefan Banach (1892–1945) created and investigated a whole class of function spaces more general than the particular space of Hilbert. Moreover, in the first years of this century, the American E. H. Moore (1862–1932) and the French mathematician Maurice Fréchet both sought to generalize still further Volterra's and Hilbert's work with functionals, in order to establish a genuine *general analysis*, a calculus of relations between two aggregates whose elements are completely abstract or arbitrary in nature. General analysis is a study of functions in which *neither* independent nor dependent variable need be a number. For that matter, the generality is so great that the independent variable need not even be a function, so that one is no longer dealing with a function of a curve or a function of a surface or a function of any function, but merely with a function of some completely abstract entity. Of course the generalized functions and their analysis include the other types as special cases.

The first task in setting up a general analysis is similar to that of Hilbert in imparting a structure to his function space. Moore and Fréchet had to provide definitions and postulates that would apply to functions where the nature of the variables is completely unspecified. Fréchet attempted to formulate a structure that would resemble as closely as possible the corresponding definitions and postulates of classic analysis. This is analogous to Hilbert's efforts to create for his function space a structure similar to that of Euclidean spaces. But let us first see how Moore proceeded. He used a principle of generalization that was practiced by mathematicians long before he asserted it explicitly. He stated that *the existence of analogies between central features of various theories implies the existence of a general abstract theory which includes the particular theories and unifies them with respect to those central features.*

Applying his principle, Moore developed a theory of integral equations and eigenvalues which is a generalization of the analogous theory of Hilbert. Fréchet's form of general analysis, described by its author in a series of memoirs starting in 1904, is better known and more readily applicable than the Moore theory. This is due to several factors, one of which is that Moore did *not* generalize *continuity* or *differentiability* of ordinary functions. But these attributes of functions are the essence of any form of analysis and are the very ones which Fréchet took great pains to specify.

Fréchet emphasized the infinitesimal (analytic) properties of a functional, and concentrated on the functional relation itself rather than on the nature of the independent variable. When that variable is a curve, surface, or function of some kind, one can emulate Hilbert and conceive of it as a point of some function space. Fréchet indicated that if such a space is to have any resemblance to ordinary spaces, however, one needs a way of recognizing when two points (or the two functions they represent) are neighboring. This can be done if one can define a *distance* between the two points (two functions). But what meaning can be given to "nearness" if variables are completely abstract or unspecified?

Fréchet's answer to this last question had best be considered later, in our discussion of *analytic topology* (Chapter 25). He does, however, give a simple example of a suitable definition of the distance between two functions that are defined and continuous in some interval. Figure 23.6 indicates that in the interval [0, 1] the maximum difference in functional values for the pair of continuous functions graphed is 2 units. This, Fréchet indicates, would be a suitable measure of the distance between the two functions or their corresponding points in function space.

Like Moore, Fréchet listed a number of basic principles and salient features of his brand of general analysis, for example: "Those properties which, in the theory of ordinary numerical functions, arise only in the handling of the most complicated, most difficult, least practical functions, are the characteristics that are the simplest, most practical, in fact

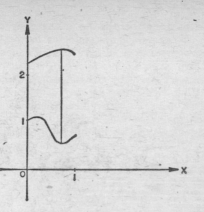

Figure 23.6

indispensable attributes of functionals or functions of generalized variables."[*]

To illustrate this aspect of his theory, Fréchet alludes to the property of *semicontinuity*. This concept is due to René Baire (1874–1932), one of the most brilliant contributors to real analysis (*not* general analysis). If one presents this "advanced" semicontinuity of *functionals*, there are available illustrations which are both simple and profound. For example, in the isosceles triangle ABC (Figure 23.7a) let $AB = 5$ in., $AC = BC = 10$ in. Joining the midpoints as indicated gives $AE = EF = FD = DB = 5$ in. so that the zigzag line $AEFDB$ measures 20 in. Joining midpoints of the triangles AEF and FDB as indicated (Figure 23.7b) will produce 8 segments, each 2.5 in. long, and a 20 in. zigzag line. Joining midpoints in the four triangles formed will again give a zigzag line measuring 20 in., etc. As the process continues, the zigzag line will get closer and closer to the 5 in. base of the triangle (Figure 23.7c). We can see this intuitively or we can use the above definition of Fréchet to fix the distance between the two functions—the zigzag line and the straight line base. The maximum vertical height of the zigzag line will measure this distance, and this will get smaller and smaller. In books on mathematical recreations, this example is often used to produce the fallacy $20 = 5$.

---

[*] Maurice Fréchet, *L'analyse générale et les ensembles abstraits, Revue de métaphysique et de morale*, Vol. 32 (1925).

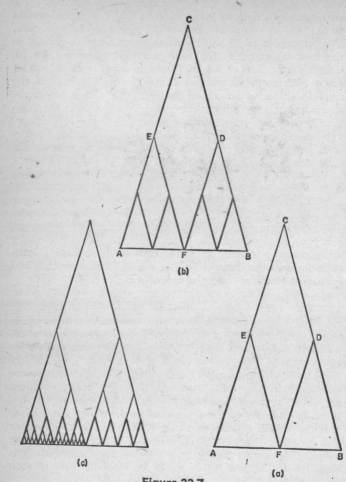

Figure 23.7

But from our present point of view, interest lies in the fact that the *length* of the zigzag line is a function of this line, that is, the length is a *functional*. To each zigzag line there corresponds a specific length. If we wish to add some variety to our picture, we can carry out the above process with a taller isosceles triangle, one with legs 40 in. or 400 in. each. To every zigzag line thus obtained, there would then correspond a length of 80 in. (800 in.), and we could obtain 80 in. (800 in.) lines as close as we please to the 5 in. base. We can repeat all of this by using shorter or longer legs in the isosceles triangle, for example, legs measuring 2.6 in. with a zigzag line of 5.2 in. The *functional* (the length of any such zigzag line) is *not continuous* at the base of the triangle, since the length of the zigzag line does *not* necessarily approximate closely the length of the base as the position of the line gets close to the position of the base. However, the functional has the property that Baire called *lower semicontinuity*. Put very crudely, this means that all the different zigzag lines (with lengths 5.2, 20, 80, 1000, 1,000,000, 1,000,000,000, etc.) we can possibly draw, as close to the base as we please, have a *lower bound*, namely 5 in., but *no* upper bound. (By analogy, for *upper semicontinuity* there would be an *upper* but *not* a lower bound.)

The definition of continuity of an ordinary real function, $y = f(x)$, at the point (a, b) (Chapter 22) requires that y approximate b within an arbitrarily small standard ϵ, providing x is in the interval $(a - \delta, a + \delta)$. This definition and Figure 22.4 indicate that the inequalities,

$$y > b - \epsilon \qquad y < b + \epsilon$$

must both be satisfied when x is in the interval selected. It was Baire who reached a generalization by making the requirement less stringent. If we require that only the first inequality, $y > b - \epsilon$, be satisfied (when x is in a sufficiently small interval containing a), we have the definition of *lower semicontinuity* at (a, b). If, on the other hand, we insist only on the second inequality, *upper semicontinuity* is defined. In the case of the functional in the above illustration, y is the length of the zigzag line, and $b = 5$. It is evident that $y > 5 - \epsilon$ for every choice of ϵ (with corresponding value of δ yielding zigzag lines close to the base of the triangle) but that $y < 5 + \epsilon$ cannot be satisfied for any such (ϵ, δ) pairs.

Now we must reveal that the concept of lower semicontinuity enabled the Italian analyst, Leonida Tonelli (1885–1946) to effect a revolution (1921) in the methodology of the calculus of variations. We note, in passing, the marked contribution of the Italian school to functional analysis. After Volterra there was Salvatore Pincherle (1853–1936), who considered the "qualitative" aspects of Volterra's functions of lines. Tonelli's ideas embedded the calculus of variations in the more general functional analysis, and they were carried further by Silvio Cinquini, a leading contemporary Italian analyst. In the United States, the direct methods of Tonelli were extended by Lawrence M. Graves and led to very significant results in the work of Edward J. McShane. For a lucid explanation of the new methods and their superiority in the theoretical aspects of the subject there is no better exposition than that of Cinquini,* or for a complete history of their development, on an advanced level, an account by McShane.†

With Volterra's "functions of lines" and his integral equations, and with the general analysis of Fréchet and Moore, we have carried to recent times one of those two main streams that started with Pythagoras, namely the channel of the "infinite processes," that is, the mathematics of the Continuum. But, in a sense, we have got ahead of our story, for it was Georg Cantor, as pointed out in one of the first chapters in this book, who created the modern philosophy of the infinite that is the foundation for any type of general analysis. Once more we have arrived at a point where, in accordance with the program explained in the Introduction, we must go round the spiral of analysis again, but at a more advanced level than that of the previous full circle.

* S. Cinquini, *Il Calcolo delle Variazioni,* Zanichelli, Bologna, 1940.
† E. J. McShane, "Recent Developments in the Calculus of Variations," *Semicentennial Addresses of the American Mathematical Society,* New York, 1938, pp. 69 ff.

Chapter 24

Infinite Hierarchy

There are mysteries within mystery, gods above gods . . .
That's what is called infinity.

Jean Cocteau

Before discussing those notions which, as Einstein once said, precipitated the fiercest "frog-mouse" battle in mathematical history, let us see what manner of man created them. Georg Cantor (1845–1918) came by his imaginative traits naturally, for his heritage was an artistic one. On his mother's side there had been a long line of painters, pianists, violinists, and conductors. Cantor's father tried to force him to be practical and insisted at first that he train for the profession of engineering, but consented finally to his pursuing his bent for pure mathematics. Just before he was thirty, Cantor published his first revolutionary paper on the theory of the *infinite*. The facts as well as the method were fundamentally new in mathematics and marked the man of genius.

Cantor's personal life, like that of so many gifted men, was unhappy. He earned his living by teaching at second-rate colleges. The most tragic fact of all was the mathematical and personal animosity of his teacher, Leopold Kronecker (1823–1891). The latter disagreed violently with Cantor's point of view, and to this day pitched battles are being fought regularly between Kronecker and Cantor adherents. No decisive victory has been achieved by either side as yet. Poor Cantor lacked the stamina to be a revolutionary; he took things so much to heart that he went out of his mind and spent his last days in a mental hospital.

Whether or not Cantor's notions will stand the test of

time, they are presented here for their beauty and because they have probably been one of the greatest stimuli in recent years toward placing mathematics on a firm logical foundation. No discussion of modern mathematics would be complete without what Hilbert called "the most admirable fruit of the mathematical mind, and one of the highest achievements of man's intellectual processes."

The trouble in the household of the infinite actually started some 2400 years before Cantor's day when, as we have seen, the Pythagoreans attempted to measure the diagonal of a unit square in a finite number of steps. During the same early period the paradoxes of the sophist Zeno of Elea added considerable fuel to the flames. Zeno was a follower of the Greek philosopher and mystic, Parmenides. Teacher and pupil alike stressed the doctrine that the world of sense is nothing but an illusion, and therefore Zeno concentrated on the destruction of a single but ubiquitous concept associated with the external world, namely *motion*. "If motion, which pervades everything," thought Zeno, "can be shown to be self-contradictory, and hence unreal, then everything else must assume the same unreal quality. By convincing people of the unreality of motion, I can best teach the doctrine of Parmenides and successfully discredit the world of the senses."

Thus it was that Zeno propounded four famous paradoxes on motion, which philosophers and mathematicians are still discussing. Zeno, in pushing Parmenides' notions, may or may not have been guilty of "sophistry." Nevertheless it takes a pretty clever man to get himself talked about for over two thousand years. Among those who have given serious thought to these puzzling questions are Thomas Aquinas, Descartes, Leibniz, Spinoza, and Bergson. Zeno's paradoxes in some form have been used as arguments for all the theories of space, time, and infinity that have been propounded from his day to ours.

The point at issue in the first two of Zeno's arguments is essentially the same. He presented these puzzles as:

I. The Dichotomy. There is no motion because that which is moved must arrive at the middle (of its course) before it arrives at the end. (And of course it must traverse the half of the half before it reaches the middle, and so on *ad infinitum*.)

In other words, to cover a distance of 1 yard, one must

reach the ½ yard point, before that the ¼ yard, before that the ⅛, and so on, *ad infinitum*. How is it possible to reach an infinite number of positions in a finite time?

II. The Achilles. The slower when running will never be overtaken by the quicker; for that which is pursuing must first reach the point from which that which is fleeing started, so that the slower must necessarily always be some distance ahead.

A modern version of this states that Achilles can run 1000 yd. a minute while a turtle can run 100 yd. a minute. The turtle is placed 1000 yd. ahead of Achilles. Zeno's argument states that Achilles can never overtake the turtle, for when Achilles has advanced 1000 yd., the turtle is still 100 yd. ahead of him. By the time Achilles has covered these 100 yd., the turtle is still ahead of him, and so on, *ad infinitum*, as the following table shows.

Position	Achilles	Tortoise
1	0	1 0 0 0
2	1 0 0 0	1 1 0 0
3	1 1 0 0	1 1 1 0
4	1 1 1 0	1 1 1 1
5	1 1 1 1	1 1 1 1. 1
6	1 1 1 1. 1	1 1 1 1. 1 1
7	1 1 1 1. 1 1	1 1 1 1. 1 1 1
	etc.	etc.

The trouble here is essentially the same as in the first paradox. If Achilles must occupy an *infinite* number of positions in order to overtake the tortoise, will he ever be able to do this in a *finite* time? Thus the solution of both these puzzles will be a matter of clarifying notions about "infinity."

The first real solution of such problems connected with infinity was propounded by Cantor in 1882. He attacked the core of all the trouble by furnishing a new number concept to replace the usual idea of *counting*. Unconsciously man assumes that, in order to have complete numerical knowledge concerning a collection, we should be able to pass its terms in review, one by one. In the case of the Dichotomy, if we wish to count the positions that must be reached—the halfway mark, the quarter, the eighth, the sixteenth, etc.—we shall never finish. Or, in the case of Achilles and the tortoise, if we imagine an umpire to say "Stop—Go!" when Achilles reaches the 1000 yd. mark (and the turtle the 1100 yd. mark), to repeat this when he reaches the 1100 yd. mark (and the turtle the 1110 yd. mark), to repeat it again at the third stage, the fourth stage, and so on, then Zeno's contention would be true in practice and Achilles would never overtake the tortoise.

But, as we have seen in previous chapters, it is actually possible or even necessary to reason about a collection without going through such an enumeration as that described. This may be illustrated even in the case of finite collections. We can speak of "Americans" without having a personal acquaintance with each citizen of the United States. We can do this because we know the essential characteristic that each individual has if he belongs to the group, and that he lacks, if he does not. So it is with infinite aggregates. They may be known by their characteristics even though we cannot complete the task of counting them, one by one.

To appreciate the substitute Cantor offered for ordinary counting, let us review the process of matching, or one-to-one correspondence, which was used even by primitive man. Cantor was the first to formalize that notion as a criterion for determining the cardinal number of a set. To illustrate a matching, Cantorian style, let us pair each natural number with its double, as follows:

1	2	3	4	5	6	7	8	$\cdots$	n	$\cdots$
2	4	6	8	10	12	14	16	$\cdots$	$2n$	$\cdots$

Then, since we have agreed that two sets of things are equal in number when they can be paired in one-to-one fashion, there are as many numbers in our first set as in the second; that is, the cardinal number of the entire set of natural numbers is the same as the cardinal number of the *proper subset* of *even* natural numbers. Evidently we have illustrated a collection that is *numerically equal to a part of itself!*

Again, let us take a part $A'B'$ of line segment AB, and compare the number of points in the two. We move $A'B'$ to the position indicated, draw AA' and BB' meeting in P (Figure 24.1). Then we pair the points of $A'B'$ with those of AB.

To find the partner of any point on $A'B'$, such as C', draw PC' and extend it to meet AB in C. Then C and C' are partners. On the other hand, to find the partner of any point on AB, as D, draw PD and let it meet $A'B'$ in D'. Then D and D'

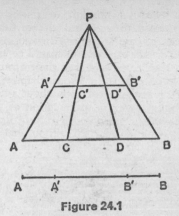

Figure 24.1

are partners. For every point on $A'B'$ we have a point on AB, and for every point on AB we have one on $A'B'$. In other words, there is a *one-to-one correspondence between the points of AB and those of A'B'*; that is, there are as many points in part of AB as in all of AB. Once again, *the whole of something is numerically equal to one of its parts.*

The Cantorian points of view was actually anticipated by Galileo, who showed that there is a one-to-one correspondence between the integers and their squares, although the latter set of numbers is only part of the first. The correspondence is

1	2	3	4	5	$\cdots$	n	$\cdots$
1	4	9	16	25	$\cdots$	n^2	$\cdots$

Galileo merely saw in this discovery a puzzling fact and did not develop the matter further. Infinity did not appear in mathematics as a mature concept until it was discovered by Bernhard Bolzano (1781–1848), who paved the way for Dedekind and Cantor.

A set of things, whether they are numbers or curves, points or instants of time, speeds of temperatures, is said to be *infinite* if it can be put into *one-to-one correspondence with one of its parts*. In Zeno's paradox, the Dichotomy, we see that the argument hinges on the fact that a moving point will occupy an infinite number of positions. The positions to which allusion is made in the paradox are

$$1/2, \; 1/4, \; 1/8, \; 1/16 \cdots$$

In the fact that these can be put into one-to-one correspondence with the infinite set of positive integers lies the proof that the number of positions to be occupied is infinite. Thus we have the correspondence

$1/2$	$1/4$	$1/8$	$1/16$	$\cdots$	$1/2^n$	$\cdots$
1	2	3	4	$\cdots$	n	$\cdots$

Then if one-to-one correspondence is a criterion of equality, there is nothing remarkable about having a finite length contain an infinite number of positions. Again, in the Achilles paradox, we have an infinite set of positions. The tortoise's positions can be put into one-to-one correspondence with Achilles', as we see in the table on page 299, and each can be put into one-to-one correspondence with the positive integers. We have

Achilles	0	1000	1100	1110	1111	1111.1	1111.11	etc.
Tortoise	1000	1100	1110	1111	1111.1	1111.11	1111.111	etc.
Integers	1	2	3	4	5	6	7	etc.

Therefore both the turtle and Achilles occupy an infinite number of positions. The fact that puzzled Cantor's predecessors is this: If Achilles were to catch up with the tortoise, the places where the tortoise had been would, on the one hand, be only part of the places where Achilles had been, and on the other, would be equal in number to Achilles' positions (on account of one-to-one correspondence). Thus, by stating as an axiom that the whole of something *can* equal a part, Cantor was able to deny the argument of this paradox.

We have just proved that the natural numbers form an infinite set. They are said to constitute a *countable* or *denumerable infinity*, and any set that can be put into one-to-one correspondence with them is also countable or denumerable. Since the even natural numbers (or the odd) can be put into one-to-one correspondence with all the natural numbers, there is a countable infinity of even natural numbers and a countable infinity of odd natural numbers. Likewise, since the positions

$$1/2, \ 1/4, \ 1/8, \ 1/16, \ \text{etc.}$$

of Zeno's Dichotomy can be put into one-to-one correspondence with the integers, they constitute another illustration of a countable set.

Just as the mathematician has numerals, 1, 2, 3, etc., that name the finite numbers, he has symbols for the *transfinite* ones as well. He represents a countable infinity of objects by the first letter of the Hebrew alphabet $\aleph_0$ (read *aleph null*). The null or zero subscript was used because Cantor hoped to be able to find other examples of infinite sets and then be able to arrange them in order of magnitude: $\aleph_0$, $\aleph_1$, $\aleph_2$, etc.

Is the set of all positive rational numbers countable? If we consider the vast number of rational fractions *between* 0 and 1, those between 1 and 2, those between 2 and 3, etc. we begin to suspect that we are on the verge of something new. Consider the fractions between 4 and 5 and select any two, such as 4 1/4 and 4 3/4. Note that between these two there are others, such as 4 3/8 and 4 5/8. Between the last two are 4 7/16 and 4 9/16 and so on, *forever*. Between each pair of whole numbers we have an amazing assemblage of fractions! Surely, since there is an infinity of whole numbers and between each pair there appears to be an infinity of rational fractions—in other words, an *infinity of infinities*—surely this aggregate should tower over the *countable infinity!* But such is not the case. The positive rational fractions are merely a one-to-one match for the positive natural numbers, and therefore merely constitute a countable infinity! There are only $\aleph_0$ positive rational fractions.

The argument follows. Take a common fraction at random, say 3/5. Notice that the sum numerator and denominator is 8. Notice, too, that there are many fractions having this same sum of numerator and denominator. Arranged in the order of increasing numerators, they are

$$1/7, \ 2/6, \ 3/5, \ 4/4, \ 5/3, \ 6/2, \ 7/1$$

Any other sum will similarly give rise to a set of fractions. Thus one can conceive of a tabulation of the various finite sets corresponding to different sums:

Sum	Rational Numbers				
2	1/1				
3	1/2,	2/1			
4	1/3,	2/2,	3/1		
5	1/4,	2/3,	3/2,	4/1	
6	1/5,	2/4,	3/3,	4/2,	5/1
7	1/6,	2/5,	3/4,	4/3,	5/2,	6/1
etc.					

By this procedure we are bound to arrive sooner or later at any positive rational number the reader may designate. If he mentions 99/100, we shall reach that with the sum 199. If he mentions 157/211, we shall arrive at that with the sum 368. Whole numbers will appear among the fractions, such as 4/2 or 4/1, for example. Also the same integer may be repeated, as in 2/1 and 4/2. The same fraction may appear repeatedly as 1/2, 2/4, 3/6, etc. We shall agree, however, to take each but once in the matching process that follows, in which each fraction is matched with an integer and each integer with a fraction.

1/1	1/2	2/1	1/3	3/1	1/4	2/3	3/2	4/1	1/5	$\cdots$
1	2	3	4	5	6	7	8	9	10	$\cdots$

In this way a one-to-one correspondence is set up, and we see that the set of positive rational fractions can be matched with the set of natural numbers. Thus the set of positive rational fractions, even though an infinity of infinities, is after all merely *countable* or *denumerable*.

Let us now carry out some transfinite arithmetic and see whether in the process we can obtain further illustrations of countable sets. If we were to add one element to a countable set, what would the effect be? For example, let us add the element 0 to the countable set of all even natural numbers, to form the set of even whole numbers (non-negative even integers). Then we can set up the one-to-one correspondence

0	2	4	6	8	$\cdots$	$2n - 2$	$\cdots$
1	2	3	4	5	$\cdots$	n	$\cdots$

The bottom row contains $\aleph_0$ (aleph null) elements. Then, since there are $\aleph_0$ even natural numbers, as a result of the matching on page 300, the top row contains $1 + \aleph_0$ elements. Therefore

$$1 + \aleph_0 = \aleph_0$$

If we were to add two, three, four, or any finite number of elements to the aggregate of even integers, we could once more match the enlarged set with the natural number aggregate. For example, the latter set can be matched with the collection, $\{-6, -4, -2, 0, 2, 4, 6, \ldots\}$. Therefore, for any natural number k,

$$k + \aleph_0 = \aleph_0$$

An analogous equation can never arise in dealing with *finite* cardinals. In fact, $k + a \neq a$ if k and a are finite cardinals greater than zero.

Again, since the odd and even subsets of the natural numbers are both countable, there are $\aleph_0$ odd natural numbers as well as $\aleph_0$

even natural numbers. The union of those two sets is the aggregate of *all* natural numbers. Hence

$$\aleph_0 + \aleph_0 = \aleph_0$$

or

$$2\aleph_0 = \aleph_0$$

Again, for a *finite*, nonzero cardinal a, $a + a \neq a$ and $2a \neq a$.

By uniting the sets in the three rows below, one obtains the set of natural numbers:

$$1, 4, 7, 10, \ldots, 3n - 2, \ldots$$
$$2, 5, 8, 11, \ldots, 3n - 1, \ldots$$
$$3, 6, 9, 12, \ldots, \quad 3n \quad , \ldots$$

Therefore

$$\aleph_0 + \aleph_0 + \aleph_0 = \aleph_0$$

or

$$3\,\aleph_0 = \aleph_0$$

and similarly, if m is any positive integer, $m\,\aleph_0 = \aleph_0$

If we examine the tabulation of positive rational numbers on page 303, we observe that the first column contains all the rationals with numerator 1. These rationals can be matched with the set of natural numbers thus:

$$\frac{1}{1}, \frac{1}{2}, \frac{1}{3}, \frac{1}{4}, \ldots, \frac{1}{n}, \ldots$$

$$1, 2, 3, 4, \ldots, n, \ldots$$

Therefore there are $\aleph_0$ rationals in the first column. In the second column there are all the rationals with numerator 2, and they can also be matched with the set of natural numbers so that there are $\aleph_0$ of these, etc. for *each* column. Hence

$$\aleph_0 + \aleph_0 + \aleph_0 + \cdots = \aleph_0$$

There are as many columns as there are different numerators. The possible numerators are

$$1, 2, 3, 4, \ldots, n, \ldots$$

or there are $\aleph_0$ numerators and hence $\aleph_0$ columns. Therefore the above equation says that a countable infinity of countable infinities is still countable, or

$$\aleph_0 \times \aleph_0 = \aleph_0$$

that is,

$$(\aleph_0)^2 = \aleph_0$$

Multiplying both sides of this equation by $\aleph_0$ yields

$$(\aleph_0)^3 = (\aleph_0)^2 = \aleph_0$$

Continuing in the same way,

$$(\aleph_0)^m = \aleph_0$$

where m is any positive integer.

Are there *noncountable* sets? We shall now show that the set of all real numbers between 0 and 1 is such a set. This set includes all the rational fractions between 0 and 1 as well as all the irrationals within the same boundaries. In Chapter 2 *decimal* expansions were used for these real numbers. It was shown that a rational fraction may have a terminating expansion like $1/4 = 0.25$ or a *repeating* pattern like $3/11 = 0.272727 \ldots$ but that for irrational numbers the expansion is always an infinite, nonrepeating one. Now in the case of terminating fractions like $1/4 = 0.25$, we shall always use the nonterminating decimal $0.25000 \ldots$ and avoid the alternative expansion $0.24999 \ldots$.

But this is all preliminary to proving that the set of real numbers between 0 and 1 is *not* countable. Suppose that someone claims that he has found a scheme for putting this set into one-to-one correspondence with the aggregate of natural numbers, and suppose further that the first few real numbers matched with natural numbers are as follows:

1	0.4 1 5 2 3 7 . . .
2	0.2 8 9 9 9 9 . . .
3	0.7 3 2 0 6 5 . . .
4	0.1 8 3 7 3 7 . . .
5	0.3 5 8 0 9 1 . . .

. . . .

. . . .

No matter what sort of plan anyone uses, there will always be at least one real number missing from his list. It is possible to construct such a decimal fraction as follows: For the tenths place, select a digit different from the tenths place of the first number in the list and different from 0 and 9*; for the hundredths place, select a digit different from 9 and different from the hundredths place of the second number on the list; for the thousandths place, select a digit different from 9 and from the thousandths place of the third number on the list; etc. Thus the first digits selected might initiate a decimal like 0.15326. . . . When (conceptually) the so-called *diagonal process* (see diagonal lines in above list) is continued on and on, a real number is obtained that differs from each number in the list in at least one decimal digit (the one between the diagonal lines) and hence is not equal to any number on that list. Thus we have seen how to construct a real number between 0 and 1 which cannot be in any list like the one suggested above. Therefore the cardinal number of the set of reals between 0 and 1 must be greater than $\aleph_0$. The symbol for this new transfinite number is C, chosen because the interval in question is a *continuum* (Vol. 1, page 38).

We shall see that there are transfinite cardinals greater than C, in fact, infinitely many of them. It might be natural, then, to ask whether there are any transfinite cardinal numbers between $\aleph_0$ and C. Only recently have mathematicians been able to provide a satisfactory answer to this question. Cantor was unable to discover any set of the desired intermediate cardinality, and hence he guessed that there was no such aggregate. His conjecture came to be known as the *continuum hypothesis*, namely, that there is no cardinal number greater than $\aleph_0$ and smaller than C.

After Cantor, different mathematicians "purified" set theory, that is, based it on an abstract postulate system. One such axiomatization, for example, is due to Ernst Zermelo (1871–1956) and Abraham Fraenkel. Then, in 1938, using the Zermelo-Fraenkel system, Kurt Gödel demonstrated that one can safely *assume* Cantor's continuum hypothesis as an additional postulate in set theory. In other words, he proved that the continuum hypothesis is consistent with the Zermelo-Fraenkel axioms. Gödel had broken substantial ground, but he had not said the last word, since he had neither proved the continuum hypothesis nor shown that it is

---

* The reason we avoid 9 in each case is that we wish to produce a real number *not* in our list. If 9's are permitted, our selection of digits might merely lead to an alternative representation of some rational number actually in our list. We exclude 0 as a selection for the first place lest the selection of digits lead to 0.000 . . . = 0, which is a boundary of the interval (0, 1) but not a number within that interval.

undemonstrable, in other words, *independent* of the other
set theory postulates. That the latter fact holds was defini-
tively established by Paul J. Cohen in 1963 in the same fashion that had been used to demonstrate that the parallel postulate is independent of the other axioms of Euclidean
geometry (Chapter 3). Thus Cohen exhibited a model, a
very subtle one, of a *non*-Cantorian set theory in which the
continuum hypothesis is negated (while the other postulates
of set theory hold true). Later we shall see how Cohen's
non-Cantorian theory handles other logically troublesome
issues of Cantor's theory. At this point we can summarize
the situation by saying that the continuum hypothesis can
be assumed or denied, depending on the applications one has
in mind.

But let us return to the development of *Cantorian set theory*. The transfinite number C is the cardinal number corresponding to the interval $I = (0, 1)$. Using that interval as
our universal set, let us now consider some of its subsets, for
example, R, the set of rational numbers between 0 and 1,
and R', the complement of the rational set, that is, the set of
irrationals between 0 and 1. Then, using the symbolism of
Chapter 6,

$$I = R \oplus R' = R \cup R'$$

Now select any (irrational) number in R', for example $\sqrt{5}$, and
form the countable set,

$$E = \left\{ \sqrt{5}, \frac{1}{2}\sqrt{5}, \frac{1}{3}\sqrt{5}, \ldots, \frac{1}{n}\sqrt{5}, \ldots \right\}$$

Let $\bar{E}$ represent the complement of E in R', that is, the residual set of irrationals between 0 and 1 after the numbers
in E are removed. Now the set $R \cup E$ is countable because
it is the union of two countable sets, the rationals and the
set E described above. Let $F = R \cup E$. Then $I = F \cup \bar{E}$.
Also we know that $R' = E \cup \bar{E}$. Now we see that I and R'
can be matched because their component subsets can be
matched, $\bar{E}$ as a subset of I with $\bar{E}$ as a subset of R', the
countable subset F with the countable subset E. Hence I and
R' have the *same cardinal number* C. In other words,
"whole equals part" once more. There are C irrationals in
$(0, 1)$ even though the irrationals form a proper subset of
all the C real numbers in $(0, 1)$.

The statement $R \cup R' = R' \cup R = I$ now has the corollary

$$\aleph_0 + C = C + \aleph_0 = C$$

Put otherwise, $C = C - \aleph_0$, which means that removing a countable infinity from a continuum does *not* diminish the latter's magnitude. Consider

$$C - \aleph_0 - \aleph_0$$

The number C can be substituted for the difference represented by the first two terms, and thus we arrive at the result

$$C - \aleph_0$$

which, as we have shown, is equal to C. By the same sort of reasoning we can see that

$$C - \aleph_0 - \aleph_0 - \aleph_0 - \cdots = C$$

What this means is that if from *any* aggregate whose cardinal number is C (the set of reals or the set of irrationals in the interval $(0, 1)$, for example) we *remove* a countable infinitude of elements and then another countable infinity and then another—forever, thus taking away a countable infinity of countable infinitudes—the power of the original set is undiminished and its cardinal is still that of the continuum. When a Pythagorean or a school student in any age first encountered $\sqrt{2}$, $\sqrt[3]{5}$, or some other irrational number, the experience seemed strange. But now we see that, from a statistical point of view, an irrational should be considered the *usual* type of number and a rational as exceptional, since there are incredibly more incommensurables than commensurables in the world of real numbers.

Since we speak of a "universe" of real numbers, we had better extend our story to show that irrationals will predominate in a larger interval of real numbers as well as in the entire set of real numbers. As a minor preliminary, we remark that if instead of taking reals *between* 0 and 1, we include the number 0 or the number 1 or both, the cardinal of the set is still C, that is, $1 + C = C + 1 = 2 + C = C + 2 = C$. In fact, it can be shown that $m + C = C + m = C$ where m is any natural number.

By pairing every real number between 0 and 1 with its double, and every number in $(0, 2)$ with its half, we find that C is the cardinal number for all reals in the interval

(0, 2); by pairing the reals of (0, 1) with their trebles and those of (0, 3) with their thirds, C is shown to be the cardinal for reals in the interval (0, 3), etc., so that C is the cardinal for reals in (0, n) where n is any positive integer. Put otherwise,

$$C + C + C + C + \cdots \ (n \text{ times}) = C$$

or

$$nC = C$$

By pairing 0.3 with 1.3, 0.72 with 1.72, $\sqrt{0.5}$ with $1 + \sqrt{0.5}$, x with $1 + x$, where x is any real between 0 and 1, we establish a one-to-one correspondence between the reals of (0, 1) and those of (1, 2). By pairing x with $\frac{1}{2}x - \frac{1}{3}$, we establish a one-to-one correspondence between the reals of (0, 1) and those of $(-\frac{1}{3}, \frac{1}{6})$. In general, we can match the reals of (0, 1) with the reals in *any* finite interval. Therefore C is the cardinal for any such interval. We shall use the symbol [0, 1,] to signify reals between 0 and 1 inclusive, and the symbol [0, 1) if 0 is included but not 1, and (0, 1] if 1 is included but not 0. Then

$$[0, 1] \cup (1, 2] \cup (2, 3] \cup \ldots$$

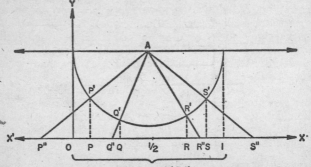

Unit Interval (0,1)

Figure 24.2   One-to-one correspondence between the point set (0, 1) and the real line. A typical point P of the interval (0, 1) is matched with a point P' of the semicircle, and the latter point is then matched with P'' on the real line (a procedure which can be carried out in reverse).

will signify *all* non-negative reals and

$$(0, -1] \cup (-1, -2] \cup (-2, -3] \cup \cdots$$

all negative reals. In both these cases the corresponding cardinal number will be

$$C + C + C + C + \cdots \text{ (forever)} = \aleph_0 \times C$$

and hence the cardinal for *all* reals is $2 \aleph_0 \times C$, which reduces to $\aleph_0 \times C$. But the diagram of Figure 24.2 indicates that the cardinal number of the set of *all* reals is C, because this set is in one-to-one correspondence with the reals between 0 and 1. Therefore

$$\aleph_0 \times C = C$$

Now let us show that

$$C \times C = C^2 = C$$

If we consider the unit square of Figure 24.3 there is a unit segment corresponding to each point between 0 and 1

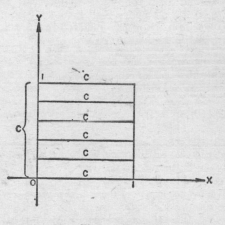

Figure 24.3

on the Y-axis. Each segment has C points and there are C segments, therefore $C \times C = C^2$ points. The Cartesian coordinates of any point within the square will be a *pair* of real numbers between 0 and 1, such as $(\frac{1}{3}, \frac{1}{2})$ or $(\pi/4, 3/8)$. We shall write the real numbers involved as *infinite* decimals just as we did in a previous argument. The points in question then become $(0.33333 \ldots, 0.50000 \ldots)$ and $(0.7853981 \ldots, 0.375375 \ldots)$. Now it is possible to establish a one-to-one correspondence between these number pairs and the real numbers between 0 and 1. We match any number pair with the *single* number formed by alternating the decimal digits of the pair. Thus the first pair above is put into correspondence with $0.3530303030 \ldots$ and the second with $0.7387553397851 \ldots$. Conversely, the single real number $0.695427 \ldots$ is mated with the number pair $(0.652 \ldots, 0.947 \ldots)$. Therefore the cardinal number of the set of points within the square is the same as that of the segment $(0, 1)$, that is

$$C \times C = C^2 = C$$

A similar argument will show that the number of points within a unit cube is C, or

$$C \times C \times C = C^3 = C$$

and, in general, $C^n = C$, where n is any positive integer.

The fact that there are no more points in a square or cube than in a line segment is rather a shock to our intuitive notion of what facts ought to be. Let us point out then that the sort of matching used to show that two sets of things have the same *cardinal* number is not at all concerned with the *order* of the elements in the sets. Points that are close together on the segment $(0, 1)$ may be mated with points far apart in the unit square. When, in Chapter 2, it was stated that $(0, 1)$ constitutes a *linear continuum*, this fact depended in an essential way on the arrangement of the numbers in the *order* of increasing magnitude.

Having examined addition and multiplication combinations involving $\aleph_0$ and C, we turn to the issue of still greater "infinities," cardinals larger than C. There are infinitely many of these larger cardinals, as a consequence of the fact that given any set, finite or infinite, a set with a higher cardinal number can always be obtained by taking all possible subsets of the given set. For example, the set of elements $\{\alpha, \beta, \gamma\}$ has the cardinal number 3. By proceeding in the fashion of Chapter 13, it can be shown that there are 8 subsets (proper or improper) of the given set. Again, a set with cardinal number 4 has 16 subsets. In general, if the cardinal number of a finite set is n, there will be 2^n subsets. One can prove this by applying the fundamental principle of permutations (Chapter 13) and reasoning that in forming a subset there are two possibilities for each member of the given set, namely, to include the member in a subset or to exclude it. Therefore there will be $2 \cdot 2 \cdot 2 \cdots$ (n times) possibilities in all. There is also a special theorem which proves that $2^n > n$ for every cardinal number n, *finite* or *transfinite*.

As a consequence of this theorem, $2^{\aleph_0} > \aleph_0$, and $2^C > C$. There is a *special theorem* establishing that $2^{\aleph_0} = C$. Then by the first of the two inequalities just listed, $C > \aleph_0$, and we have three distinct transfinite cardinals in increasing order of size, namely, $\aleph_0$, C, and 2^C. Let us use S to symbolize 2^C. Then by the special inequality theorem to which we have alluded, $2^S > S$, and there is a fourth and greater transfinite cardinal. If this fourth cardinal is used as an exponent for 2, a fifth transfinite cardinal results, and so on *ad infinitum*, producing an infinite sequence of transfinite cardinals arranged in increasing order of magnitude.

Our many illustrations of the arithmetic of cardinals, finite and transfinite, might be summarized by saying that their addition and multiplication satisfy closure, commutative, associative, and distributive laws. But the "peculiarities" of the transfinite cardinals make it impossible to carry out "normal" subtractions and divisions with them. These results occur because, in reasoning about cardinal numbers, one-to-one matching is the sole criterion. But another very important factor, that of *order*, is essential to a handling of questions related to Cantor's theory and to other mathematical subjects as well. In the case of infinite sets, we have just seen how vital order can be in matters of geometric dimension, where a mere matching of elements without consideration of their order can make a line segment the equivalent of a square or a cube or an n-dimensional cube with $n > 3$. This destruction of dimensionality was accomplished by changing the natural order of the real numbers in the $(0, 1)$ interval.

It must be noted that one cannot literally arrange or rearrange the huge infinitude of numbers of a continuum like $(0, 1)$; it is rather that one conceives of some particular arrangement or order, like that of increasing magnitude, or that of the rationals on page 303. One focuses on a *binary relation* containing pairs of elements in a particular class, a relation like "less than" or "earlier than," and then this relation gives rise to a certain "arrangement." But one might select the relation "greater than" instead of "less than" and thus generate a different "arrangement" or ordering of the same set. In fact, as some examples cited earlier have indicated, changing the ordering of an infinite set may sometimes produce startling results. The point to be emphasized is that a definition of order will not be found in the nature of the class to be "arranged," since the ordering need not be unique. Instead, the issue is one of defining some sort of *relation* that provides the protocol by which certain elements can be conceived as lower or earlier, and others as later or higher.

Particular types of relation were discussed earlier (Chapter 7). But now we must define a kind of relation suitable to our next objective, which is an exposition of Cantor's theory of transfinite ordinal numbers. Therefore we define a *full preference relation,* sometimes called a *simple ordering* or a *linear ordering.* Given a particular aggregate, a *full preference relation* is one with the three attributes listed below. By describing its effect on the elements of the given class, these characteristics tell how the order rule works.

(1) *Asymmetry:* If x and y are elements of the given class such that x precedes y, then y cannot precede x.

(2) *Transitivity:* If x, y, z are three distinct elements of the class such that x precedes y and y precedes z, then x precedes z.

(3) *Connectedness:* (*Comparability* of *all* pairs of distinct elements in the given set, thus making the rule "full.") If (x, y) is *any* pair of distinct elements of the class, then x must precede y, or y must precede x.

It is obvious that these properties are satisfied by the relation $<$ (less than) within various sets of real numbers, and hence $<$ is a full preference relation for such sets. But one can adduce specific instances where one or more of the required characteristics is lacking. For example, property (1) is lacking if the relation "is brother or sister of" is applied to the children of a family. If x is the brother or sister of y, then y is the brother or sister of x. The relation is *symmetric*, not asymmetric. There is a failure in transitivity when the relation "is the father of" is applied to an aggregate of people. If x is the father of y, and y is the father of z, then it is not true that x is the father of z. Hence the particular relations cannot establish simple orderings of the set of people.

An ordering of a set by a given relation may fail to be "full," that is, not all pairs of distinct elements may be comparable. Thus, connectedness is lacking in the following example: The members of a certain organization are to be seated in "order" at a banquet table. The rule of protocol states that members of Committee I are to be seated ahead of those of Committee II, and these are to be seated ahead of members of Committee III, etc. Now if x and y are members of the same committee, the rule will *not* tell whether x is to precede y or y is to precede x. Hence the rule does *not* establish a *full* preference relation for seating.

Cantor required that order be added to the structure of infinite sets prior to assigning an *ordinal* number to these aggregates. In defining the ordinal number of such an ordered class, he first considered its cardinal number. Thus the finite cardinal number "five" or the symbol 5 is not limited to particular descriptions like 5 pictures or 5 neutrons, etc., but is a way of characterizing *all* possible sets of a certain type, namely those with "fiveness" as a common attribute. The elements of any one of these sets are in *one-to-one correspondence* with those in another. Now Cantor required a particular *ordinal number* to characterize all *ordered* aggregates of a certain type, namely, those having the *same cardinal* number and "arranged" in *similar fashion*. Another way of stating this is to say that two ordered sets have the same ordinal number if they are *isomorphic* with respect to order. This means that in matching the sets, *order is preserved*. Thus order is preserved in the one-to-one matching if when element x precedes element y in the first ordered aggregate, then x', in the second ordered set, the mate of x, precedes y', the mate of y. Thus the ordered sets $\{A, B, C\}, \{C, A, B\}, \{A, C, B\}$, etc. are isomorphic with respect to order. To prove this, consider any pair of such sets, for example, $\{A, B, C\}$ and $\{C, A, B\}$. We note that, in the second ordered set, C, A, B are mates of A, B, C, respectively, in the first ordered set. In the first sequence we can make the three statements: A precedes B, B precedes C, A precedes C. The test of preservation of order requires that we substitute the mates of A, B, and C, respectively, in these statements and find that the results are true in the second sequence. Doing so, we have C precedes A, A precedes B, C precedes B. This is a correct description of the second arrangement.

In the same way, one can establish order isomorphism between *any* pair of the six different ordered sets formed by permuting the elements of $\{A, B, C\}$. Hence those six sets all have the same order type, so that the *ordinal* 3 corresponds to any one of the six arrangements. In the same way the $n!$ arrangements of n elements are all of the same Cantor ordinal type, namely, n. Then if we consider the non-negative integers or whole numbers arranged in order of increasing magnitude, $\{0, 1, 2, 3, 4, 5, \ldots, n, \ldots\}$, each number after the first is the *ordinal* number for the set of numbers preceding it. Thus 5 is the order type of $\{0, 1, 2, 3, 4\}$ and n is the ordinal for $\{0, 1, 2, \ldots, n-1\}$. In other words, the set of natural numbers $\{1, 2, 3, \ldots, n, \ldots\}$ can be considered to represent *either* all nonzero finite cardinals or all finite ordinals. When arranged in order of increasing magnitude, this most basic set can be described not only as ordered, but also as *well-ordered*, by which is meant that *every* nonempty subset has a first element. Examples of well-ordered sets are $\{a, \beta, \gamma, \delta\}$, $\{6, 5, 4, 3, 2\}$, or any *finite* order.

But there are ordered sets that are not well-ordered. For example, the rational numbers in order of size is not a well-ordered set because it contains subsets like the set of rationals greater than 4. That subset (arranged in order of size) has no first number, since thare is no next rational that comes immediately after 4. Again,

$$\{\ldots, -4, -3, -2, -1, 0, 1, 2, 3, 4, \ldots\}$$

is ordered but not well-ordered, for such subsets as the integers less than 2, or integers less than 3, or integers less than −4, etc. have no first elements.

An *ordinal number* is often defined as the order type of a well-ordered set. Well-ordered sets have an ordinal number and other special properties that make them very important in mathematical reasoning. Among these is the fact that they have a definite beginning and a next term after any term except the last (if there is a last). One of the chief uses of well-ordered sets is in the method of *mathematical induction*, which readers may have studied at school. That method makes use of the well-ordering of the natural numbers. Cantor planned to generalize the technique to a process of *transfinite induction*.

In creating *transfinite* ordinal numbers, Cantor sought to enlarge the set of finite ordinals so that the extended set would be well-ordered. Since the set of ordinals *after* all the finite ordinals was to be nonempty, the well-ordering property required that there must be a *first* ordinal immediately after the entire sequence of finite ordinals (natural numbers). The successor to the natural number (finite ordinal) sequence is a *transfinite* ordinal describing the order type of that sequence. Cantor symbolized that first transfinite ordinal by ω. Then if the enlarged set of ordinals is to be well-ordered and if there are to be ordinals after ω, there must be a *first* ordinal immediately after ω. Cantor labeled this new transfinite ordinal $\omega + 1$. It is the order type of $\{1, 2, 3, \ldots; \omega\}$. After $\omega + 1$, there must be the ordinals $\omega + 2$, $\omega + 3$, etc. Then after the entire sequence

$$\{\omega, \omega + 1, \omega + 2, \ldots, \omega + n, \ldots\}$$

there is a first or next ordinal which Cantor labeled 2ω. It is followed by $2\omega + 1$, $2\omega + 2$, ... After the entire sequence thus formed there are the further transfinite ordinals 3ω, $3\omega + 1$, $3\omega + 2$, ... Thus Cantor conceived of his ordinals as the following well-ordered set, where each ordinal gives the type of the ordered set preceding it:

$$
\begin{array}{llllll}
1, & 2, \ldots, & & n, \ldots; \\
\omega, & \omega + 1, & \omega + 2, \ldots, & \omega + n, \ldots; \\
2\omega, & 2\omega + 1, & 2\omega + 2, \ldots, & 2\omega + n, \ldots; \\
3\omega, & 3\omega + 1, & 3\omega + 2, \ldots, & 3\omega + n, \ldots; \\
\multicolumn{4}{c}{\cdots\cdots\cdots\cdots\cdots\cdots\cdots\cdots\cdots\cdots\cdots}
\end{array}
$$

$$
\begin{array}{llllll}
\omega^2, & \omega^2 + 1, & \omega^2 + 2, & \ldots, & \omega^2 + n, & \ldots; \\
\omega^2 + \omega, & \omega^2 + \omega + 1, & \omega^2 + \omega + 2, & \ldots, & \omega^2 + \omega + n, & \ldots; \\
\omega^2 + 2\omega, & \omega^2 + 2\omega + 1, & \omega^2 + 2\omega + 2, & \ldots, & \omega^2 + 2\omega + n, & \ldots;
\end{array}
$$

As we have said, Cantor's ordinal type ω describes the order type of the natural numbers arranged in order of magnitude, that is, the order type of each of the following *sequences* (Chapter 22) and many others as well:

$$1, 2, 3, 4, \ldots, n, \ldots$$
$$0, 1, 2, 3, \ldots, n - 1, \ldots$$
$$2, 1, 3, 4, \ldots, n, \ldots$$
$$3, 2, 1, 4, \ldots, n, \ldots$$

Observe that a countable set need *not* be a sequence, that is, an ordered set with cardinal $\aleph_0$ need not be of order type ω, for if we consider the first two rows of our lengthy tabulation of ordinals, we have a single ordered set containing $\aleph_0 + \aleph_0 = \aleph_0$ elements, and yet its order type is 2ω, the ordinal which follows the first two rows. We can also consider the first three rows, with a total of $\aleph_0$ elements and order type 3ω, etc. Thus a countable set has a single cardinal, $\aleph_0$, but an infinite number of ordinals, depending on the way its elements are arranged.

Not all sums of finite and transfinite ordinals are to be found in our lengthy list of such ordinals. Thus, whereas $\omega + 1$ is listed, $1 + \omega$ does not appear. The former is the order type of the set formed by placing a single symbol ω *after* all the natural numbers, and $1 + \omega$ is now defined to be the order type of the sequence formed by placing a single element *ahead* of any sequence. Thus one can place the symbol 0 ahead of the sequence of natural numbers to obtain the sequence of whole numbers

$$\{0, 1, 2, 3, \ldots, n - 1, \ldots\}$$

But that is just one of the sequences already cited as having order type ω. This signifies that $1 + \omega$ is *not* a new ordinal, since it is identical with ω. As a further consequence, $1 + \omega \neq \omega + 1$. Our example illustrates what is true in general: Addition involving sums of finite and *transfinite* ordinals is *not commutative*.

We have seen that a finite set has only one order type but that an infinite set may have many orders. Thus since well-ordering is desirable for some important purposes, perhaps when a set is *not* well-ordered, the desired property can be achieved by rearrangement of terms. The ordered set

$$\{\ldots, -5, -4, -3, -2, -1, 0, 1, 2\}$$

(reading from left to right) is not well-ordered, but if we reverse it to form

$$\{2, 1, 0, -1, -2, -3, -4, -5, \ldots\}$$

this result (reading from left to right) is well-ordered. The positive rationals arranged in order of size do not form a well-ordered set, but the rearrangement on page 303 is one way of accomplishing well-ordering. Since any *countable* set can be put into one-to-one correspondence with the natural number sequence and that sequence is well-ordered, every countable set, if not already well-ordered, can be arranged in such a way as to be well-ordered. Finally, there is a famous theorem generalizing this fact to all infinite sets. The proof would carry us beyond the scope of this work, but the statement is: *Every set can be well-ordered.*

Cantor's theory of the infinite was his answer to Zeno's paradoxes and other antinomies, "monsters," scandals, that revealed the need of a good foundation for calculus and analysis in general. But his *Mengenlehre* (theory of sets) generated its own paradoxes and that was why Zermelo and Fraenkel, as well as P. Bernays, von Neumann, and others, saw the need to place the subject on a firmer foundation. Since we have just been talking about transfinite ordinals, let us examine a contradiction which plagued Cantor in 1895–1896 and which Burali-Forti (1861–1931) revealed in 1897. Cantor believed the infinite aggregate of *all* ordinals (ordered according to increasing magnitude) to be well-ordered. Then, using his own principle of formation, he realized it would be possible to create a new ordinal, the next *after* those in the set under consideration and symbolizing the type of order in that class. Herein lies the contradiction: If we are considering the class of *all* ordinals, how can there be a new ordinal outside this class, *not* part of the "all"?

To take an antinomy arising out of the sort of reasoning we used with cardinals, we recall from previous chapters that a given set may be a class of classes. In other words, the elements of a set may themselves be sets. As such a set Bertrand Russell offered for consideration the class of *all* those classes that are *not* members of themselves, and posed this question: Is the set of sets so described a member of itself? If the answer is negative, then it is a class that does *not* contain itself, hence must belong to the class of classes in question, thus does contain itself, and we have a contradiction. If the answer is affirmative, the class is a member of the "all" and is therefore a set that does *not* contain itself, which contradicts the fact that we have just affirmed that it is a member of itself.

Since the above argument may be difficult to follow, we offer another version due to Russell. In a certain village the village barber shaves *all* those men and only those who do not shave themselves. Who shaves the barber? If he is one of those men who do not shave themselves, he must be shaved by the barber (himself) and hence he does shave himself, a paradoxical situation. If, on the other hand, it is claimed that he is someone who shaves himself, then he cannot be shaved by the village barber, which contradicts the fact just asserted namely, that he, the barber, is someone who does shave himself.

These "all" paradoxes of *Mengenlehre* arose around the beginning of the twentieth century, but in the sixth century B.C. Epimenides the Cretan said, "All Cretans are liars," and in the fourth century B.C. Eubulides gave a better formulation of the same "liar paradox" by asserting, "What I am now saying is a lie." This paradox occurs in each case because the quoted sentence, if true, must by what it says be false, and if false, must by what it says be true.

The paradoxes were the motivation for Zermelo, Fraenkel, and all the other mathematicians who provided pure set theory with a foundation that would exclude dilemmas of the kind we have illustrated. The general idea is to *restrict* the wide latitude in Cantor's conception of a set as any collection whatsoever, an idea we have used repeatedly (in informal discussions). As early as 1908, Russell proposed to overcome contradictions by saying that one may *not* gather all sorts of entities into a single aggregate, but must limit a set to things of the *same type*. He presented a *theory of types* by which "individuals" are considered of type 0, classes of individuals are considered of type 1, classes of classes are of type 2, sets of classes of classes are of type 3, etc. Then individuals may be elements of a class; classes may be elements of a class of classes; a class of classes may be an element of a set of classes of classes, etc. Anything of type n may be an element of a class of type $n + 1$, so that the latter class will contain as members only entities of the same type.

Russell's theory of types explains paradoxes by stating that they involve a confusion of types; that is, they disobey the membership rules just stated. Thus when, in the first version of the barber paradox, we speak of a "class that is (or is not) a member of itself," we are committing the error of considering a class (type 1) to be (or not to be) a member of itself (type 1). This is wrong because an entity of type 1 can only be an element of a set of type 2. In other words, a class *cannot* be a *member* of itself. It can only be an element of a class of classes. (It can, of course, be a subset of itself, but that is not what the barber paradox asserts.)

There is also a hierarchy of types of language. At level 0 there are words referring to individuals; at level 1 there are statements about individuals; at level 2 there are assertions about statements, etc. If one keeps the levels distinct, no statement can refer to itself, since it must refer to an entity at the level just beneath it. Thus Eubulides' claim, "*This* statement is false," is ruled out of consideration, and the "liar paradox" is resolved. One may, for example, permissibly state, at level 1, "Epimenides was a Cretan," then at level 2, "The statement just made is true," then at level 3, "Our illustrative level 2 statement has a permissible logical format."

In 1904 Zermelo had dealt with an issue involving a type 2 aggregate. He had given a proof of the famous *well-ordering theorem*, in which he made an assumption about a class of classes. This postulate has come to be known as Zermelo's *axiom of choice* and, like the continuum hypothesis, was a logical challenge to logicians and pure mathematicians from Zermelo's day until just recently, when discoveries of Gödel and Paul Cohen shed new light on the issue. Gödel and Cohen accorded the selection axiom the same treatment that they had given the continuum hypothesis. In other words, Gödel proved Zermelo's axiom to be *consistent* with the other postulates of abstract set theory, and Cohen showed that the axiom of choice is *independent* of the other postulates. Therefore one is free to include the moot axiom in a *Cantorian* set theory, or to substitute for it an assumption *negating* it in a *non-Cantorian* set theory. Cohen offered different substitutes for the axiom of choice, just as the parallel postulate is negated in different ways in Lobachevskian and Riemannian non-Euclidean geometries.

But let us now examine the actual content of the axiom of choice. In that assumption Zermelo extended to infinite classes a familiar procedure with finite sets. Thus we regularly elect *representatives* to city councils. We may consider each district as a set of people and then our set of districts becomes a class of non-overlapping classes; one representative is *chosen* from each district, and the city council is the class of the representatives. Zermelo idealized this *finite* empirical situation and assumed that such a set of representatives could also be selected when the number of classes is infinite. His axiom states: For *any* class of non-overlapping classes there exists at least one class which contains one representative element from each class of the aggregate of classes.

Some of the foremost analysts of this century—Borel, Baire, Lebesgue, and others—objected to Zermelo's assumption on various technical grounds. Thus one can choose representatives for Congress simultaneously, or one after another. The critical analysts are willing to permit the latter procedure (in theory) even when the number of classes is denumerably infinite, but object to selecting all representatives simultaneously, by a *single* act of choice, as it were. A major bone of contention is therefore the lack of a *constructive* method for obtaining the representative class in certain situations. A suggestion as to the nature of the difficulty is found in the following story, which is part fact, part legend. In the early days of Cantorian theory, the son of an American multimillionaire was a graduate student in mathematics at Göttingen. So great was his talent that the university professors predicted he would be a leading mathematician of the next generation. Then suddenly he announced he would return to the United States to become a partner in his father's business and would renounce mathematics except as an amateur hobby. One of his fellow students decided to remonstrate with him and arrived on the scene as the American was directing his valet in the packing. The German youth was astounded to see that several trunks were filled with layers and layers of shoes, and his amazement increased when the valet opened a closet that revealed shelves completely filled with *more* shoes.

In spite of his innate courtesy, the advocate of pure science could not help exclaiming "So many pairs!"—whereupon he received the rejoinder, "Nevertheless a countable number!"

"Why, oh why are you doing this foolish thing? Why give up a career for which you are so well qualified?" the young man pleaded.

Legend has it that the departing American felt obliged to put up a strong defense and responded, "I am discouraged because mathematics is ultimately baffling. For example, my father has had a pair of shoes delivered to me almost every other day since I have been at the university, and my valet has been keeping track by numbering the pairs, writing the integer 1 inside the left shoe of the first pair to arrive, the integer 2 inside the left shoe of the second pair to arrive, and so on, inscribing successive integers for successive pairs in order of arrival. But with each pair of shoes comes a pair of socks; hence I know that I have as many pairs of socks as pairs of shoes. Still, I can't give my valet a constructive rule telling exactly how to choose the sock which is to bear the number 1 or 2 or 3 or 4, etc. Therefore, even if a mathematician like Cantor were to conceive of an infinity of pairs or sets of indistinguishable entities (like socks), mathematics does not give constructive laws of selection needed to prove facts related to such sets."

Actually, since even a multimillionaire could not provide an *infinity* of pairs of *socks*, the difficulties with Zermelo's axiom is only suggested by the story, but does not really exist for a *finite* number of pairs however large this finite number. But more valid objections to Zermelo's axiom arose from the following situation. He used his postulate in the proof of the well-ordering theorem, which states that *every set* can be well-ordered. From that theorem it follows that the aggregate of real numbers between 0 and 1 inclusive can be well-ordered. Nevertheless, no one to date has been able to exhibit such a well-ordering. This failure caused mathematicians to examine Zermelo's proof to see whether he had erred in some way. In the process they proved the well-ordering theorem equivalent to the axiom of choice. What this means is that not only can the well-ordering theorem be deduced from the axiom, but conversely, if the possibility of well-ordering every set is assumed to be true, Zermelo's axiom can be deduced as a theorem. Thus, doubts about the universal possibility of well-ordering entail doubts about Zermelo's axiom. Another feature in the situation is the use of an "existence proof." Some modern logicians refuse to accept a proof that something exists or something can be done (a set can be well-ordered, for example). Such critics say that a valid proof not only must show that a thing can be done but must contain an exact method for carrying out the process.

Cohen, however, settles the issue, as already stated, by showing how one can consistently *assume* either the axiom of choice or its negation. It all depends on whether one's attitudes or the applications one desires call for Cantorian or non-Cantorian set theory. Cohen has even presented different forms of the negation and, in each case, has specified how large an infinity of sets it is possible to "choose from" as well as which infinities are too large to choose from (for the particular negation assumed).

This chapter has emphasized the Cantorian theory of *infinite* aggregates, but sets whose cardinal number is finite are not to be considered of minor importance in mathematics. In fact, we shall see later that the "intuitionist" school of logic employs only the latter type of aggregate and would bar infinite classes except for those that can be *constructed* by adding one element at a time *ad infinitum*.

Again, methods for determining cardinal number and ordinal type have been stressed, but properties of *operations* with sets, like addition or union, were more important when we treated the *algebra* of classes in Chapter 6. Now, as an immediate sequel to the present discussion, the theory of infinite sets will be related to the modern subject of *topology*.

Chapter 25

Angelic Geometry

Hermann Weyl (1885–1955), a leading mathematician of the recent era, once remarked that the angel of topology and the demon of abstract algebra are engaged in a war where each battle is a struggle for the soul of another branch of mathematics. The two subjects in question do, in fact, lie at the root of almost all of modern pure mathematics. The "fiendish" member of the fundamental pair has been developed to some extent at various points in previous chapters, and now the "loftier" of the two opponents will be considered.

Topology might be described as the *general study of continuity*, that concept whose manifold aspects have challenged philosophers and mathematicians from Pythagoras' day to our own. In the nineteenth century Cantor and Dedekind considered many types of *geometric* continua which were point sets in a plane or in space or on a surface, on a hypersurface, etc. Since the associated problems were always couched in geometric language, topology was at first considered a sort of geometry, and the Cantorian study of general continua, where different point aggregates are specified and limiting points, neighborhoods, and the like are defined, came to be called *point-set topology* or, alternatively, *analytic topology* because the concepts and methods are characteristic of modern analysis. Today all such topics, in particular those aspects we have treated in Chapters 22, 23, and 24, are generalized in the subject which provides the conceptual background for modern analysis and which, appropriately, is called *general topology*.

A different technique for handling the properties of continua is found in the *combinatorial topology* whose modern phase was launched by Henri Poincaré in a series of memoirs from 1895–1904. At that time topology was still considered a branch of geometry and was called *analysis situs*, analysis of situation. Poincaré wrote:[*]

Analysis situs is a purely *qualitative* subject where quantity is banned. In it two figures are always equivalent if it is possible to pass from one to the other by a continuous deformation, whose mathematical law can be of any sort whatsoever as long as continuity is respected. Thus a circle is equivalent to any sort of closed curve but not to a straight-line segment, because the latter is not closed. Suppose that a model is copied by a clumsy craftsman so that the result is not a duplicate but a distortion. Then the model and the copy are not equivalent from the point of view of metric geometry or even from that of projective geometry. The two figures are, however, topologically equivalent. . . .
    It has been said that geometry is the art of applying good reasoning to bad diagrams. This is not a joke but a truth worthy of serious thought. What do we mean by a poorly drawn figure? It is one where proportions are changed slightly or even markedly, where straight lines become zigzag, circles acquire incredible humps. But none of this matters. An inept artist, however, must *not* represent a closed curve as if it were open, three concurrent lines as if they intersected in pairs, nor must he draw an unbroken surface when the original contains holes.

The above quotation from Poincaré indicates that topology is not concerned with the issues of Euclidean geometry —the measurement of lengths, areas, volumes, angles, the making of scale drawings or enlargements. Again, topology is not limited to the rules of projective geometry, where straight lines may change in position but may never be distorted into curves, and circles may be transformed into ellipses and vice versa but may not acquire humps or altogether arbitrary closed contours. All of this would naturally suggest the question: Can there be any use in a "geometry" like topology that permits enormous freedom in transforming figures into others that are to be considered equivalent?
    It is not our purpose to answer the above question fully at this point, but we shall indicate briefly that some important aspects of physical theories are rooted in topology. There is, for example, the "finite but unbounded" space of relativity. Einstein's *unbegrenzt* signifies "without limitation in the form of boundaries." This is the equivalent of Poin-

---

[*] H. Poincaré, *La valeur de la Science*, Flammarion, Paris, 1905, p. 44.

caré's term *closed*, which makes curves like the circle and ellipse, lines like the periphery of a polygon, surfaces like a sphere all closed (*unbegrenzt*). A line segment or arc is not closed, because its end-points are *boundaries*. Surfaces that are not closed are the circular disk, which has a boundary in its peripheral circle, and the circular annulus, which is bounded by two concentric circles. Einstein used the term "finite" in a metric sense, and therefore, in accordance with Poincaré's statement, the property involved is not a topological one. In relativity, a finite space is one that is not inconceivably large but where one can say, for example, in the case of a circle, that its length is less than 50 ft., or in the case of a sphere, that its area is less than 1000 sq. ft. Topologists handle finiteness of geometric figures somewhat differently.

Again, other features of physical reality are topological. Thus we see that in a straight-line universe (Figure 25.1) an insect journeying from *A* to *C* would have to pass through *B* because *B* is *between* *A* and *C*. Thus "betweenness" is a *quality* associated with geometric situation (*analysis situs*). In a circular universe (Figure 25.1) an insect

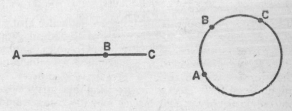

Figure 25.1

would *not* have to pass through *B* to reach *C*, since he could travel around the circle by an alternative route. In fact, we can make *no* unique "between-ness" statement about three points on a circle, for instead of saying that *B* is between *A* and *C*, we could equally well claim that *A* is between *B* and *C*, or that *C* is between *B* and *A*. If we are thinking of a geometric *time* continuum, for example, and we picture it as a *directed* straight line, we can say for three instants of time—*A*, *B*, *C*,—that the time instant *B* comes *after* *A* but *before* *C* (or the reverse if the line has the opposite direction), but we cannot make such a statement if we conceive of the time continuum as a circle, an ellipse, or a polygonal periphery.

To leave Poincaré's ideas and return to Cantor's, we recall that one-to-one correspondence is the criterion for equivalence of sets as far as their cardinal number is concerned. One result of this mode of comparing aggregates is that the point sets corresponding to a line segment, a cube, a "hypercube," have the same cardinality. This affront to intuition is alleviated by the observation that, to establish the equivalence of the point sets named, the figures must be shattered, so to speak; that is, the matching is *not* continuous, because points originally close together may have as mates points far apart. The situation emphasizes that topology is *not* a mathematics of measuring and that the cardinal number of points in a figure is not an adequate description. Therefore one-to-one correspondence is supplemented by the requirement of *bicontinuity*, or continuity both ways, before two figures may be called topologically equivalent.

Figure 24.1 illustrated a one-to-one correspondence between the line segments AB and $A'B'$. In Chapter 22 we gave a rigorous definition of a continuous function of a real variable, but here we shall merely state informally that the one-to-one correspondence pictured in Figure 24.1 is a *continuous* mapping of AB onto $A'B'$ because points close together on AB are mapped onto points close together on $A'B'$. The correspondence is also a continuous mapping of $A'B'$ onto AB because points close together on $A'B'$ are mapped onto points close together on AB. Just as the ϵ, δ technique rigorized the concept of continuity in Chapter 22, the present notion of continuity can also be given suitable mathematical rigorization. But we shall merely state informally that Figure 24.1 illustrates a *bi-unique, bicontinuous* correspondence between two point sets.

Two sets are said to be topologically equivalent if and only if a bi-unique (one-to-one), bicontinuous correspondence between the sets can be established. Such a correspondence is called a *homeomorphism*, and topologically equivalent sets are termed *homeomorphic*. Figure 25.2 illustrates some topologically equivalent figures and the homeomorphisms matching their points. Figure 25.3 shows figures no two of which are homeomorphic. The circle of Figure 25.4 is homeomorphic to either one of the knots, as we can see intuitively if we number points on the circle as if it were

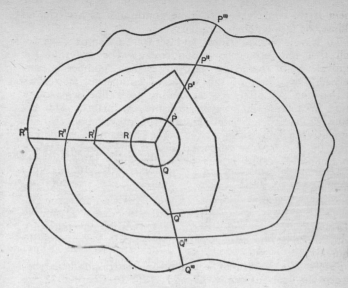

Figure 25.2

a clock, 1,2,3, . . . , 12 and imagine infinitely fine sub-divisions. We can assign the same numbers to corresponding points in the knots. Then points with numbers 4.1782 and 4.17819, say, will be close together on the clock as well as on the knots. We observe that the topological equivalence of the three figures is in no way dependent on the matching of points in the surrounding space. In topology each figure would be considered an entire space in itself, as it were.

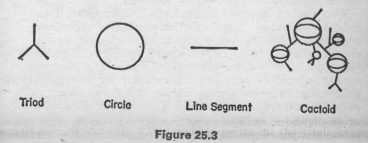

Triod   Circle   Line Segment   Cactoid

Figure 25.3

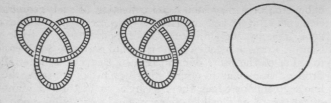

Figure 25.4

This fact leads to a warning about the traditional "continuous deformation" or "stretching and bending without tearing" or "rubber-sheet" descriptions of topological equivalence, where deformations may possibly involve an external space in which a configuration is embedded. If figures can be deformed into one another, they are homeomorphic, but Figure 25.4 indicates that the converse is false. Either knot is equivalent to the circle, but no amount of stretching, bending, etc. would deform it into a circle. Such a knot would have to be broken or else deformed in a *4-dimensional space* to convert it into a circle by mere bending and stretching. Therefore it is better not to consider deformation as the definition of homeomorphism and to rely instead on the original concept of bi-unique, bi-continuous correspondence between two configurations. For those who are fond of the "rubber-sheet" notion there is consolation, since this idea is embodied in a special, exceedingly important concept called *homotopy*. If one does wish to consider configurations as embedded in some space—for example, the curves on a surface—then deformation within the surface can be considered. A curve which (remaining within the surface) can be deformed continuously into another curve is said to be *homotopic* to the latter. Thus the knots and the circle (Figure 25.4) are *not* homotopic in the plane, but are homotopic in 4-dimensional space.

Difficulties arose in topology because continua were conceived as *geometric* and there are two essentially different ways of regarding a geometric figure. One can see it from Cantor's point of view, as an ensemble of its individual points, or one can consider it as a whole, as Euclid did. In the latter case it is a point or a line segment or a triangle or a circle or a plane or a sphere or a cylindric surface or a cube, etc.; or it may be a *finite* collection of such geometric elements. But if one replaces the segment or triangle or cube, etc. by its (infinite) set of points, one is back to Cantor. From a lay viewpoint it would certainly seem easier to think of the *finite* combination of elements in a tetrahedron or triangular pyramid—the 4 points or vertices, the 6 line segments or edges, the 4 triangles or faces. The number of elements or "cells" of each kind, plus the mode of *combining* them or fitting them together (the paper pattern, as it were) is often called the *combinatorial skeleton* of the particular continuum, in this case a tetrahedral surface. The study of properties of continua after this fashion is called *combinatorial* or *algebraic* topology, since algebraic symbols and formulas are used for the combinatorial schemes and the reasoning is carried out by means of algebraic concepts and operations. If issues of general (point-set) topology arise, one covers the set with a combinatorial mesh-work of cells, then subdivides these repeatedly into finer cells until ultimately the points are reached, much in the manner suggested by the nested intervals of Chapter 2 or by the way a foot-rule can be divided into inches, then half-inches, quarter-inches, etc. (*ad infinitum*, in theoretical mathematics). Sometimes it is not necessary to carry out the process of subdivision indefinitely in order to trap all points as the net grows finer and finer. If a continuum has a property called "compactness," it turns out to be possible to cover all its points by means of a *finite* number of cells. In some continua, one traps the points by a finite number of *overlapping* patches. In all that we have just said it is evident that the two kinds of topology, combinatorial and general, are not divorced from one another but that there is an interplay of concepts and methods. However, the matter of fusing the two types into a single logical whole has not yet been accomplished, and all attempts to do so have thus far been frustrated by the excessive difficulties that arise. Nevertheless one can say that either kind of topology is concerned with *topological spaces*.

What then is a *topological space*? It is just a set (space), finite or infinite, endowed with a "topology." Crudely speaking, the "topology" assigned can be considered to specify the subsets that are "neighborhoods," and such specification makes it possible to arrive at definitions of "limit" and "continuity." But the idea of a "neighborhood" is not purely qualitative (topological) since it has a *metric* connotation, for some measurement of distances would seem to be required to decide which points are close enough to a given point to be part of its "neighborhood." Hence the more general nonmetric conception of an "open set" is introduced. Specifically, one assigns a "topology" to a given universal set I, that is, one converts it into a *topological space*, by selecting a collection of subsets of I and postulating that these subsets are to be labeled *open sets*. The subsets of the collection can be chosen somewhat arbitrarily except that the collection must be closed with respect to certain operations, and the subsets pronounced to be "open" must also have properties resembling those of the metric "neighborhoods" which they generalize. Hence the following three conditions must be satisfied:

(1) The empty set $\emptyset$ and the universal set I are open sets.
(2) The *union* (logical sum) of any aggregate of open sets (that is, the set of elements belonging to at least one open set of the aggregate) is an open set.
(3) The *intersection* (logical product) of any two open sets is an open set.

To provide an illustration and also to show that a set S can be provided with *different* "topologies," in other words, can be structured to form *different* topological spaces, let us return to the universe $I = \{\alpha, \beta, \gamma\}$ of Chapter 6. In that chapter we saw that I contains eight subsets. We can endow I with a topology by specifying that only $\emptyset$ and I are to be considered open sets. (Observe that the three requirements listed above would be satisfied.) At the other extreme, we might topologize I by postulating that all eight subsets are "open." Or I might be converted into a topological space by defining the class of open sets as

$$\left\{\emptyset, I, A = \{\alpha, \beta\}, C' = \{\alpha\}\right\}$$

where the symbols A and C' have the same meaning as in Chapter 6. The reader can readily show that this "topology" has the required properties and that the same is true of the "topologies" $\{\emptyset, I, A, A'\}$, $\{\emptyset, I, A, B'\}$.

A fundamental problem of either combinatorial or general topology is one of classification, of subdivision of topological spaces into different types. This is done in many scientific situations by means of a special kind of binary relation called an *equivalence relation* (illustrated in Chapter 21 by "equivalence modulo *m*"). If, for example, we have on cards the names of all subscribers to a magazine, and wish to arrange the cards in alphabetic order, we may consider the binary relation on the set of subscribers defined by ρ = "has the same initial letter in his surname." Then as we sort the cards we place them in different packs according to this criterion, all cards in one pack being *equivalent* in the sense that the surnames start with A or with B, etc. To subdivide each pack further we could use other equivalence relations. In a sense, names like Bentley, Billings, Brown are equivalent, if, say, we are talking about a fictitious character, Mr. B_____, or guessing a name in a game or puzzle where the initial letter is the only hint.

To give a formal definition, we now state that a binary relation ρ on a set S is an equivalence relation if, and only if, ρ is

(1) *Reflexive*: $x \, \rho \, x$ where x is any member of S;
(2) *Symmetric*: If $x \, \rho \, y$, then $y \, \rho \, x$, where x and y are members of S;
(3) *Transitive*: If $x \, \rho \, y$ and $y \, \rho \, z$, then $x \, \rho \, z$, where x, y, z are members of S.

Parallelism is an equivalence relation dividing the lines of a plane into sets in each of which the lines are "equivalent" in the sense of having the same direction. Likewise, congruence, similarity, and projectivity effect a subdivision of geometric figures into sets of equivalent figures. In similarity geometry, for example, a scale drawing or an enlargement is equivalent to the original figure and may be substituted for it, and thus only a single category is involved. In topology, homeomorphism is an equivalence relation; a sphere is topologically equivalent to a polyhedron, an arc to a line segment, a knot to a circle. Just as we speak of the types {0, 1, 2, 3, 4} when congruence modulo 5 is the equivalence relation, we may speak of *the* line segment, *the* circle, *the* sphere as types. In number theory with modulus 5, we may substitute 6 or 21 for 1; 200 or 315 for 0; 14 or 1019 for 4; etc. In topology we may substitute a convex polygon or a star polygon for a circle, or a Euclidean plane

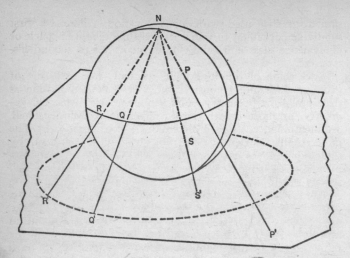

Figure 25.5   Stereographic projection

for a punctured sphere. That the last of these substitutions is correct can be proved by the process of *stereographic projection* (Figure 25.5) (used in making maps that represent angles correctly and hence give a true representation of small neighborhoods of each point on the earth). The diagram indicates that when one point is removed from the spherical surface (in this case, the North Pole), there is a bi-unique, bicontinuous correspondence between its points and those of the tangent plane at the South Pole.

Thus we have already mentioned several types of configuration or topological equivalence class—*the* arc, *the* circle, *the* sphere, *the* punctured sphere. It might seem natural to extend the classification so as to include *the* sphere in Euclidean 4-space, *the* sphere in Euclidean 5-space, etc., or since we cannot visualize these, to their analytic equivalents,

$$x^2 + y^2 + z^2 + w^2 = 1$$
$$\ldots x_1^2 + x_2^2 + x_3^2 + \cdots + x_n^2 = 1$$

To limit the classification of types so that it is not overpowering, it would seem sensible to follow a procedure similar to that used with alphabetization, where we first subdivide according to initial letters, then take each pack or equivalence class and subdivide it according to second letters, etc.

If we think of topology in its original sense as a sort of geometry, we might consider the first crude subdivision as that into plane geometry, solid geometry, 4-dimensional geometry, or more exactly into 1-dimensional, 2-dimensional, 3-dimensional, . . . , n-dimensional configurations. The only trouble is that we are not sure what we mean by *dimension* in the topological sense. We have already explained what is meant by the term as applied in "Euclidean" spaces. But topological spaces are far more general in nature and in some instances dimension cannot be specified by the definitions used for special cases. Let us then defer temporarily the consideration of how dimension is defined in topology. A satisfactory definition can be given, and the dimension of a topological space can be proved to be a topological property of the space, that is, an invariant under homeomorphism, so that spaces can be classified according to dimension. Since we may imagine that all the topological spaces have now been sorted into packs labeled 0, 1, 2, 3, 4, . . . , according to dimension, let us study the subclassification. Topology has advanced to the point where complete classification for dimensions 0, 1, 2, has been achieved (at least for spaces which are "compact manifolds"). For more complicated spaces or those of dimensionality 3 or higher, the classification problem has not yet been solved.

When a surface is called a *manifold*, the term signifies that the neighborhood of every point on the surface is homeomorphic to the interior of a circle. A Euclidean plane and a sphere are manifolds. In the former case a neighborhood of a point is identical with the interior of a circle. On a sphere, the neighborhood of a point can be deformed by being flattened out into the interior of a circle. A mathematical cone (Figure 7.11), we recall, looks like an hourglass. It is *not* a manifold because the neighborhood of the vertex, the point where the two "nappes" of the cone meet, is not homeomorphic to the interior of a circle. The reason for this failure is suggested if we try to deform the neighborhood by flattening it out. Except at the vertex, two points of the cone would go into one point of the flat area so that the correspondence would be two-to-one instead of one-to-one.

We have explained (page 331) the importance of "compactness" as a property making it possible to cover certain manifolds with a *finite* number of "cells." Hence, let us remark further that for the special topological spaces we shall consider, whenever we speak of a *compact* 2-dimensional manifold, the term *compact* will correspond to what we have called a *closed* surface confined to a finite portion of space. The topologist defines compactness more generally by avoiding the metric concept of "finite portion of space." He bases his definition on *intrinsic* properties of a surface, that is, those that do not depend on the surrounding space. In what follows, then, whenever we refer to a *surface*, we shall mean a compact 2-dimensional manifold.

The classification of surfaces is almost as simple as that of modular congruence, where {0, 1, 2, 3, 4} represents all types of integer modulo 5, or {0, 1, 2, 3, . . . , $m-1$} represents all types of integer modulo m. In Figure 25.6 we have indicated an ordinary *torus* (shaped like a doughnut or inner tube), a torus with two holes (like a pretzel), and a torus with three holes. The fundamental theorem for surfaces states that the types are *the* sphere, *the* torus with

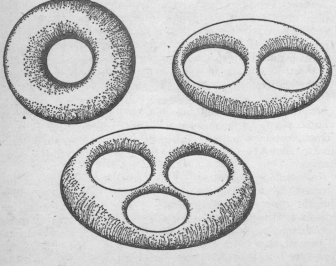

Figure 25.6

one hole, *the* torus with two holes, . . . , *the* torus with *m* holes, etc., where *m* is any positive integer. This is seen to be strictly analogous to the classification of integers modulo *m*.

In a simple classification problem like alphabetization we can place any name in the proper category if we can read, and know the alphabet, and it is not difficult to place 1019 modulo 5. One merely divides by 5 and obtains the remainder 4, which makes 1019 cquivalent to 4 (modulo 5). But to classify some strange abstract topological surface by proving it homeomorphic to a sphere or a torus with *m* holes might be exceedingly difficult for a novice, or even an expert in topology. Unless we have special information about the surface, or a "hunch," how can we tell whether to try to set up the correspondence with an ordinary torus or one with a thousand holes?

In any case, the direct resort to formulating homeomorphisms is not an easy one. However, the use of topological *invariants* is of great assistance in the problem of classification, numerical invariants in particular. What we mean by a numerical *invariant* can be illustrated in elementary mathematics. Every cubic polynomial has exactly 3 linear factors. There are an infinite number of different cubic polynomials but the *number* of linear factors, 3, is the same in every case. This is a numerical invariant for the set of all cubic polynomials. By analogy, what we seek is a *number* that is the same for sphere, ellipsoid, polyhedron, and all surfaces topologically equivalent to these. Again, 2 is the *numerical* invariant which specifies for quadratic polynomials the number of linear factors that *any* such polynomial must have. The analogous numerical invariant is different for quartic, quintic, etc. polynomials, so that all algebraic polynomials can be *classified* according to the number of linear factors. Thus anyone who asks for a quadratic polynomial with linear factors $(x + 1)$, $(x - 3)$, and $(2x + 5)$ is talking nonsense.

In topology, after we find a numerical topological invariant for *the* sphere, we must find the analogous number for *the* torus. If, as in the case of algebraic equations, we obtain a different number for each type of surface, these numerical invariants will furnish a criterion for classification.

Let us start with polyhedra (surfaces whose faces are polygons). In Figure 25.7 we have illustrated a few of those studied in school geometry. There are the five regular

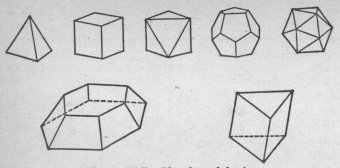

Figure 25.7   Simple polyhedra

(Platonic) polyhedra, a prism, and a frustum. These are all simple (or "simply connected") polyhedra, which means intuitively that they contain no holes. Figure 25.8 illustrates some nonsimple polyhedra. We tabulate the number of vertices, edges, faces, for each simple polyhedron:

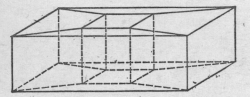

(a)

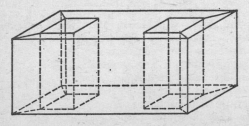

(b)

Figure 25.8   Nonsimple polyhedra

	Vertices (n_0)	Edges (n_1)	Faces (n_2)
Regular tetrahedron	4	6	4
Cube	8	12	6
Regular octahedron	6	12	8
Regular dodecahedron	20	30	12
Regular icosahedron	12	30	20
Triangular prism	6	9	5
Frustum of a hexagonal pyramid	12	18	8

These numbers vary from figure to figure, but it is easy to check that in every case

$$n_0 - n_1 + n_2 = 2$$

where n_0, n_1, n_2 represent the number of vertices, edges, faces, respectively. If a count is made for other simple polyhedra, the same result will be obtained, and it can be *proved* that, for all simple polyhedra,

$$n_0 - n_1 + n_2 = 2$$

This fact was first observed by Descartes, and rediscovered a century later by Euler. It is customary to refer to the proposition as *Euler's theorem*. If we deform a polyhedron or if we inflate it so that edges and faces become curved, if we continue the inflation until the surface becomes spherical (Figure 25.9), the numbers n_0, n_1, n_2 will remain the same, and no matter what type of polyhedron we deform or inflate,

$$n_0 - n_1 + n_2 = 2$$

for all the resulting surfaces, and finally for the sphere (subdivided into the curvilinear polygons into which the polyhedral faces have been deformed).

We have found our first numerical topological invariant. It is usually called the *Euler characteristic*, or just the *characteristic* of a surface. We can now state: The Euler characteristic of the sphere is 2.

Figure 25.8 illustrates nonsimple polyhedra with Euler characteristics, $16 - 32 + 16 = 0$ and $24 - 44 + 18 = -2$, respectively. When inflated sufficiently they can be deformed into an ordinary torus and a torus with two holes,

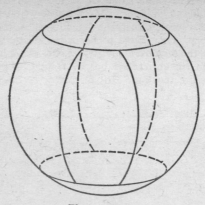

Figure 25.9

respectively (where both surfaces are subdivided into curvilinear polygons). Then the characteristics of the torus and the torus with two holes are 0 and −2, respectively.

In topology it is proved that if the number of holes in a torus is p, its Euler characteristic is $2 - 2p$. The number p can be given a more precise and fundamental topological meaning than "number of holes" and is then appropriately named the *genus* of the surface. For a sphere, the genus is 0. When $p = 0$ is substituted in the formula $2 - 2p$, the correct Euler characteristic, 2, results. All ordinary surfaces can then be classified according to either genus or characteristic. In the former case, one of the numbers $\{0, 1, 2, 3, 4, 5, \ldots\}$ can be assigned to the surface, and in the latter, one of the numbers $\{2, 0, -2, -4, -6, -8, \ldots\}$.

One does not usually picture a surface as a composite of vertices, edges, polygonal faces, but merely as the set of its points. Still it is possible to cover a surface with curvilinear polygons (in many different ways). Then, in order to standardize procedures, one can break the polygons down into triangles so that there is a *triangulation* of the surface. The surface becomes a polyhedron, and one can obtain its Euler characteristic by simple counting. Then one can classify the surface as to type. It can be proved that no matter what subdivision into polygons (triangles) is used, the characteristic has the same value, as seems natural if it is really an intrinsic property of the surface.

This was the whole story of surfaces up to the day of A. F. Moebius (1790–1868). After his contribution to topology, it was revealed that the "ordinary" surfaces are just *half* the story. They came to be called *oriented* surfaces in contrast to the *nonoriented* surfaces of Moebius. We shall now explain the difference between these two types.

If we use the rectangle *ABCD* of Figure 25.10 as the pat-

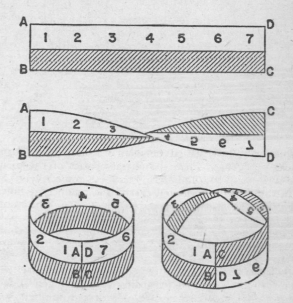

Figure 25.10   Cylinder and Moebius strip

tern for a surface and bring *AB* and *CD* together so that *A* coincides with *D* and *B* with *C*, we obtain a finite portion of a cylindric surface. Let us start again, and this time, giving the paper a slight twist, reverse the direction of *DC* so that now *D* coincides with *B* and *C* with *A*. The resulting surface is known as a *Moebius strip*, and the reversal of the direction of *DC* involved in its construction is a heuristic clue to its *nonorientability*. This surface and similar ones (made by giving two, three, four, etc. twists to the rectangle before identification of the edges) have been a happy source of recent parlor magic. If the reader should attempt the "tricks" we now describe, we advise that he draw the median line EF, that he make BC relatively long, AB narrow, in order to facilitate handling, that he use Scotch tape to make the seam binding AB and CD.

Now if one wishes to contrast cylinder and Moebius band, one can cut the cylindric surface along the median line. As expected, it falls into two parts. If the Moebius strip is cut along its median line, the unexpected results; it does not fall in two, but becomes a Moebius band with two twists instead of one. It can be proved that this two-twisted band is homeomorphic (topologically equivalent) to a cylindric surface. We can suggest why this is so by starting with the rectangular pattern of Figure 25.10, twisting it twice before seaming AB and DC together. This time we observe that we must identify D with A, and C with B, as in the case of the cylinder, so that the Moebius band with two twists and the cylindric surface have the same *combinatorial* pattern.

Now let us return to the original Moebius strip with a single twist, where the direction of CD is reversed before seaming. We imagine that a watch is placed with its center at the midpoint of the seam $AB(CD)$, and that the time indicated on its face is 11:45, so that the minute hand points to 9 and the hour hand to 12. We start sliding the watch to the left, that is, in the direction indicated by the minute hand. We keep going so that the center of the watch remains on the median line and its back is in contact with the surface. When the watch first returns to the seam, it will be on the side of the paper invisible to us, with its back towards us. If the paper and the watch case were transparent, we would see the minute hand still pointing to the left, but the hour hand would point down instead of up. From *our point of view* the direction of rotation has been reversed, since originally the direction along the minor arc from 9 to 12 was *clockwise* and now it is *counterclockwise*.

In all of this we are thinking *not* of the physical paper band and a real watch but of an abstract mathematical surface and watch, without any thickness and completely transparent. The physical experiment can be carried out with a transparent pliable plastic pattern for the strip and a watch crystal with the hands painted on it as pointing to 9 and 12.

The Moebius strip is called *nonorientable* because it is not possible to *fix* the direction of rotation around a point of this surface. A surface is called *orientable* if it is possible to draw a small directed circle at each point (either clockwise or counterclockwise) so that the little circles at points close together will have the same direction. We can see that this is desirable if we think of the analytic processes in mathematics. In trigonometry the positive sense of rotation is conventionally fixed as *counterclockwise*. An angle +30° signifies one-twelfth of a revolution in the counterclockwise direction, and −30° implies the same rotation in the opposite direction, and the trigonometric functions associated with the two rotations will, in general, be different. For example, sine 30° = 0.5, sine (−30°) = −0.5. Calculus and other analytic subjects use the trigonometric facts and formulas in addition to other processes where orientation is important. None of this mathematics would be valid in physical applications if circles and hence angles might change their algebraic signs without the awareness of the surveyors, astronomers, and draftsmen, who shift their tools slightly or observe objects in some small region of the earth or heavens. In a cosmos like a Moebius strip some of our science and mathematics would have to be modified.

We emphasize that the Moebius surface is nonorientable because we cannot arrange to have circles at neighboring points agree on direction. The device of the moving watch seems to guarantee, in the beginning, that neighbors will agree, but in the end we see that some close to the seam may pronounce a certain rotation clockwise, whereas others nearby, but on the other side of the seam, will declare the same rotation to be counterclockwise.

Another way of indicating the nonorientability of the Moebius band is to compare it once again with the cylindric surface. We would say that the latter surface has two sides, in the sense that one could paint the inside of a cylindric tank white and the outside red. In drawing a circle or other continuous closed path starting on the red side, one remains on that side, and similarly for the white side. One cannot go from red to white or vice versa without crossing over the top. But the center of the watch in our illustration has described a continuous closed path on the Moebius strip and succeeded in getting to the other side without crossing "over the top," that is, over any boundary. Since a continuous closed path must always be confined to one side of a surface, mathematicians call the Moebius strip one-sided or unilateral. To show this in "parlor magic" style, one may decide to color a Moebius band by taking a piece of colored chalk whose length is equal to the width of the strip, then placing it along the seam and sliding it to the left, always perpendicular to the median line. The chalk will color the surface as it progresses, and if one continues on and on for a sufficient distance, he will find that he has colored the entire surface and that he might have saved effort by dipping the band into a pail of paint. Thus nonorientability and one-sidedness are just two different ways of describing a particular topological aspect of a Moebius band. Mathematicians prefer the notion of nonorientability because it is an *intrinsic* property and does not depend on the surrounding space. This is the same issue discussed in the differential geometry used in relativity. In the present case we would say that an insect confined to a Moebius strip could discover its nonorientability by making a closed tour around it. To see that it is one-sided requires observation from a vantage point in the surrounding space.

Since we have said that a strip with two twists is homeomorphic to a cylinder, the former must be two-sided or orientable. The reader may experiment with coloring such a band in order to see that the continuous motion of the chalk, no matter how prolonged, will not color the entire strip, and that it is possible to start with a different color on the reverse side of the seam and never run into the first. This suggests that for 2, 4, 6, 8, . . . or any even number of twists a Moebius band is two-sided or orientable, and for 1, 3, 5, 7, . . . or any odd number of twists, one-sided or nonorientable.

As stated earlier, any compact orientable 2-dimensional manifold can be classified according to either its genus or its Euler characteristic; that is, it can be typed as a sphere or some sort of torus. There is, in theory, a way of closing up a Moebius strip so as to form a compact manifold. Then for the resulting surface and other nonorientable, one-sided types of surface, there is a complete classification by numerical invariants which is parallel to that explained earlier for the ordinary surfaces. Finally, the fundamental theorem of the topology of surfaces is: *Two surfaces are equivalent if and only if they are both orientable or both nonorientable and have the same characteristic number*. This, speaking crudely, makes the classification of surfaces as clear-cut as the alphabetization of cards. When some exceedingly abstract 2-dimensional point set is involved, one must first determine whether or not it is orientable. Then after covering its surface with polygons (triangles), one counts vertices, edges, faces, in order to obtain the characteristic. The two facts place it in a specific category.

Returning to the pattern (Figure 25.10) for the cylinder, we can follow the identification of edges AB and CD of the rectangle by the identification of the other pair of opposite sides as indicated in Figure 25.11. The cylindric surface is no longer bounded by two edges, but is closed by identification and becomes a torus. All the vertices of the rectangular pattern coalesce into a single one, so that $n_0 = 1$. The identification of opposite sides leaves only 2 edges, so that $n_1 = 2$. There is only one face, the rectangle itself, so that $n_2 = 1$. Then the characteristic is

$$n_0 - n_1 + n_2 = 1 - 2 + 1 = 0$$

which checks with the previous result for the torus.

If we consider removing boundaries, that is, closing the cylindric surface, we can carry out the first two steps in Figure 25.11 and then identify the free edges of the rectangle after giving them *opposite* directions (Figure 25.12). This construction *cannot* be carried out in physical space without having the surface intersect itself as indicated in Figure 25.12, which pictures a *nonorientable torus* or *Klein bottle*, named after Felix Klein, who was the first to point

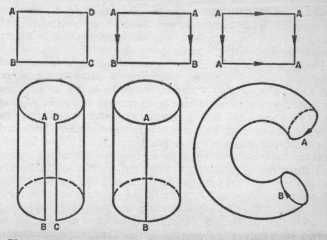

Figure 25.11   Torus formed from combinatorial pattern

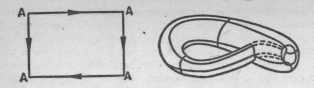

Figure 25.12   Klein bottle formed from combinatorial pattern

out its pattern and properties. The nonorientability can be seen to arise from identifying the lengths of the rectangular pattern in the same way one seams the widths in constructing the Moebius strip. In 4-dimensional space it would be possible to carry out the construction of the twisted nonorientable torus without having it intersect itself. Lewis Carroll, the mathematical author of *Alice in Wonderland*, described the Klein bottle in his story "Sylvie and Bruno," where he called it the Purse of Fortunatus. We observe from its rectangular pattern that this Purse has the same Euler characteristic, 0, as the untwisted torus. That is why, in the fundamental theorem of the topology of surfaces, the characteristic is *not* sufficient for classification, and the orientability must also be known.

If we were 4-dimensional creatures, we could readily see how, for the Moebius strip, the identification indicated in Figure 25.13 must close it, producing a surface which can be proved to be homeomorphic to the *projective plane*, the plane in which the 2-dimensional figures of projective geometry can be located. The *pattern* shows that, after identification, $n_0 - n_1 + n_2 = 2 - 2 + 1 = 1$, so that the Euler characteristic of the *projective plane* is 1. We remark that the projective plane is an alternative choice to the closed Moebius strip for the fundamental compact nonorientable 2-dimensional manifold, playing the same role as the sphere does among orientable manifolds.

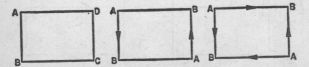

Figure 25.13 Combinatorial pattern for the projective plane

Not all point sets or topological spaces are 2-dimensional, however. Before determining the facts just mentioned, one must know the dimension of the set involved. The Peano curve (Figure 22.1), which is a helpful illustration in many of the logical issues of topology, will assist us once more. It is described by the continuous motion of a moving point. Hence, intuition says it should be 1-dimensional. On the other hand, it fills a square, which would make it appear 2-dimensional. After all, we have just seen how one might convert a square into a cylinder or Moebius strip, and the Peano curve will then cover such a surface. What is its dimensionality, and how can one determine dimension in general?

The problem of obtaining a suitable definition of dimension for the very general spaces of topology is once again a matter of taxonomy, of classifying all possible topological spaces into 0-dimensional, 1-dimensional, 2-dimensional, . . . , n-dimensional aggregates. Let us return to the line segment and square which Cantor proved to contain the same number of points and see if we can find a topological property of each that will help to define dimension. What we seek is some qualitative property of the segment that will hold for an arc, zigzag line, wavy curve, that is, for any topologically equivalent figure, but will not be true for the square and its equivalents. Earlier we mentioned the case of an insect traveling in a straight line cosmos. Let us say that it has traveled from A to C on the straight-line segment in Figure 25.1 and now wishes to make the return journey. In the interim, however, some catastrophe has destroyed B. There is now a hole where B was originally located, and the return trip is impossible. Suppose that an insect lives, instead, within a square (Figure 25.14a). Then if the original trip took place along the path ABC, the re-

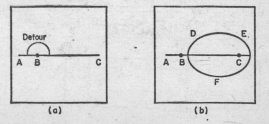

(a)   (b)

Figure 25.14

moval of B does not prevent a return journey from C to A, because a detour is possible. To make the trip impossible would require a disaster destroying all points along some entire path (Figure 25.14b) like DEF, so that no avenue of return in any direction is possible. If the insect is to be prevented from returning to A, it will take not merely a great many points but a certain arrangement of these points to block the way. In Figure 25.14b we notice that the simplest kind of point set or "space" that will cut point C off from point A is what we are tempted to term *1-dimensional*. This gives us the idea of saying that a square or some other space is 2-dimensional, if when you wish to join two of its points, it requires a one-dimensional set to prevent you from doing so. We cannot call this statement a definition because we don't precisely know what it means for a set to be one-dimensional, and hence it would not be logical to use the idea of one-dimensionality to explain the notion of two-dimensionality. However, we have made very definite progress. For the situation which confronts us now is a very familiar one in mathematics. We are faced with an *induction*. To explain three-dimensionality we need the notion of two-dimensionality; to explain two-dimensionality it is sufficient to understand one-dimensionality. When we have done this, we are prepared at once, *by induction*, (that is, one step at a time) to define all higher dimensions.

You notice that there are two features to this projected dimension theory. First, it is in some sense a negative approach. We converted the idea of having enough "room" into an idea of "obstacles," of being unable to do something when certain point sets are removed from our space. Second, we have hitched our wagon to mathematical induction, a very powerful and beautiful mathematical tool. This approach to the problem is due to Poincaré, who gave it in a form considerably more precise than we have.

In mathematical inductions it is customary to start with the case $n = 1$, but in the dimension theory of topological spaces, one goes back to the completely empty set $\emptyset$ for which a *negative* dimensionality, -1, is postulated. Now let us consider a set consisting of two isolated points, A and B (Figure 25.15). If you wish to move from A to B, you cannot, since there are no points in between. You are blocked from the very start by the empty set, $\emptyset$. Because motion is blocked by the empty set, which has dimension -1, the dimensionality of our space of two points is one

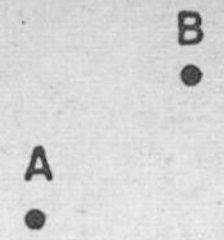

B
●

A
●

Figure 25.15 A 0-dimensional space

-higher. Hence it is 0-dimensional. A space consisting of one point is *a fortiori* 0-dimensional. Since it is not empty, it cannot have dimensionality −1, and if its dimensionality were higher than zero, we would have the contradiction that part of the above two-point space is of higher dimension than the whole. If we have a space of three points or any finite number of points, it is readily seen that the argument for the two-point space can be repeated. Hence any space containing a finite number of points is 0-dimensional. If the countably infinite set of natural numbers {1, 2, 3, . . .} is graphed on the real number line, there are gaps or empty spaces between the points. Therefore motion between any pair of points is impossible; that is, it is blocked by the empty set. Hence the set of natural numbers is 0-dimensional. Any countable set can be matched with it and given a matching topology so that all countable sets become *equivalent* topological spaces of the *same dimension*. Thus the countable set of all rational points, for example, would be 0-dimensional. Although the set of irrational points is not countable, it can be proved that it is 0-dimensional.

This brings us to the meaning of a 1-dimensional space. It is one where movement between any pair of points can be blocked by a 0-dimensional space. Then a straight line is 1-dimensional because, as we have seen, a single point blocks motion. What about a circle or any closed curve? On the circle of Figure 25.1 the removal of the single point B will not block motion between A and C. If, however, in Figure 25.1 we also remove a point from the longer arc from A to C, motion from A to C will be impossible. Since it requires the removal of two points, that is, a 0-dimensional set, to block motion between any pair of points on the circumference, the circle is 1-dimensional. Hence any closed curve is also 1-dimensional because such a curve is homeomorphic to a circle. Next we pronounce the square 2-dimensional because it requires the removal of a 1-dimensional space to prevent the motion between any pair of points of the square. In Figure 25.14b we see that removal of a circle or closed curve will accomplish the blockage, but how do we know that there is no 0-dimensional set that would be equally effective? When we think of a point set as dense as the irrationals, for example, we might imagine that this or some similar sort of very dense 0-dimensional set might do the trick. With our limited development of general topology we are unable to prove the nonexistence of any such set, but it can actually be demonstrated that no 0-dimensional set will block the way. Similarly, when a space is to be proved 8-dimensional, one must show that motion between any pair of its points will be blocked by a 7-dimensional set but not by one of 6 or fewer dimensions.

We may feel that a lot of trouble is involved in proving a square 2-dimensional, when we were intuitively sure that this was so right along. A criterion like the one of our definition is important, however, for the varied types of sets that can be converted into topological spaces, many of which defy intuition as well as simpler methods of defining dimension. We saw that even the more or less elementary aggregate of irrational points is puzzling. Its points are as numerous as those in the entire real set and differ from it by the relatively negligible set of rationals; yet the modern topological theory of dimensionality assigns a lower dimension to the irrationals than to the reals. This is another indication that topological properties like dimensionality are qualitative and may appear, at times, to conflict with results obtained from counting or measurement. Again, we are reminded that *analysis situs* is concerned with situation, and it is the relative situation of the irrationals, rather than the length they cover, that determines a topological property.

Topology is too new a subject to have many practical applications. Perhaps its most important service, however, has been that of solving baffling problems in *other* branches of mathematics where the traditional quantitative methods have failed or are incredibly arduous. As Weyl humorously put it, the "soul" of each mathematical subject in turn is likely to be captured by topology. In applied mathematics there has been "capture" of parts of electrical network theory, industrial management science, linear programming and game theory, statistical mechanics, social psychology and other behavioral sciences by today's *graph theory*, a subject which applies the *combinatorial topology* of certain specialized 1-dimensional sets, called *graphs*.

The origin of graph theory, like that of some other combinatorial topological questions, can be attributed to Euler. In his day there were seven bridges crossing the Pregel River in Königsberg, Germany (Figure 25.16). Walking along the bridges from one bank of the river to islands in the river and then to the other bank and back was a favorite Sunday pastime. The arrangement of the bridges is indicated in the *graph* (set of vertices and connecting edges) of Figure 25.16, in which there are 4 vertices and 7 edges. Euler asked: Is the graph *unicursal*, that is, can one traverse *all* seven bridges without crossing any bridge twice? By

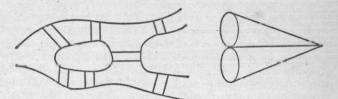

Figure 25.16   Königsberg bridges and their graph

combinatorial reasoning not unlike that used in our earlier treatment of permutations and combinations, Euler arrived at a negative answer and the following theorems:

(1) In any graph the number of *odd* vertices (an odd vertex being one that lies on an odd number of edges) is even.

(2) A graph that has no odd vertices can be described unicursally by a circuit or re-entrant route that starts at any vertex and returns to that vertex.

(3) A graph that has exactly two odd vertices can be described unicursally by a route starting at one of the odd vertices and ending at the other.

(4) A graph that has more than two odd vertices *cannot* be described unicursally.

The Königsberg bridge graph exhibits 4 odd vertices and hence, by the last theorem quoted, cannot be traversed unicursally.

In any graph the unicursal routes which pass over each *edge* exactly once are called *Euler lines* (Euler *circuits* if they are re-entrant). A "dual" concept is that of a *Hamilton line* (Hamilton circuit) which passes through every *vertex* exactly once. Since the existence of Hamilton lines (circuits) is important in many practical applications of graph theory, it is unfortunate that, in contrast to the situation with Euler lines, there are no general theorems solving the existence problem for Hamilton lines. One must still rely, to considerable extent, on trial and error.

Hamilton lines arose in connection with the recreational game to which allusion was made in the footnote on page 127 of Volume One. In a paper presented before the British Mathematical Association meeting at Dublin in 1857, Hamilton proposed and (using combinatorial analysis and group theory) solved some special cases of the following problem: In a regular dodecahedron is there a continuous route (along the edges) that passes through each of the 20 vertices exactly once? Since our problem involves only *topological* aspects of a 1-dimensional point set, we need not consider the regular dodecahedron as pictured in Figure 25.7 or as constructed in one of the commercial "go round the world" versions of Hamilton's original puzzle. In such toys there is usually a wooden dodecahedron with a nail at each vertex (which

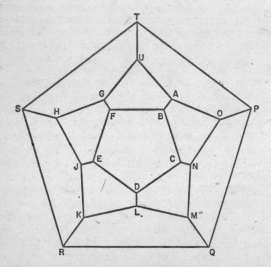

Figure 25.17   Graph of the 20 vertices and 30 edges of a regular dodecahedron

bears the name of a city—Frankfort, Brussels, Delhi, etc.) and a string to wind from nail to nail along the edges. For our purposes we can imagine the network of dodecahedron edges to be deformed and flattened into the graph of Figure 25.17. In that graph the reader can verify that the following are Hamilton circuits:

ABCDEFGHJKLMNOPQRSTUA
FBAUTPONCDEJKLMQRSHGF
FBAUTSRKLMQPONCDEJHGF

He can also observe that, although the circuits pass through all vertices, they do *not* traverse all edges.

The matter of Euler and Hamilton lines is purely topological, but when graph theory assigns lengths to edges or "weights" to vertices, quantitative elements are added to the associated problem. For example, in Hamilton's problem one might give the distance (by air) between each pair of adjacent cities (that is, cities joined by an edge). Then there arise maximum and minimum problems, questions of optimization reminiscent of the game theory and linear programming questions of Chapter 11, and the variational issues of Chapter 23. Thus the methodology of graph theory has found the shortest route (by air) for a complete circuit (without duplication) of all the capital cities in the United States. This is a special case of the "traveling salesman problem," where the salesman must visit certain towns before returning to his home office and wishes to accomplish his task in the shortest time or as inexpensively as possible.

All of these facts indicate that even if topology has not yet reached the man in the street, it is at present a useful tool and an intriguing one to those who enjoy puzzles and mathematical recreations. Additional aspects of the subject can be revealed by considering the history of its development. We have already mentioned Euler repeatedly as a sort of founding father. Gauss, who was too modest to place his claim in the discovery of non-Euclidean geometry, appears to have also withheld most of his thoughts on analysis situs. In one of his posthumous papers, however, there is the prediction that the subject would become a matter of the greatest importance in the years ahead. In 1833 he had complained, "Leibniz initiated the geometry of situation, Euler and Vandermonde gave it momentary consideration, but after a century and a half we still know practically nothing about it." Gauss himself actually did very little to alleviate this situation. His topological work consisted of analyzing knots associated with a problem of electrostatics where linked and unlinked networks are involved. The physicist Kirchhoff (1824–1887) developed the matter fully, and his results are still of practical importance in electric network theory. Some of the more complicated problems lend themselves to elegant solutions provided, once more, by the new, fashionable graph theory.

It was Gauss's most outstanding student, Riemann, who made the first major contribution to *analysis situs,* namely, the formulation of certain abstractions which are still called *Riemann surfaces.* They solved the problem of converting general relations between complex variables into (one-valued or uniform) functions. Instead of representing the variable z in one Cartesian plane, Riemann conceived of 2 or 3 or 4 or more z-planes or sheets, according to whether the relation is a one-to-two or one-to-three or one-to-four correspondence, etc. (Figure 25.18). He pictured the sheets as

Figure 25.18   Riemann surface for the values of z when z and w are related by a one-to-two correspondence ($w^2 = z$, for example).

attached at certain special points ("branch points") and also envisioned certain abstract "bridges" enabling passage from one sheet to another. In this way he established the homeomorphism or topological equivalence of the w-plane and the many-sheeted z-plane or Riemann surface. In short, Riemann *topologized analysis,* as mathematicians are wont to say.

As far as combinatorial *analysis situs* is concerned, Poincaré is the next mathematician in chronological order. In fact, researchers today usually consider pre-Poincaré topology as trivial and name the French leader as the creator of the whole subject. Since Poincaré was a universalist who applied his magic touch to so many mathematical domains, what motivated his decade of intensive concentration on the new "geometry"? It was his attempt to solve one of the most difficult problems in all mathematics, the so-called *n*-body problem. For the simplest case, $n = 2$, that is, the 2-body problem, the solution was given by Newton. This is merely the story we told previously about his *proof* of Kepler's third law, that is, his solution of the differential equations obtained from his second law of motion and his inverse-square law of gravitational attraction. His solution gave the *approximate* orbits of two heavenly bodies, the sun and the earth, say, or the earth and the moon, etc. We emphasize the word *approximate* because the sun and a planet, or a planet and a satellite, are not two isolated bodies exerting gravitational tugs on one another. The pull of all the other bodies exerts an influence, and hence the *n*-body problem is that of determining what the *exact* course of all celestial bodies will be for all future time, or what it was in all the past, given exceedingly precise observational data *now*, or at any particular instant of time.

In 1887 King Oscar II of Sweden offered a prize for the solution of this problem. Poincaré did not solve the problem, but he was awarded the prize for his formidable attack on the special case $n = 3$, the 3-body problem (the determination of all-time orbits for sun, earth, moon, for example). It was the overpowering difficulty of the quantitative approach to the problem that motivated qualitative considerations, and this required Poincaré to formulate a rigorous geometry of situation. To explain the full meaning of the mathematics would involve a lengthy digression. Hence let us merely remark that the 3-body problem involves the solution of a system of nine differential equations.

Poincaré showed that if two of the bodies have masses that are small compared to the third, *periodic* solutions exist. Shortly before his death in 1912, he proved that certain orbits could be periodic, *provided* that a simple geometric theorem, topological in nature, is true. He was ailing and fatigued at the time and found himself unable to demonstrate the proposition on which the whole issue depended. The theorem *sounds* like an easy one, for it concerns the annular area between two concentric circles, the problem being to prove that when a certain topological transformation of this area is carried out, two of its points must remain fixed. It is hard to believe that a serious issue of dynamical astronomy can depend on such an apparently simple question. In 1913 George D. Birkhoff (whose ergodic theorem was discussed in Chapter 15) gained international fame in the mathematical world by *proving* the last theorem of Poincaré, a feat considered one of the greatest achievements in the American mathematician's long, distinguished career. Like many of the most difficult topological problems (some are still unsolved), the particular theorem sounds like an exercise in high school geometry.

In the same way, many of the famous theorems of topology sound obvious or trivial. For example, there is the *Jordan curve theorem*. Any curve homeomorphic to a circle is called a Jordan curve, and the theorem establishes that in the plane, or on the sphere, a Jordan curve divides the surface into two distinct regions which have no point in common (an "inside" and an "outside"). Figure 19.6 indicates that the theorem does not hold on the torus. Some things that appear obvious form the still unsolved problems of topology. For example, suppose that a country is subdivided into states or districts, and a map of this country is to be colored in such a way that no two states with a common boundary have the same color. (This common boundary must be a line segment and may not be a single point.) By diagramming the most intricate kinds of subdivision, the reader can convince himself, by trial, that *four* colors will always suffice. To date no proof of this "obvious fact" has been obtained even though the problem has been under investigation ever since Moebius proposed it more than a century ago.

It has been proved, however, that *seven* colors suffice for any map on the torus, however complicated the scheme of subdivision. The minimum number of colors required for a map on a specified surface is called the *chromatic number* of that surface, and furnishes another example of a topological invariant. Thus the chromatic number of the torus is 7, and topologists hope to be able to prove that the chromatic number of the plane is 4.

As emphasized earlier, the topological invariants connected with a surface or space help to characterize it, and therefore by establishing the inequality of Euler characteristics, chromatic numbers, or other numerical invariants, one can demonstrate that two abstract manifolds are not homeomorphic, and thus belong to different classifications. Such use of invariants is much easier than attempting to prove directly that no homeomorphism exists for two configurations.

The chromatic number is an invariant arising through the subdivision of a surface, and in general, topology arrives at characterizations of manifolds by studying the nature of the submanifolds which can be embedded in them. For example, invariants of a surface can be derived from the curves which can be drawn on these surfaces. Thus, on a sphere, an ordinary closed curve like a circle or an ellipse can be contracted continuously into a point without leaving the surface. On the other hand, a meridional or a latitudinal circle on a torus (Figure 25.19a) cannot be contracted con-

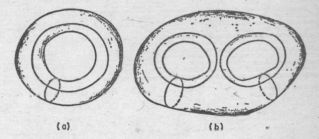

(a)   (b)

Figure 25.19   Variation in connectivity and Betti number on different surfaces

tinuously into a point without breaking away from the surface. This situation was described earlier (Chapter 19) as a matter of *connectivity*, a property associated with the possibility of *connecting* any point of a surface with any other by means of a continuous path. Thus, on a torus, even if a meridional and a latitudinal circle are drawn, it is still possible to connect any point of the surface with any other without crossing these circles; that is, they do not fence in any portion of the surface. By contrast, a single circle, or any simple closed curve, can serve as a dividing line on a spherical surface. Hence the sphere is said to be *simply connected*, whereas the torus is described as being *multiply connected* or having a higher order of connectivity. But another way the topologist handles this question is to apply the notion of *homotopy* or continuous deformation. On a simply connected surface any simple closed curve can be deformed continuously into any other, or all closed curves are equivalent, if homotopy is the criterion. This is not the case on nonsimply connected surfaces.

Instead of studying closed curves from the point of view of homotopy, one may relate them to the Jordan curve theorem, and examine their bounding properties. The fact that in the plane or on the sphere a closed curve bounds, that is, has an "inside" and an "outside," although this need not be the case on the torus or other surfaces of higher genus, suggests a way of establishing the nonhomeomorphism of surfaces. If a third closed curve were drawn on the torus of Figure 25.19*a*, it would divide the surface into two parts, or be a boundary. But in the torus with two holes (Figure 25.19*b*), one may draw meridional and latitudinal circles around each hole (4 closed curves in all) without obtaining a boundary, that is, without dividing the surface into disjoint areas. Therefore the torus with two holes is *not* homeomorphic to the ordinary torus.

These facts are associated with numerical invariants of each surface. The maximum number of closed curves which can be drawn on a surface without dividing it into disjoint areas is a topological invariant called the 1-dimensional *Betti number* of the surface, after the Italian Enrico Betti (1823–1892). From what was stated above, the Betti numbers for the sphere, the simple torus, and the torus with two holes must be 0, 2, 4, respectively. But Riemann held priority over Betti in indicating the topological invariance for each surface of the number of non-bounding closed curves. Since the German geometer actually wished to *divide* a surface by means of closed curves, he always drew one more closed curve than Betti or Poincaré and therefore the *Riemannian connectivity number* is the minimum number of closed curves that will divide a surface into disjoint regions. Thus this number is always one greater than the corresponding Betti number. Hence the sphere, torus, and two-holed torus possess connectivity 1, 3, 5, respectively.

It seems intuitive that the Riemann-Betti-Poincaré notion should be capable of generalization to invariants associated with the dividing or bounding properties of sets or closed surfaces in a 3-dimensional manifold, and then to analogous invariants for abstract spaces of higher dimensionality. Poincaré did, in fact, develop his *homology theory* on this basis, and since he believed in the omnipotence of the group concept, it is not surprising that he applied it with fruitful results in this instance. If a closed curve C or "cycle," as it is called in topology, is the *boundary* of a region on a surface, the Poincaré theory states that "C is homologous to zero," which is symbolized by $C \sim 0$. If cycles are oriented (clockwise and counterclockwise), then $-C$ has a meaning. Since one can go round and round a closed curve, $2C$, $3C$, $4C$, etc., also have meaning. Cycles may be added and subtracted. Thus $C + C'$ and $C - C'$ are indicated in Figures 25.20a and 25.20b. If one selects a convention concerning the

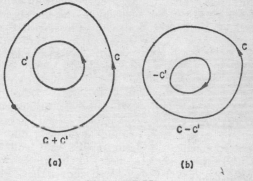

(a)   (b)

Figure 25.20

region bounded and this assumption is intuitively equivalent to having the area to the *left* of the bounding curves, then $C - C'$ bounds the annulus in Figure 25.20b, or $C - C' \sim 0$. In this case, C is said to be homologous to C'. From the point of view of homology, C and C' are equivalent. If all cycles homologous to a particular one are considered equivalent, then they can be classified as a single type. Thus homology is an equivalence relation for the classification of cycles, just as earlier in this chapter homeomorphism was an equivalence relation for spaces. The number of types of cycle, that is, the number of *homology classes*, on a manifold is an invariant of the manifold. From what has been stated above, it is easy to show that the cycle types on a manifold form a commutative or abelian group with respect to the operation of addition. Poincaré named this the *Betti group*. The concept of cycles and their homologies may be extended to 3-dimensional, 4-dimensional, . . . , n-dimensional manifolds. On higher dimensional manifolds one has not only closed curves but also closed surfaces, etc.; that is, the cycles have 1, 2, 3, 4, etc. dimensions.

Poincaré formulated the concepts of cycle and homology

more exactly by developing an algebraic or combinatorial scheme of representation for a manifold. Then he showed that the fundamental problem of homology theory is to determine the structure of the Betti groups for the 1-, 2-, 3-, . . . , n-dimensional cycles, and in particular to determine the numerical invariants associated with each Betti group. These are called the n-dimensional *Betti numbers* and the *coefficients of torsion* (in nonorientable manifolds). There is a fundamental theorem: Two orientable manifolds which have equal Betti numbers of all dimensions are topologically equivalent. After Poincaré, other significant contributions to homology theory were made by members of the Princeton school, in particular by Oswald Veblen (1880–1960), J. W. Alexander, and Solomon Lefschetz. Alexander proved the so-called duality theorem, which is a broad generalization of the Jordan curve theorem. Then this theorem was extended still further by Lefschetz and by P. Alexandroff and Pontrjagin. Lefschetz established certain "intersection" theorems and applied these to developing very important formulas for the number of points which remain fixed when a manifold is subjected to a continuous mapping onto itself. This theory of fixed points was applied in the previously mentioned research of Birkhoff and Morse.

There are a number of great names in topology today. The Princeton school is still notable, but there are also distinguished topologists outside the United States. Some of these contribute directly to the subject, whereas others apply its concepts to various branches of mathematics much as Cartan used topological concepts in differential geometry. In fact, as the twentieth century advanced, both analytic and combinatorial topology progressed far beyond their initial phases. Major developments in point-set topology are due to the modern Polish analysts and to the school of the American mathematician R. L. Moore. But the United States has contributed even more notably to the growth of combinatorial topology through the remarkable discoveries mentioned above, and those made more recently by mathematicians at Princeton and the Institute for Advanced Study. One can name specifically H. Marston Morse, A. W. Tucker, Hassler Whitney, N. E. Steenrod. Their research, exceedingly advanced in nature, contributes to the rigorization, generalization, and application of the elementary topological concepts considered in this book.

In the present and preceding chapters there has been some

indication of how the "angel of topology" is a guiding spirit in modern geometry, analysis, physics, and mathematical astronomy, but the *bon mot* of Weyl quoted at the outset of this chapter implies that *analysis situs* has penetrated into other mathematical subjects and pervades current activity. Thus topology is likely to be a most potent factor in the immediate future of mathematics.

Chapter 26

The Leonardos of Modern Mathematics

Leonardo da Vinci is the classic example of the universal genius, an increasingly rare type in human history, primarily because the advance of civilization entails more and more specialization of interests. Carl Friedrich Gauss, the towering figure who provided a glorious ending to the eighteenth century of mathematical history and propelled the nineteenth century into vital activity, was not a universalist in the same sense as Leonardo. However, his creative thought was all-encompassing within the domain of mathematics and physical science. His biography was given in Chapter 19 and his name has been mentioned in almost every chapter. His contributions to number theory, differential geometry, non-Euclidean geometry, astronomy, probability theory, the theory of functions, and topology have been discussed. Now, a century after Gauss, there is probably no living mathematician who is able to contribute so notably to so many different mathematical specialties. Twentieth-century science has reached a point where our leading thinkers usually find it necessary to devote themselves to a subspecialty of a subspecialty of a field already highly specialized. This is markedly true in mathematics, where Henri Poincaré and David Hilbert are often considered to have been the last of the universalists, with the concession that more recent additions to the mathematical Pantheon, like Hermann Weyl and John von Neumann, were still able to place the stamp of their genius on many branches of the mother science.

What manner of man can embrace all or most of mathematics in his research activities? Perhaps some clue is to be found in the biographies of the modern mathematical

"Leonardos." The personal stories of Gauss and von Neumann have already been told, but there remains the matter of examining the biographies of Poincaré, Hilbert, and Weyl. If the mathematical ideas and discoveries of all five men were presented in complete detail, they would offer a fairly complete survey of modern mathematics.

Henri Poincaré was born in Nancy in 1854, the son of Léon Poincaré, a physician whose native town was Rouen. The family was a distinguished one; Henri's first cousin, Raymond, was president of France during World War I; his sister, several years his junior, married the philosopher Émile Boutroux, and her son was a budding young mathematician when death cut his career short.

Poincaré was a delicate child and was affected badly by diphtheria and other serious illnesses of childhood. There was little romping and outdoor sport for him. Instead he received his first education at home under the kindly guidance and direction of his mother. At elementary school his greatest interest was nature study, and this was not replaced by mathematics until he was fifteen years of age. His literary aptitude manifested itself early, for a composition written by him at age nine was pronounced a "small masterpiece" by his teacher. It is not surprising then that his mature years brought membership in the *literary* section of the Institut de France, an honor never accorded to any other mathematician.

His scientific education began with a short period at the School of Forestry, where he was awarded first prize in mathematics. He left this school shortly in order to enter the École Polytechnique, and after graduating from this famous institution, he decided to become an engineer and hence attended the School of Mines. He served as an engineer at Vesoul, not far from Nancy, where on one occasion he was a member of a rescue crew after a mine explosion and fire had occurred. But his very first research papers—in the field of differential equations—attracted the attention of leading French mathematicians, and he was offered a teaching position at Caen. In 1881, when he was twenty-seven, he was called to the University of Paris, where his academic advancement was rapid. In 1886 he became professor of mathematical physics and probability theory, and later occupied the chair in celestial mechanics. From 1904 to 1908 he held a chair in astronomy at the École Polytechnique. From 1908 to 1912 his health was poor, and at age fifty-eight he died suddenly from an embolism following surgery.

In the field of research Poincaré's total creative output was so varied in subject matter and so colossal in volume that it is almost impossible to survey it. Hence it seems best to indicate three or four of his major specialties. He carried on research in differential equations as related to both physical science and pure mathematics. Earlier in this book we quoted his belief that mathematical astronomy is a major scientific subject. The fact that he was the primary figure in the creation of modern combinatorial topology has been emphasized and illustrated.

Poincaré was an exceedingly modest man. That, along with his belief that the world of mathematics should be an international one, made him often give credit to foreign (non-French) mathematicians for work that he had done himself. To honor the Italian mathematician Enrico Betti, Poincaré named certain topological entities Betti numbers (Chapter 25), although Poincaré, not Betti, had discovered them. The story is similar for the Fuchsian functions, where Poincaré wished to compliment the German analyst Lazarus Fuchs (1833–1902). There is a mathematical joke to the effect that Poincaré called certain functions Kleinian because Felix Klein had nothing to do with them. This is not quite accurate, however. About 1881 Poincaré had initiated his theory of *automorphic functions,* a generalization of elliptic functions (Chapter 7), which are themselves a generalization of ordinary trigonometric functions. He was unaware that Klein held priority. When the latter wrote a letter to apprise Poincaré of this fact, he immediately gave Klein's name to all subsequent automorphic functions, and in fact to much of their theory which he himself developed, single-handedly, after Klein had a nervous breakdown. One thing is certain: the French leader extended himself in generosity to mathematicians of other nationalities.

During the years when Poincaré was working on automorphic functions he also carried on research in algebra and number theory, and during every period of his professional life he gave some of his best thought to mathematical astronomy. His results appeared in the three volumes of his *Méthodes nouvelles de la mécanique céleste,* published in 1892, 1893, and 1899. Then he published another three volumes in 1905, 1909, 1910, this work being en-

titled *Leçons de mécanique céleste*. This was more peda-
gogical and practical than his earlier three-volume treatise,
which had been largely mathematical and theoretical, and
so revolutionary in its point of view that it was considered
comparable to Laplace's *Mécanique céleste*. As sequels to
these astronomical works there were his *Leçons sur les
figures d'équilibre d'une masse fluide* and his *Leçons sur les
hypothèses cosmogoniques*. But it is impossible to make a
suitable selection of Poincaré titles from some five hundred
research papers, thirty books on mathematical physics and
astronomy, numerous philosophic and popular works on
science.

A remark on these last is, however, in order. Around the
turn of the century Poincaré started to write a series of
monographs to popularize important aspects of mathematics,
physical science, and the philosophy of science. In these
books he exhibited his literary talent and his ability as a
lucid expositor. E. T. Bell claims that "workmen and shop-
girls could be seen in the parks and cafés of Paris avidly
reading one or other of Poincaré's popular masterpieces in
its cheap print and shabby paper cover."[*] If this sounds like
an exaggeration, let us say that these very monographs are
very popular in France at the present time, and in their
English translations are best sellers among paperbacks on
science in the United States today.

It is evident that Poincaré's life was "all work and no
play." One would like to think that he found his trips for
the purpose of lecturing at mathematical or scientific con-
gresses a sort of vacation. One of these brought him to the
United States in 1904, when he was one of the guest speakers
at the St. Louis Exposition. Like most mathematicians he
enjoyed music, and he was very happy in the midst of his
family—his wife, son, and three daughters.

David Hilbert was born just eight years after Poincaré,
on January 23, 1862, in the city of Königsberg in East
Prussia. We have the word of Hermann Weyl that Hilbert's career was comparable to that of the other mathematical "Leonardos" we have named: "The world looked
upon David Hilbert as the greatest mathematician living in
the first decades of the twentieth century." Weyl gave one
important reason for this evaluation:

[*] E. T. Bell, *Men of Mathematics*, Simon and Schuster, New York, 1937,
p. 530.

At the International Mathematical Congress in Paris in 1900 David Hilbert, convinced that problems are the life-blood of science, formulated twenty-three unsolved problems which he expected to play an important role in the development of mathematics during the next era. How much better he predicted the future of mathematics than any politician foresaw the gifts of war and terror that the new century was about to lavish upon mankind! We mathematicians have often measured our progress by checking which of Hilbert's questions have been settled.*

Because Weyl was himself a universalist, it was recognized that he was the person best qualified to write a critical biography of Hilbert. Therefore, when the latter died in 1943, leading scientific societies throughout the world called on Weyl to write an account of the great leader's life and work. One of the best and fullest of such eulogies was the one Weyl wrote for the Royal Society of London.† We quote some excerpts from that biography.

Hilbert was descended from a family which had long been settled in Königsberg and had brought forth a series of physicians and judges. During his entire life he preserved uncorrupted the Baltic accent of his home. For a long time Hilbert remained faithfully attached to the town of his forbears, and well deserved its honorary citizenship which was bestowed upon him in his later years. It was at the University of Königsberg that he studied, where in 1884 he received his doctor's degree, and where in 1886 he was admitted as Privatdozent; there, moreover, he was appointed Ausserordentlicher Professor, in 1892, succeeding his teacher and friend Adolf Hurwitz, and in the following year advanced to a full professorship. The continuity of this Königsberg period was interrupted only by a semester's studies at Erlangen, and by a travelling scholarship during the year before his habilitation, which took him to Felix Klein at Leipzig and to Paris where he was attracted mainly to Ch. Hermite. It was on Klein's initiative that Hilbert was called to Göttingen in 1895; there he remained until the end of his life. He retired in the year 1930.

In 1928 he was elected to foreign membership of the Royal Society.

Beginning in his student years at Königsberg a close friendship existed between him and Hermann Minkowski, his junior by two years, and it was with deep satisfaction that in 1902 he succeeded in bringing Minkowski also to Göttingen. Only too soon did the close collaboration of the two friends end with Minkowski's death in 1909. Hilbert and Minkowski were the real heroes of the great

---

* Hermann Weyl, "A Half-Century of Mathematics," *American Mathematical Monthly*, Vol. 58, No. 8 (October 1951), p. 525.

† Royal Society of London, *Obituary Notices of Fellows*, Vol. 4, No. 13 (November 1944), pp. 547 ff.

and brilliant period, unforgettable to those who lived through it, which mathematics experienced during the first decade of this century in Göttingen. Klein ruled over it like a distant god, "divus Felix," from above the clouds; the peak of his mathematical productivity lay behind him. Among the authors of the great number of valuable dissertations which in these fruitful years were written under Hilbert's guidance we find many Anglo-Saxon names, names of men who subsequently have played a considerable role in the development of American mathematics. The physical set-up within which this free scientific life unfolded was quite modest. Not until many years after the first world war, after Felix Klein had gone and Richard Courant had succeeded him, towards the end of the brief period of the German Republic, did Klein's dream of the Mathematical Institute at Göttingen come true. But soon the Nazi storm broke and those who had laid the plans and who taught there with Hilbert were scattered over the earth, and the years after 1933 became for him tragic years of ever deepening loneliness.

Hilbert was of slight build. Above the small lower face with its goatee there rose the dome of a powerful, in later years bald, skull. He was physically agile, a tireless walker, a good skater, and a passionate gardener. Until 1925 he enjoyed good health. Then he fell ill of pernicious anaemia. Yet this illness only temporarily paralyzed his restless activity in teaching and research. He was among the first with whom the liver treatment, inaugurated by G. R. Minot at Harvard, proved successful; undoubtedly it saved Hilbert's life at that time.

Hilbert's research left an indelible imprint on practically all branches of mathematical science. Yet in distinct successive periods he devoted himself with impassioned exclusiveness to but a single subject at a time. Perhaps his deepest investigations are those on the theory of number fields. His monumental report on the "Theorie der algebraischen Zahlkörper", which he submitted to the Deutsche Mathematiker-Vereinigung, is dated as of the year 1897, and as far as I know Hilbert did not publish another paper in this field after 1899. The methodical unity of mathematics was for him a matter of belief and experience. It appeared to him essential that—in the face of the manifold interrelations and for the sake of the fertility of research—the productive mathematician should make himself at home in all fields. To quote his own words: "The question is forced upon us whether mathematics is once to face what other sciences have long ago experienced, namely to fall apart into subdivisions whose representatives are hardly able to understand each other and whose connexions for this reason will become ever looser. I neither believe nor wish this to happen; the science of mathematics as I see it is an indivisible whole, an organism whose ability to survive rests on the connexion between its parts." Theoretical physics also was drawn by Hilbert into the domain of his research; during a whole decade beginning in 1912 it stood at the centre of his interest. Great, fruitful problems appear to him as the life nerve of mathematics. "Just as every human enterprise prosecutes final aims," says he, "so mathematical research needs problems. Their solution steels the force of the investigator." In his famous lecture at the International Congress of Mathematicians at Paris in 1900 Hilbert tries to probe the immediate future of mathematics by posing twenty-three unsolved problems; they have indeed, as we can state to-day in retrospect, played an eminent role in the development of mathematics during the subsequent forty-three years. A characteristic feature of Hilbert's method is a peculiarly direct attack on problems, unfettered by any algorithms; he always goes back to the questions in their original simplicity. When it is a matter of transferring the theory of linear equations from a finite to an infinite number of unknowns he begins by getting rid of the calculatory tool of determinants. A truly great example of far reaching significance is his mastery of Dirichlet's principle which, originally springing from mathematical physics, provided Riemann with the foundation of his theory of algebraic functions and Abelian integrals, but which subsequently had fallen a victim of Weierstrass's pitiless criticism. Hilbert salvaged it in its entirety. The whole finely wrought apparatus of the Calculus of Variations was here consciously set aside. We only need to mention the names R. Courant and M. Morse to indicate what role this direct method of the Calculus of Variations was destined to play in recent times. It seems to me that with Hilbert the mastering of single concrete problems and the forming of general abstract concepts are balanced in a particularly fortunate manner. He came of a time in which the algorithm had played a more extensive part, and therefore he stressed strongly a conceptual procedure; but in the meantime our advance in this direction has been so uninhibited and with so little concern for a growth of the problematics in depth that many of us have begun to fear for the mathematical substance. In Hilbert simplicity and rigour go hand in hand. The growing demand for rigour, imposed by the critical reflections of the nineteenth century upon those parts of mathematics which operate in the continuum, was felt by most investigators as a heavy yoke that made their steps dragging and awkward. Full of longing and with uneasiness they looked back upon Euler's era of happy-go-lucky analysis. With Hilbert rigour figures no longer as enemy, but as promoter of simplicity. Yet the secret of Hilbert's creative force is not plumbed by any of these remarks. A further element of it, I feel, was his sensitivity in registering hints which revealed to him general relations while solving special problems. This is most magnificently exemplified by the way in which, during his theory of numbers period, he was led to the enunciation of his general theorems on class fields and the general law of reciprocity.

We shall now recall Hilbert's most important achievements. In the years 1888–1892 he proved the fundamental finiteness theorems of the *theory of invariants* for the full projective group. His method, though yielding a proof for the existence of a finite basis for the invariants, does not enable one actually to construct it in a concrete individual case. Hence the exclamation by the great algorithmician P. Gordan, at the appearance of Hilbert's paper: "This is not mathematics; this is theology!" It reveals an antithesis which reaches down to the very roots of mathematics. Hilbert, however, in further penetrating investigations, furnished the means for a finite execution of the construction.

His papers on the theory of invariants had the unexpected effect of withering, as it were overnight, a discipline which so far had stood in full bloom. Its central problems he had finished once and for all. Entirely different was his effect on the *theory of number fields*, which he took up in the years 1892–1898. It is a great pleasure to watch how, step by step, in a succession of papers ascending from the particular to the general, the adequate concepts and methods are evolved and the essential connexions come to light. These papers proved of extraordinary fertility for the future. On the pure theory of numbers side I mention the names of Furt-wängler, Takagi, Artin, Hasse, Chevalley, and on the number-and-function theoretical one, those of Fueter and Hecke.

During the subsequent period, 1898–1902, the *foundations of geometry* are nearest to Hilbert's heart, and he is seized by the idea of axiomatics. The soil was well prepared, especially by the Italian school of geometers. Yet it was as if over a landscape, wherein but a few men with a superb sense of orientation had found their way in murky twilight, the sun had risen all at once. Clear and clean-cut we find stated the axiomatic concept according to which geometry is a hypothetical deductive system; it depends on the "implicit definitions" of the concepts of spatial objects and relations which the axioms contain, and not on a description of their intuitive content. A complete and natural system of geometric axioms is set up. They are required to satisfy the logical demands of consistency, independence, and completeness, and by means of quite a few peculiar geometries, constructed *ad hoc*, the proof of independence is furnished in detail. The general ideas appear to us to-day almost banal, but in these examples Hilbert unfolds his typical wealth of invention. While in this fashion the geometric concepts become formalized, the logical ones function as before in their intuitive significance. The further step where logic too succumbs to formalization, thus giving rise to a purely symbolic mathematics—a step upon which Hilbert already pondered at this epoch, as a paper read to the International Congress of 1904 proves, and which is inevitable for the ultimate justification of the role played by the infinite in mathematics—was systematically followed up by Hilbert during the final years of his mathematical productivity, from 1922 on. In contrast to L. E. J. Brouwer's intuitionism, which finds itself forced to abandon major parts of historical mathematics as untenable, Hilbert attempts to save the holdings of mathematics in their entirety by proving its formalism free of contradiction. Admittedly the question of truth is thus shifted into the question of consistency. To a limited extent the latter has been established by Hilbert himself in collaboration with P. Bernays, by J. von Neumann, and G. Gentzen. In recent times, however, the entire enterprise has become questionable on account of K. Gödel's surprising discoveries. While Brouwer has made clear to us to what extent the intuitively certain falls short of the mathematically provable, Gödel shows conversely to what extent the intuitively certain goes beyond what (in an arbitrary but fixed formalism) is capable of mathematical proof. The question of the ultimate foundations and the ultimate meaning of mathematics remains open; we do not know in which direction it will find its final solution nor even whether a final objective answer can be expected at all. "Mathematizing" may well be a creative activity of man, like language or music, of primary originality, whose historical decisions defy complete objective rationalization.

A chance occasion, a lecture in 1901 by the Swedish mathematician E. Holmgren in Hilbert's seminar dealing with the now classical paper of Fredholm's on *integral equations*, then but recently published, provided the impulse which started Hilbert on his investigations on this subject which absorbed his attention until 1912. Fredholm had limited himself to setting up the analogue of the theory of linear equations, while Hilbert recognized that the analogue of the transformation on to principal axes of quadratic forms yields the theory of the eigenvalues and eigenfunctions for the vibration problems of physics. He developed the parallel between integral equations and sum equations in infinitely many unknowns, and subsequently proceeded to push ahead from the spectral theory of "completely continuous" to the much more general one of "bounded" quadratic forms. To-day these things present themselves to us in the framework of a general theory of Hilbert space. Astonishing indeed is the variety of interesting applications which integral equations find in the most diverse branches of mathematics and physics.

It was also due to his influence that the theory of integral equations became a world-wide fad in mathematics for a considerable length of time, producing an enormous literature, for the most part of rather ephemeral value. It was not merit but a favour of fortune when, beginning in 1923 (Heisenberg, Schrödinger) the spectral theory in Hilbert space was discovered to be the adequate mathematical instrument of quantum physics. This later impulse led to a re-examination of the entire complex of problems with refined means (J. von Neumann, M. Stone, and others).

This period of integral equations is followed by Hilbert's physical period. Significant though it was for Hilbert's complete personality as a scientist, it produced a lesser harvest than the purely mathematical phases, and may here be passed over. I shall mention instead two single, somewhat isolated, accomplishments that were to have a great effect: his vindication of Dirichlet's principle; and his proof of a famous century-old conjecture of Waring's, carrying the statement that every integer can be written as a sum of four squares over from squares to arbitrary powers. The physical period is finally succeeded by the last one, already mentioned above, in the course of which Hilbert gives an entirely new turn to the question concerning the foundation and the truth content of mathematics itself. A fruit of Hilbert's pedagogic activity during this period is the charming book by him and Cohn-Vossen, *Anschauliche Geometrie*.

This summary, though far from being complete, may suffice to indicate the universality and depth of Hilbert's mathematical work. He impressed the seal of his spirit upon a whole era of mathematics. And yet I do not believe that his research work alone accounts for the brilliance that radiated from him, nor for his tremendous influence. Gauss and Riemann, to mention two other Göttingers, were greater mathematicians than Hilbert, and yet their immediate effect upon their contemporaries was undoubtedly smaller. Part of this is certainly due to the changing conditions of time, but the character of the men is probably more decisive. Hilbert's was a nature filled with the zest of living, seeking the intercourse of other people, and delighting in the exchange of scientific ideas. He had his own free manner of learning and teaching. His comprehensive mathematical knowledge he acquired not so much from lectures as in conversations with Minkowski and Hurwitz. "On innumerable walks, at times undertaken day by day," he tells in his obituary on Hurwitz, "we browsed in the course of eight years through every corner of mathematical science." And as he had learned from Hurwitz, so he taught in later years his own pupils—on far-flung walks through the woods surrounding Göttingen or, on rainy days, as peripatetics, in his covered garden walk. His optimism, his spiritual passion, and his unshakable faith in the value of science were irresistibly infectious. He says: "The conviction of the solvability of each and every mathematical problem spurs us on during our work; we hear within ourselves the steady call: there is the problem; search for the solution. You can find it by sheer thinking, for in mathematics there is no *ignorabimus*." His enthusiasm did get along with criticism, but not with scepticism. The snobbish attitude of pretended indifference, of "merely fooling around with things" or even of playful cynicism, did not exist in his circle. Hilbert was enormously industrious; he liked to quote Lichtenberg's saying: "Genius is industry." Yet for all this there was light and laughter around him. Under the influence of his dominating power of suggestion one readily considered important whatever he did; his vision and experience inspired confidence in the fruitfulness of the hints he dropped. It is moreover decisive that he was not merely a scientist but a scientific personality, and therefore capable not only of teaching the technique of his science but also of being a spiritual leader. Although not committing himself to one of the established epistemological or metaphysical doctrines, he was a philosopher in that he was concerned with the life of the idea as it realizes itself among men and as an indivisible whole; he had the force to evoke it, he felt responsible for it in his own sphere, and measured his individual scientific efforts against it. Last, not least, the environment also helped. A university such as Göttingen, in the halcyon days before 1914, was particularly favourable for the development of a living scientific school. Once a band of disciples had gathered around Hilbert, intent upon research and little worried by the toil of teaching, it was but natural that in joint competitive aspiration of related aims each should stimulate the other; there was no need that everything come from the master.

His homeland and America among all countries felt Hilbert's impact most thoroughly. His influence upon American mathematics was not restricted to his immediate pupils. Thus, for instance, the Hilbert of the foundations of geometry had a profound effect on E. H. Moore and O. Veblen; the Hilbert of integral equations on George D. Birkhoff.

A picture of Hilbert's personality should also touch upon his attitude regarding the great powers in the lives of men; social and political organization, art, religion, morals and manners, family, friendship, love. Suffice it to say here that he was singularly free from all national and racial prejudices, that in all questions, political, social, or spiritual, he stood forever on the side of freedom, frequently in isolated opposition to the compact majority of his environment. Unforgotten by all those present remains the unanimous and prolonged applause which greeted him in 1928 at Bologna, the first International Congress of Mathematicians at which, following a lengthy struggle, the Germans were once more admitted. It was a telling expression of veneration for the great mathematician whom every one knew to have risen from a severe illness, but at the same time an expression of respect for the independent attitude, "au dessus de la mêlée", from which he had not wavered during the world conflict. He died in Göttingen, Germany, in 1943, at the age of eighty-one, when he succumbed to a compound fracture of the thigh brought about by a domestic accident.

Weyl, Hilbert's biographer, is the last, in chronological order, of the modern Leonardos with whom the present chapter is concerned. Because Weyl was a universalist, it was a group of mathematicians, rather than a single specialist who wrote his biography, namely, Professors M. H. A. Newman, H. Davenport, P. Hall, G. E. H. Reuter, and

L. Rosenfeld. Each one of these men is an expert in a particular one of Weyl's specialties and hence is able to explain Weyl's role in the area in question.*

Hermann Weyl was born on 9 November 1885, the son of Ludwig and Anna Weyl, in the small town of Elmshorn near Hamburg. When his schooldays in Altona ended in 1904 he entered Göttingen University as a country lad of eighteen, and there remained (except for a year at Munich), first as student and then as Privatdozent, until his call to Zurich in 1913. Of these days he said (in the obituary of Hilbert for this Society, 1944), "Hilbert and Minkowski were the real heroes of the great and brilliant period which mathematics experienced during the first decade of the century Göttingen, unforgettable to those who lived through it. Klein ruled over it like a distant god, 'divus Felix,' from above the clouds." Among those nearer to his own age whom he found there were Carathéodory and Harald Bohr, Courant, Zermelo, Erhard Schmidt.

While still a schoolboy he had picked up in his father's house an old copy of the *Critique of Pure Reason*, and absorbed with enthusiasm Kant's thesis of the *a priori* nature of Euclidean geometry. But in Göttingen Hilbert had just completed his classical work on the foundations of geometry, with its host of strange "counter"-geometries. Kantian philosophy could not survive this blow: Weyl transferred his allegiance to Hilbert. "I resolved to study whatever this man had written. At the end of my first year I went home with the 'Zahlbericht' under my arm, and during the summer vacation I worked my way through it—without any previous knowledge of elementary number theory or Galois theory. These were the happiest months of my life, whose shine, across years burdened with our common share of doubt and failure, still comforts my soul."

In spite of the great variety of mathematical stimulation of the Göttingen years, this was the only period of comparable length in which he devoted himself to a single branch of mathematics—analysis, and to a single theme, the problems that arose naturally out of his dissertation, on singular integral equations. Towards the end of this period two causes combined to turn his attention to wider fields. First, in the session 1911–1912 he lectured on the theory of Riemann surfaces, and was led by his sense of the inadequacy of existing treatments to plunge deep into the topological foundations. Secondly, in 1913 he accepted the offer of a chair at the Institute of Technology in Zurich, where his colleague for one year was Einstein, who was just then discovering the general theory of relativity. Weyl was soon launched on the series of papers on relatively and differential geometry which culminated

* Royal Society of London, *Biographical Memoirs of Fellows*, Vol. 2 (1956), pp. 305 ff.

in the book *Raum-Zeit Materie*. Later still this work led on, through his analysis and generalization of the Lie-Helmholtz space-problem, to his third great theme, the representation theory of the classical groups, and its application to quantum theory.

In the decade 1917–1927, he was at the height of his powers. A stream of papers appeared, not only on his main themes, but on any mathematical topics that interested him—and that meant in almost all parts of mathematics. (A glance at the papers listed in the bibliography under the year 1921 will give some impression of the spread of his interests at this time.) He was ready to defend this universality, this refusal to put all his effort into making steady and systematic progress in one field. "My own mathematical works were always quite unsystematic, without method or connexion. Expression and shape are almost more to me than knowledge itself. But I believe that, leaving aside my own peculiar nature, there is in mathematics itself, in contrast to the experimental disciplines, a character which is nearer to that of free creative art. For this reason the modern scientific urge to found Institutes of Science is not so good for mathematics, where the relationship between teacher and pupil should be milder and looser. In the fine arts we do not normally seek to impose the systematic training of pupils upon creative artists."

The years at Zurich were happy ones, during which, he says, the worst that happened to disturb his peace was a series of offers of chairs by foreign universities; "for such decisions worried me." In the *Rückblick* he tells amusingly how, when he received his first invitation to Göttingen, to succeed Klein in 1923, he walked his wife Hella round and round a block in Zurich till nearly midnight, then jumped on the last tram to telegraph acceptance—and refused. The second invitation, to succeed Hilbert in 1930, he accepted, after still more painful hesitations. But his short stay as professor in Göttingen was clouded over by the threat of coming political events. In 1933 he decided that he could not stay in Germany after the dismissal of his colleagues by the Nazis, and he accepted an offer of permanent membership of the Institute for Advanced Study, then newly founded in Princeton. There he worked as a member till his retirement in 1951, and he remained an emeritus member till his death in 1955, spending half his time there and half in Zurich. Of the Institute he said that it is the finest workshop for a mathematician that it is possible to imagine.

He married in 1913 Helene Joseph, the daughter of a doctor in Ribnitz in Mecklenburg, and there were two sons of the marriage. All who were visitors at the Weyls' house in Mercer Street will remember her charm and gaiety. She shared to the full his taste for philosophy and for imaginative and poetical literature, and was the translator of many Spanish works, including the writings of Ortega y Gassett, into German. She died in 1948.

In 1950 he married Ellen Bär, born Lohnstein, of Zurich, and from that time had the happiness of spending half of each year in Zurich. He died suddenly, of a heart attack, on 9 December 1955.

The last public event of his life was the seventieth birthday gathering, at which he was presented with a volume of "Selecta" from his own works. A wider circle of his friends had a last happy glimpse of him at the Amsterdam Congress in 1954, where he delivered the address on the work of the Fields Medallists (Kodaira and Serre), a *tour de force* which showed him, in his sixty-ninth year, well abreast of those new theories which have changed the face of mathematics in the last twenty years.

Few mathematicians have left so clear an impression of themselves in their work. His life-long interest in philosophical problems, and his conviction that they cannot be separated from the problems of science and mathematics, has left its mark everywhere in his work. In the last year of his life he wrote a brief philosophical autobiography, which he called "Erkenntnis und Besinnung," a title which he explained in these words. "In the intellectual life of man there can be clearly distinguished two domains: the domain of *action* (Handelns), of shaping and construction to which active artists, scientists, technicians and statesmen devote themselves; and a domain of *reflexion* (Besinnung) of which the fulfilment lies in insight, and which, since we struggle in it to find the *meaning* of our activity, is to be regarded as the proper domain of the philosopher." The essay itself traces with affectionate detachment the philosophical progress of the young Weyl, from Kant through Husserl's "Phenomenology" and Fichte's Idealism to his discovery in 1922 of the medieval mystic Eckehart, who gave him for a time "that access to the religious world which I had lacked ten years earlier. . . . But my metaphysical-religious speculations, aroused by Fichte and Eckehart, never came to a clear conclusion; that was in the nature of things." He turned, under the stimulus of writing his book on the philosophy of science (1927) to the astringent pages of Leibniz. "Auf den metaphysischen Hochflug folgte die Ernüchterung.

In mathematical logic, too, things seemed a little less sure at the end of his life than at the beginning, "the world becomes strange, the pattern more complicated," but he held steadily to his view that postulation cannot replace construction without the loss of significance and value. This belief he held so seriously that he deliberately kept away throughout his life from those mathematical theories which make essential and systematic use of the Axiom of Choice.

The literary graces with which he liked to adorn his work gave it an unmistakable flavour. Who else, in the austere pages of the London Mathematical Society, would sum up the outcome of Minkowski's "unexpected difficulties" in the geometry of numbers in the words: "But of him it might be said, as of Saul, that he went out to look after his father's asses, and found a kingdom"? And who else would have found in *Der Rosenkavalier*, of all places, an apt and serious quotation for his chapter on "Ars Combinatoria" (genetics)? It was a particularly cruel fate that imposed upon him "the yoke of a foreign tongue that was not sung at my cradle." Under this handicap he did not resign himself to writing in a drab and timid style, but used his adopted language as boldly and colloquially as his own—sometimes, it is true, with results which were surprising as well as pleasing.

The mathematical form of his presentations was even more characteristic than his literary style. His strong preference for arguments that stem from the central core of the problem, rather than verifications—even easy verifications—by computation, and his liking for pregnant verbal statements where others might use symbols, more easily seized by the mathematician's eye, sometimes made close demands on the reader's attention, but the reward was doubly great when the passage was understood. But his absorption in conceptual analyses and general theories never extinguished his zest for formal mathematical detail. He considered examples to be the life-blood of mathematics, and his books and papers are full of them. In the obituary of Hilbert he mentions with admiration the many examples by which Hilbert illustrated the fundamental theorems of his algebraic papers—"examples not constructed *ad hoc*, but genuine ones worth studying for their own sake!" The *dictum* of Hilbert on the subject, in *Mathematical Problems*: "The solution of problems steels the forces of the investigator: by them he discovers new methods and widens his horizon. One who searches for methods without a definite problem in view is likely to search in vain:"—this he took as a precept in his own mathematical life.

He was indeed not only a great mathematician but a great mathematical writer. His style was leisurely by modern standards, but it had a wonderful richness of ideas. His discoveries will surely not only long survive as mathematics, but will be read in his own incomparable accounts of them.

Throughout his life Weyl continued to write papers from time to time on topics in *analysis*, but the long series of papers (1908–1915) in which (following Hilbert's precept) he applied the new theory of integral equations to eigenvalue problems of differential equations establishes most clearly his stature as an analyst.

The papers written in this period fall into two groups. In the first (1909–1910) the theory of singular eigenvalue problems is developed for ordinary differential equations.

The second early group of papers in analysis are on the asymptotic distribution of natural frequencies of oscillating continua, *e.g.* membranes, elastic bodies and electromagnetic waves in a cavity with reflecting walls.

Weyl's outstanding quality as an analyst is already shown by these early papers. In all of them the argument moves by clearly visible steps, each involving difficult work.

In 1913 there appeared *Die Idee der Riemannschen Fläche*. This book, in which Weyl revealed his full powers for the first time, marked the beginning of the widening of his mathematical interests. By its declared subject it belonged to analysis, and indeed it contained a masterly exposition of the classical theory of algebraic and analytic functions on Riemann surfaces, culminating in a proof of the uniformization theorem. But it was the plan, revolutionary at that time, of placing "geometrical" function theory on a basis of rigorous definition and proof, hitherto enjoyed only by the Weierstrass theory, that gave the book its unique character, and forced Weyl to plunge deep into the *topology* of manifolds. In his Lectures on Algebraic Functions of 1891–1892 Felix Klein had shown that the notion of a Riemann surface need not be tied to the multiple-sheeted coverings of a sphere to which Riemann had confined himself, but could be extended to include any surface provided with *local uniformizing variables* (conformal maps of the members of an open covering onto a circular domain). When Klein delivered his lectures there were no means available of giving exact form to these ideas: the lack of topological notions made it impossible even to define a Riemann surface precisely. In 1910 and 1911 L. E. J. Brouwer published his papers on the topology of simplicial manifolds. Weyl saw at once that here was the basis for an exact treatment of Klein's ideas, with Hilbert's proof of the Dirichlet Principle as the instrument for establishing the existence of differentials on the surface. To these ingredients, which, as might be expected, he modified and simplified to suit his purpose, he added others of his own. In order to prove, as he wished, that the "analytisches Gebilde" can itself be regarded a surface, he needed a thoroughgoing axiomatic definition of a surface, which should make it clear that the "points" can be mathematical objects of any kind (in this case pairs of power series). The notion of a *neighbourhood-space*, as a set in which certain subsets are associated with each point as its neighbourhoods, had been introduced by Hilbert in 1902, but his definition remained unused and almost unnoticed. Weyl revived and clarified Hilbert's definition, and showed for the first time how it could be applied. The conditions which make the restriction to manifolds were not separated, as they would be today, from the general topological axioms, but the notion of a *topology* as a designated family of subsets, was clearly brought into view. He could now define a *surface* to be a (connected) triangulable 2-manifold, and a *Riemann surface* to be a surface on which, for each point p_0, certain complex-valued continuous functions are designated *regular at p_0*, again subject to suitable axioms.

Another of the new ideas which Weyl brought to his task had to wait more than twenty years to be independently rediscovered in more general form by topologists. This was the isolation of the topological part of the proof of the duality between the differentials and the 1-cycles on the surface.

Still another substantial contribution made in this book to the topology of the subject is the treatment of the covering surface. This notion had been used by Poincaré, but only Weyl's exact definitions and proofs made clear what precisely are the parts played by the topological and the function-theoretic properties.

It is natural that some of these pioneering topological chapters should appear somewhat rugged to modern readers. Weyl himself published a new edition in 1955 in which he got rid of the troublesome triangulation condition, and cast many of the definitions into the clearer forms which forty years of progress in topology had made possible.

It is convenient to mention here another contribution of Weyl to topology, though its connexion with continuous manifolds would have seemed remote when it was published. This was the short series of papers (1923–1924) written in Spanish, on "combinatorial analysis situs," that is the axiomatic theory of cell-complexes. A good deal of the material was of an expository character and Weyl himself seems to have attached little importance to the papers; but in fact this was the first appearance in the literature of a homology theory based on an axiomatic definition of abstract cell-complexes.

Weyl's interest in *general relativity*, and through it in *differential geometry*, began through his giving a course of lectures on the subject in Zurich after the departure of Einstein to Berlin—lectures which were the nucleus from which the book *Raum-Zeit-Materie* grew, through a series of revisions and expansions, to the great treatise of 1923 (5th edition). This book is too well-known to need lengthy description. It gave Weyl his first opportunity to combine discussion of the philosophical questions in which he was so deeply interested with technical mathematics. On the mathematical side, it is distinguished, as might be expected, for the precision of the results. Nowhere else, for example, is there to be found so thorough and exact a discussion of the central orbit, finishing with rigorous inequalities for the maximal and minimal distances—a useful piece of information for discussion of the motion over long periods of time.

Weyl's own principal contribution to the subject was his "unified field theory" of gravitation and electricity—the beginning of the quest on which Einstein spent so many fruitless years. The two papers of Weyl on the subject have been more influential in differential geometry than in relativity theory. Weyl took up Levi-Cività's idea (1917) of the "parallel displacement" of a vector, but made the decisive innovation of freeing it entirely from dependence on a Riemann metric. This was the starting point of the rapid development of projective differential geometry ("geometry of paths") which took place, particularly in the United States under the leadership of Oswald Veblen.

In his papers on gravitation and the electron Weyl took up the notion introduced by Einstein in one of his attempts at a "unified field theory" of attaching a local set of axes (*Vierbein*) to each point of space-time. By using this method to express the relation between a spinor-field and the metric of general relativity, Weyl found a natural interpretation of the Vierbein in terms of the spin, which has proved fruitful in the hands of later workers. He also pointed out in these papers the possibility of representing a fermion [Chapter 13] field by a pair of 2-component spinors distinguished by definite, and opposite, senses of rotation which on spatial reflexion go over into each other. When the mass is zero the 4-component wave equation degenerates into two uncoupled 2-component equations describing these two oriented spinors. This non-conservation of parity, thought at first to be little more than a mathematical curiosity, has turned out to be an essential property of the so-called weak interactions between fermions of small mass ("leptons"). It is now established that neutrinos are indeed describable by the 2-component formalism introduced by Weyl.

From relativity Weyl turned, by a natural transition, to the problem of finding the "inner reason" for the structure of general metric space, i.e., deducing the Riemann assumption of a metric based on a quadratic form from axioms about the group of "movements" in the space [Chapters 17, 19, 20]. For the classical constant-curvature spaces Helmholtz had characterized the group of movements as the smallest which allows free mobility, i.e., contains just one element which carries a point, a directed line through the point, and so on, into another arbitrary system of the same kind. He sketched a proof, which was made exact by Lie, that such a group coincides with the group of linear transformations leaving a quadratic form invariant. Weyl's problem was to formulate and prove a corresponding theorem for infinitesimal geometry. This he did by analyzing the meaning of the assumption that the metric, i.e., the group of movements, uniquely determines the affine connexion, and he showed that this assumption and the conservation of volume suffice to characterize the group of infinitesimal rotations at a point as the set of linear transformations that leave a non-degenerate quadratic differential form invariant.

In Hilbert's development of axiomatic mathematics two stages can be seen. The first is the setting up of branches of mathematics as theories of pure structure, that is to say, as theories about sets in which some subsets are distinguished, in accordance with certain conditions. The distinguished subsets may be given such picturesque names as "open set," "straight line," or "pair of elements and their product," but it is the conditions they satisfy, not their names, that make one subject differ from another. The second stage is the formalization of set theory itself, which in the first stage was treated "naively."

Axiomatic theories in the first sense were quite congenial to Weyl, who, as we have seen, was himself the first to give recognizable axiomatic characterizations of two central concepts of modern mathematics, topological neighbourhood-spaces and cell-complexes, and in the *Mathematical analysis of the space-problem* found axioms for Riemannian geometry. No logical problems need be posed by such theories, provided that illustrative examples or "models" can be made out of the real numbers, and provided, of course, that the real numbers are accepted as secure. Hilbert's treatment of the second stage, which amounted to reducing mathematics to the properties of the grammar of the sentences expressing its theorems, was highly repugnant to Weyl. He perhaps took too seriously the comparison sometimes made between making a proof according to Hilbert's "rules of procedure," and playing a game of chess. The object of the comparison is to illustrate the surprising and important fact that formal logical systems can be described objectively without reference to their intended meaning, but Weyl saw in this a degradation of mathematics. "Hilbert's mathematics may be a pretty game with formulae, more amusing even than chess; but what bearing does it have on cognition, since its formulae admittedly have no material meaning by virtue of which they could express intuitive truths?" He quotes with approval Brouwer's aphorism. "To the question, where shall mathematical rigour be found, the two parties give different answers. The intuitionist says: in the human intellect, the formalist: on paper."

His own first incursion into the field was in the monograph *Das Kontinuum*, and he never departed greatly from the position he there took up (though he published a more extended exposition in 1921). A characteristic opening paragraph declared his purpose. "In this little book I am not concerned to disguise the 'solid rock' on which the house of analysis is built with a wooden platform of formalism, in order to talk the reader into believing at the end that this platform is the true foundation. What will be propounded is rather the view that the house is largely built on sand. I believe I can replace this shaky part of the foundation by strong and reliable supports, but they will not carry everything that is nowadays generally believed to be secure. The rest I abandon: I can see no other possibility."

The "sandy part" was the part of mathematics which (he said) involves a "vicious circle," namely the kind of definition called "impredicative"* by Russell, who also saw here a danger to the

* When a set M and an object m are so defined that m is a member of M but is defined only by reference to M, the definition of M or of m is called *impredicative*. An impredicative definition can be found in each of the paradoxes of logic and the theory of sets.

stability of mathematics. As a measure of protection against the appearance of "semantic" paradoxes Russell had enunciated the principle: "No totality can contain members defined in terms of itself." It was to give formal expression to his principle that Russell introduced the "ramified" theory of types, of which Weyl's *Kategorien* and *Stufen*, in *Das Kontinuum*, are a version. The proliferation of real numbers of different types makes analysis quite intractable and led Russell to the desperate expedient of the Axiom of Reducibility, which simply postulates that for every sentence with a single free variable, x, of level a, there exists a "first-order" sentence defining the same class, that is a sentence of the lowest type possible for sentences with the free variable x. In 1949 Weyl rejected this way out of the difficulty. "Russell, in order to extricate himself from the affair, causes reason to commit hara-kiri, by postulating [the existence of an equivalent first order sentence] in spite of its lack of support by any evidence."

His own cure was the drastic one of allowing only "first order" definitions, and throwing away the parts of mathematics that failed to survive the purge. This means that bounded sets of real numbers need not have least upper bounds, and that we may not, in general, form the set, $P(E)$, of all subsets of a given set. He carried out in detail, in the book, the development of analysis as far as it would go on this basis. His set theory was of a genetic kind, only such sets being admitted as could be built up from "ground categories" by the use of allowed principles of construction. It thus resembled the Zermelo system (to which he refers) later developed by von Neumann; but in place of the more powerful Zermelo operations, he uses only the combination of Boolean operations and quantification of type-0 variables, by means of a recursive iteration scheme. The theory of real numbers to which this leads is of the sort that has been made familiar by the Intuitionists. The extent of the sacrifice involved is much more accurately known at the present day. The movement of logic is now toward a re-interpretation of classical proofs in a constructive sense, rather than a policy of voluntarily jettisoning certain of the most powerful instruments of proof, which is unlikely to recommend itself to mathematicians in general. Nevertheless a return to the "naive" acceptance of the axioms of classical set-theory as self-evident truths, on which we can confidently build up mathematics, is now out of the question; and in this change of opinion Weyl's writings certainly played an important part. Brouwer's analysis goes deeper, but his theories are to many impenetrable. It was Weyl's advocacy of the intuitionist views and his clear and attractive expositions of them, in his papers and books that first made them accessible to many mathematicians, and turned the revolutionary doctrine of his time into the orthodoxy of today.

Chapter 27

Twentieth-Century Vistas—Analysis

The "Leonardos" of modern mathematics contributed to many of its subdivisions, but the mother science also progressed notably through the research of mathematicians who devoted themselves to particular specialties. Therefore, in this and the next two chapters, we shall name some of the greatest recent mathematical specialists and describe the nature of their discoveries. The sample will be a representative one. "Scene I" will discuss modern analysts and phases of analysis. "Scene II" will feature the lives and ideas of some "demons of abstract algebra." "Scene III" will indicate aspects of the crisis in the subject which is, according to one's point of view, the basis of all mathematics or else not mathematics at all, but *metamathematics*.

Our first topic, the recent *theory of measure*, has its roots in metric geometry, where a number is assigned to a length or an area or a volume. We have seen that, in antiquity, measurement was at first considered just a case of comparison with a standard unit. Then the problem of incommensurables revealed that the question was not as simple as intuition suggests, and that it requires a consideration of infinite processes. Then when calculus was fully developed, there came the more sophisticated point of view that, for most figures, measures do *not* exist a priori but are contingent on the existence of associated limits. The evaluation of such limits became the task of integral calculus, a tool that also gives measures for many physical entities like mass, work, pressure. As scientific history advanced, both physical and abstract geometrical concepts became more complicated, and there was greater need for precise mathematical formulation.

In Cantor's theory of the infinite, one-to-one correspondence is the criterion for determining whether two sets have the same cardinal number or whether one aggregate has more elements than the other. But this does not give the "length" (or area or volume) of a point set. In fact, the interval [0, 3] has the same cardinal number of points, C, as [0, 1], although Euclidean geometry says the former is three times the latter in length. (We have used the bracket [ ] symbolism to indicate that the intervals in question include the end-points, 0 and 3 in the first case, 0 and 1 in the second.)

What sort of foot rule can we apply to infinite sets to obtain a suitable measure for such abstractions so that there may be application to their counterparts in the physical world? In dealing with the set of all real numbers, the Cartesian picture is the number axis. Here one uses a standard length for the unit interval [0, 1] and marks it off repeatedly to obtain the intervals [1, 2], [2, 3], etc. If *measure* is to be just a generalization of length, it would seem a good idea to say that the *measure* of the set of real numbers in each of these intervals is also one unit. Thus one can readily measure point sets that are intervals or finite aggregates of nonoverlapping intervals. But certain other questions present themselves naturally: If from the set of all real numbers between 0 and 1 we remove the end-points 0 and 1, what is the length or measure of the remaining set, that is, the open interval (0, 1)? Or suppose that we remove all the rational fractions that have 1 as numerator: 1/1, 1/2, 1/3, 1/4, 1/5, . . . ; what is the measure of the residue? Or suppose that we go further and remove all the rational points in [0, 1]; what length remains? In the last years of the nineteenth century, Émile Borel gave much creative thought to these and many more difficult questions of the same kind. Then, in 1902, with Borel's ideas as background, Henri Lebesgue (1875–1941) established a *general* theory of measure. He abstracted its structure from all the particular "measure theories" of the past—empirical, abstract geometrical, Borelian, etc.

In measurement in geometry, perimeters of polygons are obtained by totaling the lengths of individual sides, and area is sometimes found by subdividing a polygon into triangles, measuring these, then adding up. Such procedures assume: *The whole is equal to the sum of its parts.* In Lebesgue's *generalization* this becomes: *The measure of the logical sum or union of a finite or countably infinite number of nonoverlapping sets is equal to the sum of their measures.* (Where the number of sets is countably infinite, the existence of a measure will involve the question of convergence of a series.)

On the other hand, generalizations of measures do *not* illustrate the classic postulate which asserts that the whole is greater than one of its parts. That axiom applies to finite sets only. The essence of infinity is that the whole of an infinite collection does equal a part. Then, in general measure theory, a statement which combines finite and infinite attributes is: *The measure of a set is either equal to or greater than the measure of a proper subset.*

Again, abstraction from particular measures leads to the assumption: *The measure of a set is zero or some positive real number.* Also, it is postulated that the measure of the empty set $\emptyset$ is zero. That "nothing" and zero are *not* identical is indicated by the fact that the converse of the axiom just stated is false. If the Lebesgue measure of a class is zero, this aggregate is *not* necessarily empty. In general measure theory, a set consisting of a single point like the origin or the point $x = 1$ on the X-axis or the point $x = 3$, etc., measures zero. (The reason for this is that the interval is the basis of linear measure, and a single point can be covered by an arbitrarily small interval.) If we accept a postulate stating that for finite and countably infinite sets the whole is equal to the sum of its parts, then the measure of a set containing two isolated points is zero, as is the measure of any finite or countably infinite collection of isolated points. Now, referring to a question raised earlier, the aggregate of all fractions with numerator 1 can be shown to measure zero, and the same is true of the class of all rational numbers between 0 and 1. For this reason, when such sets are removed from the interval [0, 1], the residual set still measures 1 unit. Thus the aggregate of irrational numbers in [0, 1] measures 1 unit. More formally, if we symbolize the class removed by E and the residue by E', the logical sum or union of E and E' is the unit interval. Therefore

$$\text{(measure of } E) + \text{(measure of } E') = \text{measure of } [0, 1]$$
$$0 + \text{measure of } E' = 1$$
$$\text{measure of } E' = 1$$

Here the measure of the whole interval is equal to the measure of the part E', but is greater than the measure of the part E.

In our discussion of the calculus it was indicated that elementary measures (like areas, volumes, pressure, etc.) are expressible as definite integrals. Lebesgue observed that this was a common feature of earlier measures and generalized it for inclusion in his theory. For example, a new type of

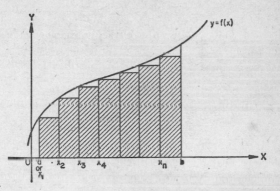

(a)

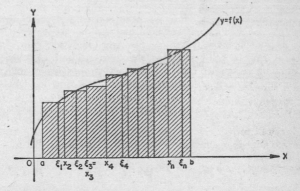

(b)

Figure 27.1   Approximating (Darboux) sums for the Mengoli-Cauchy integral

definite integral had been created by the Dutch analyst
T. J. Stieltjes (1856–1894), and Lebesgue used this to define
an important type of measure, now named Lebesgue-Stieltjes
measure in honor of both mathematicians. The Lebesgue-
Stieltjes measure is in fact the backbone of probability
theory today.

In the history of classic analysis, elementary measure and
integral calculus preceded differential calculus partly because practical problems called for measurement and partly
because the concepts involved are essentially easier in the
case of integration. History repeated itself: measure and integration of functions with arbitrary variables were developed first because they presented fewer difficulties. To
return now to the idea of integration in elementary calculus,
the Mengoli-Cauchy definite integral (Chapter 8) is defined
in a fashion suggested by Figure 27.1a, where the sum of
a set of rectangles is used to approximate the area bounded
by the segment of the X-axis between a and b, the curve
$y = f(x)$, and the ordinates at $x = a$ and $x = b$. Then the
area or definite integral can be defined as the *limit* of the
sum of rectangular areas, as the base of each rectangle gets
smaller and smaller (and the number of rectangles gets
larger and larger). More formally,

$$\int_a^b f(x) \ dx = \lim[f(x_1)\Delta x + f(x_2)\Delta x + \cdots + f(x_n)\Delta x]$$

as Δx approaches zero. Here we have taken the bases of the approximating rectangles as equal in length, for each base $= \Delta x =$
$(b - a)/n$. This is not necessary, however. The bases may vary in
length as long as each base approaches zero as a limit. Also, the approximating rectangles may be drawn with altitudes at any point
ξ_i of an interval so that in Figure 27.1b the approximating sum is

$$(x_2 - x_1) f(\xi_1) + (x_3 - x_2) f(\xi_2) + \cdots + (x_{n+1} - x_n) f(\xi_n)$$

and it can be proved that as the lengths of the intervals approach 0,
the same limit is reached as in the original definition, that is,

$$\int_a^b f(x) \ dx$$

In the Mengoli-Cauchy definition, $y = f(x)$ was assumed to be a
function continuous at each point of the interval $[a, b]$. Also, if one
wishes to use condensed symbolism, the sum of the rectangles is
indicated by

$$\sum_{i=1}^{n} f(x_i)\Delta x$$

or, alternatively, by

$$\sum_{i=1}^{n} (x_{i+1} - x_i)f(\xi_i)$$

where $\sum$, the Greek sigma, symbolizes the sum of a finite number of elements. Then

$$\int_a^b f(x)\,dx = \lim_{\Delta x \to 0} \sum_{i=1}^{n} f(x_i)\,\Delta x$$

In 1854 Riemann generalized this definition so that continuity of $f(x)$ in the interval $[a, b]$ was no longer required; that is, certain types of discontinuity were permitted at a finite number of points in this interval. Riemann merely required that $f(x)$ be *bounded* (finite in value) in the interval $[a, b]$. Then he formed the *approximating sum* (later called a *Darboux sum*)

$$L_1\Delta x + L_2\Delta x + \cdots + L_n\Delta x = \sum_{i=1}^{n} L_i\Delta x$$

where $L_1, L_2, \ldots, L_n$ are the (greatest) *lower bounds* of $f(x)$ in each interval. He also formed the approximating sum

$$U_1\Delta x + U_2\Delta x + \cdots + U_n\Delta x = \sum_{i=1}^{n} U_i\Delta x$$

where $U_1, U_2, \ldots, U_n$ are the (least) *upper bounds* of $f(x)$ in each interval. Then if the above approximating sums have the *same* limit as $\Delta x \to 0$, this common limit is the *Riemann integral* of $f(x)$ in the interval (a, b).

The great French geometer Gaston Darboux (1842–1917) showed that a function $f(x)$, which is bounded in (a, b), will have a Riemann integral in (a, b) if, and only if, the discontinuities of $f(x)$ in (a, b) constitute a set of *measure zero*.

The next generalization of the definite integral was made in 1902 by Lebesgue, whose theory of integration created a veritable revolution in analysis. Before explaining Lebesgue's idea, we must remark that the creation of this new type of integration was one more example of simultaneous discovery. Hardy pointed out that William Henry Young, Lebesgue's British contemporary,

working independently, arrived at a definition of the integral different in form from, but essentially equivalent to Lebesgue's. He had not made Lebesgue's applications; the great theorems about integrals and derivatives are Lebesgue's and his alone. But naturally Young's integral, being equivalent to Lebesgue's, "has them in it." If Lebesgue had never lived, but the mathematical world had been presented with Young's definition, it would have found Lebesgue's theorems before long. In the definition itself Young was anticipated by about two years, and it must have been a heavy blow to a man who was just beginning to find himself a mathematician; but he recognized the anticipation magnanimously, and set himself wholeheartedly to work at the further development of the theory. The phrase "the Lebesgue integral" is Young's.*

To understand the nature of the Lebesgue integral, one should compare it with the Riemann integral which it generalizes. To obtain a pertinent example of a Riemann integral, consider that in a diagram like Figure 27.1*a* the X-axis represents *time* and the interval [a, b] measures 1 month. If the interval [a, b] should be subdivided into 30 equal parts, then $\Delta x = 1/30$, that is, represents one day. Now if we think of $f(x)$ as a thermographic record of temperatures for a particular month, then $f(x_1)$, $f(x_2)$, . . . , $f(x_n)$ would represent temperatures at the same hour each day. In that case, the Darboux sum

$$f(x_1)\Delta x + f(x_2)\Delta x + \cdots + f(x_n)\Delta x$$

would be formed by multiplying each daily temperature by 1/30 and adding the products so obtained. This leads to the same result as adding the 30 temperatures for different days and dividing by 30. The latter procedure indicates that in the present instance the Darboux sum would give an "average" or mean temperature. A more representative average of temperatures during the month would be obtained from a diagram like Figure 27.1*b*, that is, from

$$f(\xi_1)\Delta x + f(\xi_2)\Delta x + \cdots + f(\xi_n)\Delta x$$

where ζ_1, ζ_2, . . . , ξ_n represent any instants of time whatsoever on different days, so that $f(\zeta_1)$, $f(\zeta_2)$, . . . , $f(\xi_n)$

* Royal Society of London, *Obituary Notices of Fellows,* Vol. 4, No. 12 (November 1943).

would be temperatures on different days but *not* necessarily at the same hour each day.

A better statistical summary would be obtained by finding the average when $\Delta x = 1$ hour or $1/720$ of a month, and an even better one by taking $\Delta x = 1$ minute or $1/43,200$ of a month, $\Delta x = 1$ second or $1/2,592,000$ of a month, etc. Thus one can consider Δx as getting smaller and smaller, that is, $\Delta x \to 0$. Then the limit of the resulting averages is the Riemann integral (or the Mengoli-Cauchy integral, since we have assumed $f(x)$ to be continuous), symbolized by

$$\int_0^1 f(x)\ dx$$

Now, although the average sought can be adequately represented by the simplest type of integral, let us see how emulators of Lebesgue might proceed. (A Mengoli-Cauchy integral or a Riemann integral is a Lebesgue integral, but

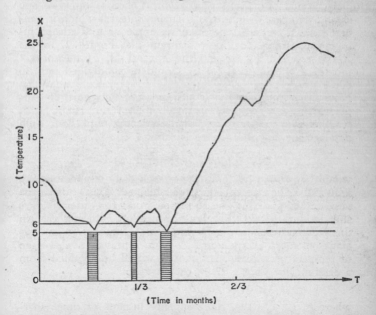

Figure 27.2   Hypothetical thermograph with rectangles whose areas total $5m_1$ in the sum approximating a Lebesgue integral

not conversely.) Suppose that the extreme temperatures during the month in question are 5° C and 25° C. We have indicated these two readings so as to form an interval on the Y-axis, the axis of temperatures (Figure 27.2). Then one procedure leading to the Lebesgue integral calls for subdivision of the interval [5, 25] on the Y-axis. Let us first divide it into 20 equal parts. Then the first small interval represents temperatures from 5° to 6°, the next one temperatures from 6° to 7°, etc. Corresponding to the first interval, one now forms the product $5m_1$, where m_1 is the total length of time during the month when temperatures were somewhere between 5° and 6°, that is, equal to or greater than 5° but less than 6°. Perhaps such temperatures occurred on a few days (Figure 27.2), so that the total time is about 1/12 of a month. Then the product required is $(5)(1/12) = 5/12$. Next the product $6m_2$ is formed, where m_2 is the total time when temperatures were equal to or greater than 6° but less than 7°. If $m_2 = 1/20$, the product required is $(6)(1/20) = 6/20$. Next $7m_3$ is formed, etc., and the Lebesgue approximating sum or mean temperature would then be

$$5m_1 + 6m_2 + 7m_3 + \cdots + 24m_{20}$$

(Note that this mean is computed by using relative frequencies in the fashion explained on pages 371 and 372 of Volume One.) A more representative temperature would be obtained by taking

$$\eta_1 m_1 + \eta_2 m_2 + \eta_3 m_3 + \cdots + \eta_n m_n = \sum_{i=1}^{n} \eta_i m_i$$

where η_1 is *any* temperature between 5° and 6°, η_2 is *any* temperature between 6° and 7°, etc.

Next, the interval from 5° to 25° can be divided into smaller parts, say 100 equal intervals, the first ranging from 5° to 5.2°, the second from 5.2° to 5.4°, etc., and a still better average, that is, a more representative monthly temperature, will then be

$$\sum_{i=1}^{100} \eta_i m_i$$

If finer and finer subdivisions are considered so that $\Delta y \to 0$, and if the approximating sums (averages) approach a limit, then this limit is called the *Lebesgue integral* of the temperature function over the interval [0, 1].

In the above case, the limiting average temperature will be the same whether the approximating sums (made up of rectangular areas) are figured by the Mengoli-Cauchy (Riemann) method or by that of Lebesgue, as one can see by carrying out the arithmetic approximations with some actual thermograph, using fine subdivisions of the X-axis with the classic method, and then using fine subdivisions on the Y-axis with the Lebesgue method. But the reason the Lebesgue integral is a powerful generalization is that, for many advanced functions, with amazingly numerous discontinuities distributed in a fashion not encountered in elementary mathematics, there is a limit for the Lebesgue sums, that is, the peculiar functions are integrable in the Lebesgue sense, but *not* in the sense of Riemann and *a fortiori* not in the sense of Mengoli-Cauchy. For example, there is the function which consists of all ordered pairs (x, y) such that x is any real number in the interval [0, 1], $y = 1$ when x is rational, $y = 0$ when x is irrational. Some of the pairs belonging to the function are (0, 1), (0.2, 1), (1, 1), $(\frac{1}{4}\sqrt{2}, 0)$, $(\pi/5, 0)$, $(\frac{1}{2}\sqrt{3}, 0)$. Figure 27.3 suggests the function, but in truth it is not possible to provide a satisfactory physical representation. The best one can do is to picture two parallel rows of infinitesimal, "densely" packed

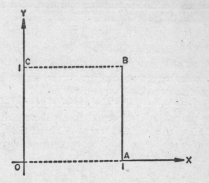

Figure 27.3   Cartesian representation of the function,

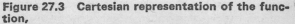
$$\begin{cases} y = 1 \text{ for } x \text{ a rational number in } [0, 1] \\ y = 0 \text{ for } x \text{ an irrational number in } [0, 1] \end{cases}$$

beads. The domain of the function is the whole interval [0, 1], and the range contains only the two numbers 0 and 1. Because the strange function we have described is discontinuous at *every point* of [0, 1] since the values of y jump back and forth between 0 and 1, the set of discontinuities has the same measure as the length of the interval, namely 1. Hence, by Darboux's theorem, our freakish function cannot have a Riemann integral over the interval [0, 1]. But let us prove directly that no Riemann integral exists. If the Darboux sums

$$L_1\Delta x + L_2\Delta x + L_3\Delta x + \cdots + L_n\Delta x$$
$$U_1\Delta x + U_2\Delta x + U_3\Delta x + \cdots + U_n\Delta x$$

are formed, they will have the values

$$0 \cdot \Delta x + 0 \cdot \Delta x + 0 \cdot \Delta x + \cdots + 0 \cdot \Delta x$$
$$1 \cdot \Delta x + 1 \cdot \Delta x + 1 \cdot \Delta x + \cdots + 1 \cdot \Delta x$$

respectively. The first of these sums has the constant value 0. Therefore its *limit* will be 0, as Δx gets smaller and smaller. The second sum has the value $n\Delta x$. If $\Delta x = 1/n$, this sum has the value $(n)(1/n) = 1$. Then if we allow n to become larger and larger as Δx gets smaller and smaller, the corresponding Darboux sum is always equal to 1. Hence its *limit* is 1. Thus the limits of the two sums, being 0 and 1, are *not* the same, and hence there is no Riemann integral.

Now consider the Lebesgue method. On the Y-axis there are just two distinct points, 0 and 1, which form the complete range of the function. The Lebesgue approximating sum is then

$$0 \cdot m_1 + 1 \cdot m_2$$

where m_1 is the measure of the set of points for which $f(x) = 0$ and m_2 is the measure of the set for which $f(x) = 1$. The first aggregate is the set of irrational points, the second is the set of rationals, and the corresponding measures are 1 and 0, respectively (page 384). Therefore the Lebesgue approximating sum is

$$0 \cdot 1 + 1 \cdot 0 = 0$$

Because the range of the function under consideration consists of the two isolated values 0 and 1, no finer subdivision of that range is possible, and the Lebesgue approximating sum does not vary but instead is equal to the constant 0.

Thus there exists a Lebesgue integral of the function over the interval $[0, 1]$ and the value of that integral is 0. Then the "area" bounded by "beads" and ordinates in Figure 27.3 measures 0, whereas intuition might mislead us into seeing a one-inch square with area 1. If, however, we think of the Lebesgue integral as an "average," then the 0 figure is justified because $0°$ "temperatures" occur at C points (of time), a much more highly infinite number than the countable infinity of rational points (of time) where "temperatures" of $1°$ occur. Thus $0°$ is the *mode* or most frequently occurring "temperature."

In the above illustration, the Lebesgue measures of certain point sets were essential. In the previous example of a temperature average, the numbers m_1, m_2, m_3, etc., the total times for which temperatures were within certain small ranges, were also measures. Specifically, m_1 is the *measure* of the set of points on the X-axis (time axis), corresponding to temperatures between $5°$ and $6°$, say, or between $5°$ and $5.2°$, etc. (depending on the fineness of subdivision on the Y-axis), and similarly for m_2, m_3, etc. In the *general case*, one is *not* necessarily dealing with functions of time (or measuring the set of rationals or the set of irrationals as in the second illustration above). Then one must either assume or prove that there actually is a *measure* for each point set involved in forming the Lebesgue approximating sums. Therefore, existence of a *Lebesgue integral* is dependent on the existence of a *Lebesgue measure*.

What exactly is Lebesgue measure? Before giving a formal answer, it would be well to summarize and add to the informal explanation given earlier in this chapter. In the first place, then, we must emphasize that the motivation for the research of Borel and Lebesgue was twofold, namely, to generalize Cantor's theory of sets, and also to investigate "difficult" point sets like those defined by *discontinuous functions*. Such aggregates began to appear toward the end of the nineteenth century—in Fourier series, in function theory, in dynamics, in probability theory, etc. The problem was to assign to each "difficult" point set an appropriate measure, that is, a *real nonnegative* (positive or zero) *number*, which is analogous to a length or an area or a volume.

Thus a measure is a *function* whose domain is some class of sets and whose range is an aggregate of nonnegative real numbers. It would then seem logical to divide an explanation of measure into two parts, first, a discussion of the *domain*, the class of sets to be measured, and second, the rules which are to govern the range.

Borel proceeded in just this way, as will now be indicated. First he formulated a class of sets, and then he presented his theory of measure for this class. He started with the elementary figures, namely, line segments or intervals, rectangles, rectangular solids (box forms), etc. on a line, in a plane, in space, etc., respectively. Restricting ourselves momentarily to a linear universe, an obvious generalization should be that to point sets made up of unions or logical sums of intervals, finite or countably infinite in number. Such intervals might be "closed" like [0, 1] or "open" like (0, 1) or "degenerate," that is, consisting of a single point like the origin or the point $x = 2$, etc. In particular, the entire X-axis or the set of real numbers would be a Borel set because it can be considered as the union of the countable infinity of intervals, [0, 1], [0, —1], [1, 2], [—1, —2], etc. Having conceived of all such logical sums of intervals, Borel next thought of "subtractions." For example, the interval [0, 1] can be removed from the real axis, leaving the set of real numbers less than 0 or greater than 1. Using the terminology of Chapter 6, one can call this set the *complement* of [0, 1]. Again, the complement of the degenerate interval consisting of the origin alone is a punctured X-axis. Also the null or empty set $\emptyset$ is the complement of the entire X-axis (set of real numbers). Borel considered that all complements of intervals and unions of intervals should be included in his special class of sets. Then with all those sets formed originally by means of union and those formed later by complementation, finite or countably infinite unions would be formed. Now if new sets should result, complements of these would be taken, and then unions formed again, etc., again and again indefinitely. The aggregate of *all* sets formed in this way is known as the *class of linear Borel sets*. Borel considered analogous procedures with rectangles in the plane, rectangular solids in space, and n-dimensional "rectangular solids" in Euclidean n-space. The resulting aggregate for all dimensions is known as the *class of Borel sets*.

What Borel did was to give a *constructive* method of assigning measures (nonnegative real numbers) to these sets such that (1) the measure of an interval or rectangle, etc. is the same as its length or area, etc., respectively; (2) sets congruent in the sense of elementary Euclidean metric geometry have equal measures; and (3) the measure of a finite or countably infinite union of nonoverlapping sets is equal to the sum of the measures of the individual sets.

But Lebesgue was able to enlarge the class of Borel sets, that is, the domain of the Borel measure function. In particular, Lebesgue was able to show that the domain of the Borel measure function did *not* include all subsets of sets whose Borel measure is zero. Just as Borel's measure reduces to a length or an area or a volume for an "elementary" figure, Lebesgue's measure agrees with Borel's when the set being measured is a Borel set. But even Lebesgue's class of sets, that is, the domain of his measure function, does *not* include all sets, as G. Vitali showed in 1905. The general problem of determining whether, in a given class of sets, a measure can be defined so as to satisfy postulates analogous to those for Borel and Lebesgue measure is a very difficult question. Nevertheless, by furnishing an abstract postulational foundation for the measure of point sets, Lebesgue provided a method more readily applicable than Borel's constructive definition of 1894. Arnaud Denjoy, a leading analyst of our day, has this to say about the matter:[*]

Lebesgue believed he had surpassed Borel in his own conception of the measure of sets. But the fact is that any sets for which Lebesgue provided a means of measurement were already susceptible of measurement by Borel's method. But what Lebesgue added to the picture, what Borel never suspected, is that there are *nonmeasurable* sets. . . . Also, after Borel had discovered how to measure sets, he did not realize that he could apply his discovery to the measurement of functions. Lebesgue's greatest claim to fame arises from the fact that he was able to use the concept of measure in this way and to deduce from it a definition of his integral.

The way Lebesgue brought the measure of sets into his formulation of the integral has already been indicated, and it has been emphasized that the existence of the Lebesgue integral is contingent on the existence of the measures m_1, m_2, m_3, etc., occurring in the Lebesgue approximating sums. A crude definition of a *measurable function* (as Denjoy and other modern analysts use the term) describes it as one for which all the measures m_1, m_2, m_3, . . . etc. in the Lebesgue

---

[*] A. Denjoy, *La théorie des fonctions de variables réelles*, Conférences du Palais de la Découverte, Université de Paris, p. 29. (Translated by the present author).

approximating sums actually exist. Borel, as Denjoy says, never had any doubts about the existence of such measures, and therefore it was necessary for Lebesgue to furnish a counterexample.

To see that there are nonmeasurable sets even within an ordinary interval, consider the linear interval $[0, \pi]$ and fit it around a circle of unit liameter (and circumference π). Now subdivide the points of the circumference into subsets with a special property as follows. If point P is a member of a subset, then so are the points whose distances from P (measured counterclockwise along the circumference) are 0, 1, 2, 3, 4, ... Observe that if $P = 0$ the point 4 will belong to the subset and will fall between points 0 and 1 on the circumference since a point at distance $\pi = 3.14$ (approximately) will coincide with 0, and therefore a point at distance 4 will coincide with a point at distance 0.86 (approximately). Similarly, a point at distance 2π will coincide with 0, and therefore a point at distance 7 will fall on top of one at distance 0.72 (approximately), etc. Again, one must assign to the same subset the points whose distances from P are 1, 2, 3, 4, . . . measured *clockwise* along the circumference. Thus starting at *any* point P on the circumference, a subset of the circumference could be formed by taking the points at distances 0, 1, 2, 3, 4, . . . , measured in either direction along the circumference. An infinite number of disjoint subsets could be formed by the method described. Then, if we accept the axiom of Zermelo (Chapter 24), one representative of each of the subsets could be selected to form an aggregate E. If E is rotated through a distance of one unit counterclockwise around the circumference, a set E_1 is formed which has no points in common with E (because each representative element in E is rotated into a *different* point of the set it represents). If E is rotated through a distance of -1, one obtains a set E_{-1} which has no points in common with E or E_1. Rotating E through a distance of 2 in either direction leads to E_2 or E_{-2}, two sets with no points in common with E, E_1, E_{-1}, or each other. Continuing the process, indefinitely, one obtains $\{E, E_1, E_{-1}, E_2, E_{-2}, . . . , E_n, E_{-n}, . . .\}$, a countable collection of non-overlapping sets which fills out the whole circumference. Moreover, since each set is formed from one of the preceding sets by a rotation, which is a rigid motion (Chapter 17), the sets are all *congruent* and should have the same measure m, where m must be zero or some positive real number. If the measure m were zero, then, by virtue of property (3) on page 395, the measure of the union of all the sets would be

$$0 + 0 + 0 + 0 + \ldots = 0$$

which contradicts the fact that the union is the whole circumference, whose measure is in truth π. Hence m cannot be equal to zero. If on the other hand, m were positive, the measure of the union would be

$$m + m + m + m + \ldots$$

This sum exceeds all numerical bounds, is "infinite," so to speak, a result which once again contradicts that fact that the circumference has the finite length π. Since m can be neither zero nor positive, no numerical measure whatsoever can be assigned to E (or to the congruent sets E_1, E_{-1}, E_2, E_{-2}, . . .) and E is *unmeasurable* (as are E_{1}, F_1, F_0, E_{-2}, . . .).

What manner of man first constructed such nonmeasurable sets, and then, in a more positive spirit, created a revolutionary concept of integration? The story of Lebesgue's life is in fact mainly an account of his studies and mathematical achievements. We shall follow his biography with that of the co-inventor of the Lebesgue integral, William Henry Young, who appears to have led a more colorful existence than Lebesgue's. Perhaps it is merely that he was fortunate to have a biographer like Geoffrey Harold Hardy, who was aware that life has a personal as well as a mathematical side, and possessed the literary ability to write a "human interest story" about a professional colleague.

Henri Léon Lebesgue was born in Beauvais in 1875. His father was a printer in modest circumstances, but a bibliophile nevertheless, who accumulated and studied from a small library of serious reading. This cultured father died while Henri was still at school, and the boy's further education was only made possible when he was granted a scholarship to the lycée of his native town, and later to a lycée in Paris. At the age of nineteen he was admitted to the École Normale Supérieure, and his first post appears to have been that of *maître des conférences* at Rennes, which he held until 1906. He then moved to Poitiers, where he was described first as *chargé de cours à la Faculté des Sciences* and later as professor. About 1912 he was called to Paris as *maître des conférences*, and he afterwards became professor at the Collège de France. He was elected to the Académie des Sciences in 1922. He was made honorary member of the London Mathematical Society in 1924, and a foreign member of the Royal Society in 1934.

His greatest contribution, as we have seen, was the replacement of some classic ideas of analysis by more general and powerful concepts. But his critical spirit first manifested itself in connection with an issue of geometry connected with developable surfaces (Chapter 19). It was explained earlier that cylinders, cones, and the set of tangents to a skew curve constitute such surfaces because they can be rolled out or "developed" on a plane, or because they are locally Euclidean. Classic differential geometry had required that developable surfaces satisfy certain regularity conditions, like possessing a continuously turning tangent plane. Lebesgue demonstrated that such conditions are not necessary. To justify this on intuitive grounds and to convince his fellow students at the École Normale, he crumpled a piece of paper in his hand in order to obtain an extremely irregular surface that fails to meet the classic requirements, but nevertheless was originally a plane surface, and hence is "developable" even when deformed. Lebesgue's formal proof, published in 1899, is said to have "*scandalisé*" Darboux. Just as Darboux was shocked by one of Lebesgue's geometric ideas, other leading mathematicians at the turn of the century reacted unfavorably to his revolutionary notions in analysis, and the French "big wigs" came close to flunking him in the defense-of-thesis examination.

In 1904 Lebesgue's *Leçons sur l'Intégration* was published. Its 1928 revision is still the standard work on the Lebesgue integral. In 1905 a paper on *Fonctions Représentables Analytiquement* contained some of the most beautiful of Lebesgue's analytic findings. The problem considered had already been solved in one way by the great René Baire. It involved the expression of discontinuous functions in terms of easier functions and, if possible, in terms of continuous functions.

Baire had classified functions as follows: In the lowest category there are the continuous functions, which Baire defined as constituting C_0, the "class zero." The limits of sequences of continuous functions are, in some instances, continuous functions and hence members of the class zero. But in other cases, the limits are discontinuous. Baire defined C_1, the "class one," as consisting of those discontinuous functions which are limits of sequences of continuous functions. Again, limits of sequences of functions in this new class are, in some cases, functions of this class. When they are not, they are functions in C_2, the Baire "class two," etc. Lebesgue gave a number of new proofs of Baire's basic theorem and proved the existence of functions in a Baire class of any assigned order. He also showed that it was possible to designate (*nommer*) a function not belonging to any Baire class. Thus Baire's classification was incomplete, and did not, from Lebesgue's point of view, include all possible real functions.

Lebesgue's integral did not generalize completely the original calculus idea of integration as *both* summation and antidifferentiation. For this reason Arnaud Denjoy, in 1912, generalized integration further; the German Perron created still another type of integral in 1914, and later there were generalizations by Stieltjes (Dutch), A. Khintchine (Russian), and P. J. Daniell (British). Lebesgue worked with the Denjoy and Stieltjes integrals as well as with his own.

Young never emphasized his own practically simultaneous discovery of the famous Lebesgue integral, Hardy recounts, among other biographical details of the English analyst's life.[*]

William Henry Young (1863–1942) was one of the most profound and original of the English mathematicians of his era.

Young was born in London on 20 October 1863. His ancestors were Ipswich people, but had been bankers in the City for some generations. His early education was at the City of London School: the headmaster, Edwin A. Abbott, had been a schoolfellow of his father. Abbott was the author of the entertaining mathematical fantasy *Flatland*, and was enough of a mathematician to recognize Young's exceptional talents, which seem indeed to have been understood much better at school than at home.

He came up to Cambridge, as a scholar of Peterhouse, in 1881. He came with a reputation to sustain and, if we are to judge him as an undergraduate and by the standards of the time, he hardly lived up to it. It is easy now to see why. The whole system of mathematical education in Cambridge was deplorable. The college teaching was negligible, the professors were inaccessible, and an undergraduate's only chance of learning some mathematics was from a private coach. Young, like nearly all the best mathematicians of his time, coached with Routh, from whom he could learn a lot. But he had many other interests, and no doubt he wasted

* Royal Society of London, *Obituary Notices of Fellows*, Vol. 4, No. 12 (November 1943), pp. 307 ff.

much of his time. He was a good, though unsystematic, chess player, and an enthusiastic swimmer and rower; and his greatest disappointment as an undergraduate seems to have been his failure to get a place in the college boat. He had always immense physical as well as mental energy, and remained an ardent oarsman all his life.

Whatever disappointments he may have had, Young seems to have been happy as an undergraduate: he said afterwards that "he never *began* to live until he went to Cambridge"; and he formed one friendship which was important throughout his career. This was with George and Foss Westcott, the sons of Professor Westcott, afterwards Bishop of Durham. Both of the Westcotts became bishops themselves later, and their influence led Young to turn his attention to theology. His family were Baptists, but he was baptized into the Church of England, became for a time superintendent of a Sunday school, and won a college theological award, the "Butler prize."

Young was a Fellow of Peterhouse from 1886 to 1892, but was never given any permanent position either by the college or the university. It was not until he was an old man that his college, in 1939, elected him an Honorary Fellow.

The next thirteen years of Young's life were spent, almost exclusively, in teaching and examining. It was common enough then for Cambridge mathematicians to earn quite large sums by private coaching, and Young set himself resolutely to do so. Here the Westcott connexion was a help, bringing him a good many pupils. He also went twice to Charterhouse as a temporary assistant master. It is difficult for any one who knew Young only later to imagine him as a schoolmaster, but he seems to have enjoyed the experience. He did much examining, at Eton and at other big schools; but primarily, through all these years, he was a coach. His position became a little more official in 1888, when Girton made him a lecturer in mathematics. "Lecturing" at Girton meant, in effect, more coaching, and after this coaching absorbed practically all his time and energy. He was working from early morning till late at night, sometimes taking two classes simultaneously in adjacent rooms, and often going without lunch.

His preferences in mathematics seem very surprising to any one familiar with his later work. He had read widely, and could teach anything in reason, but astronomy was his pet subject. "Astronomy" was the mathematical astronomy required for the tripos of those days, and a man who could make that stimulating must have been a teacher indeed. This interest lasted, and his first suggestion for "independent work," in the early days of his marriage, was one of a textbook of astronomy to be written in collaboration with his wife.

And all this time we hear not one word of research. Young was the most original of the younger Cambridge mathematicians; twenty years later he was the most prolific. Yet no one suggested to him that he might have it in him to be a great mathematician; that the years between twenty-five and forty should be the best of a mathematician's life; that he should set to work and see what he could do. The Cambridge of those days would seem a strange place to a research student transplanted into it from to-day.

I still find it difficult to visualize Young's own attitude during these early days of unproductivity. The productivity, when it did come, was so astonishing; it seems at first as if it must have been the sequel to years of preparation, by a man who had succeeded at last in finding his subject and himself. One would have supposed that any one so original, however he might be occupied, must surely have found something significant to say, but actually, the idea of research seems hardly to have occurred to Young. Mr. Cowell says that Young once told him that he "deliberately accepted ten years of drudgery," that he "fancied his knowledge of the Stock Exchange," and that he thought that he could "win his leisure" by thirty-five; but "leisure" meant freedom, comfort, reading, and travel, not a life of mathematical research. The truth seems to be that Young had really no time to think of much but his teaching; that the atmosphere of Cambridge was mathematically stifling; that no one was particularly anxious to look out for or encourage originality; and that he was too much absorbed in his routine, in his pupils and their performance, to dream of higher ambitions.

However that may be, the dreams were to come and the "drudgery" to end, and the end came quickly after Young's marriage. In 1896 he married Grace Chisholm, the second of his wrangler pupils. Mrs. Young's father was H. W. Chisholm, for many years Warden of the Standards, and her brother, Hugh Chisholm, was editor of the *Encyclopaedia Britannica*. The family carries on this tradition of distinction, and two of Young's six children are well known to us as mathematicians. The eldest son, Frank, was killed as an airman in France in 1917.

The great break in Young's life came, quite suddenly, in 1897; and here perhaps I had better quote Mrs. Young's own words. "At the end of our first year together he proposed, and I eagerly agreed, to throw up lucre, go abroad, and devote ourselves to research." It implies a revolution in Young's whole attitude to mathematics. But Mrs. Young had studied in Göttingen before her marriage, and knew what the air of a centre of research was like, so that possibly the revolution was a little less abrupt than it appears. At any rate, the Youngs left Cambridge for Göttingen in September. "Of course all our relations were horrified, but we succeeded in living without help, and indeed got the reputation of being well off." Young's "banker's instincts" had served him well.

Young's permanent home was abroad for the rest of his life, in Göttingen until 1908 and then in Switzerland, first in Geneva and afterwards in Lausanne; but the continuity of home life was much broken by his many activities. In 1901 he came back to Cambridge, and had rooms in Peterhouse during term time for some years, returning home for vacations. During 1902–1905 he was Chief Examiner to the Central Welsh Board, and seems to have thrown himself into the work with all his usual enthusiasm. His reputation was now rising, and he became a Fellow of the Royal Society in 1907, but it was not until 1913 that he obtained any definitely academic position. He was still not properly appreciated, and I can remember that, when he was a candidate for the Sadleirian chair in 1910, no one in Cambridge seemed to take his candidature very seriously.

The next few years were his years of greatest activity. He wrote a great deal—there are forty papers of his in volumes 6–18 of the *Proceedings of the London Mathematical Society* only; and in 1913 he at last became a professor. His first posts were of an "occasional," though honourable, kind. He was the first Hardinge Professor of Mathematics in Calcutta; this involved residence in India for the three winter months of the next three years. He also became Professor of the Philosophy and History of Mathematics in Liverpool, and lectured there during the summer. This was a special post created for him, and he held it until 1919, when he was appointed Professor of Pure Mathematics at Aberystwyth. Here he was as energetic as ever, but his residence abroad was sometimes a source of trouble, and disagreements about this, and about appointments to the staff, led to his resignation in 1923.

By this time Young had almost ceased his activity as an original mathematician. It had slackened for a time about 1915, but the death of his son in 1917 caused him great distress and drove him back to mathematics "as a drug." It was in this year that the London Mathematical Society awarded him the De Morgan medal. He did good work after, but none quite equal to his best, and after 1923 he wrote little. He was President of the London Mathematical Society during 1922–1924, and his last papers (including his Presidential address) were printed in its *Proceedings* in 1925. It was a little later, in 1928, that the Royal Society gave him the Sylvester medal in recognition of a life of invincible mathematical activity. Young was well over sixty now and regarded his career as a constructive mathematician as finished, but there were other openings for his activities. He had always been keenly interested in the international organization of mathematics. In 1929 he became President of the International Union of Mathematicians.

In 1932 he turned back to his other old interests: law (he had been a member of Lincoln's Inn from early days), finance, and above all languages. These included Jugoslav and Polish, two of the most intricate of Central Europe.

The end of Young's life was rather tragic, since he was cut off from his family completely by the war. Mrs. Young had left him, as they meant for a few days only, and the collapse of

France prevented her return; and his children were settled in London, South Africa and Paris. He had always been the centre of a family, and found himself imprisoned in Switzerland and practically alone. Little had been heard from him, but it is known that he died quite suddenly, that he "just went out," and that the University of Geneva, of which he was an honorary doctor, did him every honour.

It is not particularly difficult to estimate Young's rank as a mathematician. His work consists of three books and over 200 papers. Two features of it stand out on almost every page, intense energy and a profusion of original ideas. Indeed it is obvious to any reader that Young has a superabundance of ideas, far too many for any one man to work out exhaustively. One feels that he should have been a professor at Göttingen or Princeton, surrounded by research pupils eager to explore every bypath to the end. It may be that he had hardly the temperament or the patience to lead a school in this way, but he never had a chance to try.

It is not surprising that a good many of Young's theorems should have been missed and rediscovered. At his best, he can be as sharp and concise as any reader could desire; and he (or he and his wife together) could write an excellent historical and critical résumé, with just the right spice of originality. There is one particular compliment which I find it easy to pay to Young. His work stands up stoutly to critical examination. There are men who seem to me admirable mathematicians so long as they write about geometry or physics—it is easy to be impressed by what one does not understand very well. Young's best work seems to me to be his work on the subjects which I myself know best, on the theory of Fourier and other orthogonal series, on the differential calculus, and on certain parts of the theory of integration.

I will say something first about the last of these subjects, not because his work here (except that on the "Stieltjes integral") seems to me his very best, but because it is the most widely known, and because it was the occasion of a disappointment which, coming as it did right at the beginning of his active career, might easily have broken the spirit of a weaker man.

The theory of functions of a real variable has been written afresh during the last forty or fifty years. In particular, the foundations of the integral calculus have been entirely remodelled; and it is acknowledged by every one that, among those who have reconstructed them, Lebesgue stands first. The "Lebesgue integral" opens the blocked passages and smooths the jagged edges which disfigured the older theories, and gives the integral calculus the aesthetic outlines of the best "classical" mathematics. In particular it brings integration and differentiation into harmony with one another. It is Lebesgue's theorems about integrals and derivatives, the core of any modern treatment of the subject, which are his greatest achievement. Young, working independently, arrived at a definition of the integral different in form from, but essentially equivalent to, Lebesgue's.

It may seem a paradox, but it is possible that Young's work on integration, fine as it was, actually impeded his recognition. These subjects were not popular, even in France, with conservatively minded mathematicians. In England they were regarded almost as a morbid growth in mathematics, and it was convenient for men out of sympathy with Young's interests, and perhaps a little jealous of his growing reputation, to dismiss him as "the man who was anticipated by Lebesgue." It is easy enough now to recognize the absurdity of such a view: if Young had never given his definition of an integral, his reputation would not be very materially affected.

Most of this work is set out in four special memoirs. In the last of these the "Young integral" is actually defined. All these papers were written in ignorance of Lebesgue's work, and recast when Young discovered it. This spoils their continuity a little, and it is perhaps a pity that he did not leave them as they stood and add the acknowledgments necessary in appendices; the genesis and progress of his own ideas would then have stood out more clearly. In later papers, Young developed the whole theory differently, by the "method of monotone sequences." This procedure is particularly well adapted to *proofs* of theorems in the integral calculus. But I mention it here less for this reason than because it led Young to one of his admitted triumphs.

There is another important generalization of the Riemann integral, the integral first defined by Stieltjes in 1894. The Stieltjes integral covers sums as well as ordinary integrals, and has come rapidly into vogue since about 1909, primarily because of its outstanding importance in the theory of "linear functionals." In Stieltjes integration we integrate one function f with respect to another function g; the classical case is that in which f is continuous and g monotone. It was inevitable, after Lebesgue's work, that mathematicians should try to combine the two generalizations, and define the integral of any Lebesgue-integrable f with respect to any monotone g. In particular, Lebesgue had tried, but his results were not altogether satisfactory. Young solved the problem with complete success: he showed that his method of monotone sequences could be applied to this more general problem with little more than verbal changes.

The best tribute to Young's work that I can quote is that of Lebesgue himself. Referring to his own attempt, he says, "En réalité, je n'avais que très imparfaitement compris ce rôle [that of monotone sequences], sans quoi je n'aurais pas écrit . . . qu'il serait très difficile d'étendre la notion d'intégrale de Stieltjes par un procédé différent de celui que j'employais. Peu de temps après que j'eus commis cette imprudence, M. W. H. Young montrait que mon procédé était loin d'être indispensable, et que l'intégrale de Stieltjes se définit exactement comme l'intégrale ordinaire par le procédé des suites monotones. . . . Ce travail de M. Young est le premier de ceux qui ont finalement bien fait *comprendre* ce que c'est qu'une intégrale de Stieltjes. . . ."

Young's work on integration, which reaches its peak in the paper on the Stieltjes integral, was preceded and accompanied by a whole flood of papers on the theory of sets of points and its application to the general theory of functions. A considerable part of the contents of these papers is incorporated in the Youngs' book published in 1906 and, unfortunately, never revised and reprinted. But there are two other fields in which Young shows his powers at their highest. These are the theory of Fourier series (and other special orthogonal series), and the elementary differential calculus of functions of several variables.

Chapter 28

Twentieth-Century Vistas—Algebra

Let us now proceed to the next sample from the modern repertory. Since "Scene II" will present certain concepts that are important in twentieth-century *abstract algebra*, it seems appropriate to precede the discussion with a biography of one of the chief contributors to that subject, namely, Emmy Noether (1882–1935)—a biography written by one of the mathematical "Leonardos," Hermann Weyl. "Emmy Noether was a great mathematician, the greatest . . . that her sex has ever produced," he wrote.*

She was born the 23rd of March, 1882, in the small South German university town of Erlangen. Her father was Max Noether, himself a great mathematician who played an important role in the development of the theory of algebraic functions as the chief representative of the algebraic-geometric school. He had come to the University of Erlangen as a professor of mathematics in 1875, and stayed there until his death in 1921. Besides Emmy there grew up in the house her brother Fritz, younger by two and a half years. He turned to applied mathematics in later years, then became professor at the Technische Hochschule in Breslau, and by the same fate that ended Emmy's career in Göttingen was driven off to the Research Institute for Mathematics and Mechanics in Tomsk, Siberia. The Noether family is a striking example of the hereditary nature of mathematical talent, the most shining illustration of which is the Basle Huguenot dynasty of the Bernoullis.†
    Side by side with Noether at Erlangen was another mathematician, Gordan, under whom Emmy wrote her doctor's thesis

------

* Hermann Weyl, "Emmy Noether," *Scripta Mathematica*, Vol. 3, No. 3 (July 1935), pp. 201 ff.
    † For a recent instance of this phenomenon, see Chapter 30, where the mathematical activities of today's Neumann family are described.

in 1907: "On complete systems of invariants for ternary biquad-ratic forms." Besides her father, Gordan must have been well-nigh one of the most familiar figures in Emmy's early life, first as a friend of the house, later as a mathematician also; she kept a pro-found reverence for him though her own mathematical taste soon developed in quite a different direction. I remember that his picture decorated the wall of her study in Göttingen. These two men, the father and Gordan, determined the atmosphere in which she grew up.

The scientific kinship of father and daughter—who became in a certain sense his successor in algebra, but stands beside him in-dependent in her fundamental attitude and in her problems—is something beautiful and gratifying. The father was a very in-telligent, warm-hearted harmonious man of many-sided interests and sterling education.

Emmy Noether took part in the housework as a young girl, dusted and cooked, and went to dances, and it seems her life would have been that of an ordinary woman had it not happened that just about that time it became possible in Germany for a girl to enter on a scientific career without meeting any too marked resistance. There was nothing rebellious in her nature; she was willing to accept conditions as they were. Her dependence on Gordan did not last long; he was important as a starting point, but was not of lasting scientific influence upon her. Nevertheless the Erlangen mathematical air may have been responsible for making her into an algebraist. Gordan retired in 1910; he was fol-lowed first by Erhard Schmidt, and the next year by Ernst Fischer, whose field was algebra. He exerted upon Emmy Noether, I believe, a more penetrating influence than Gordan did. Under his direction the transition from Gordan's formal standpoint to the Hilbert method of approach was accomplished. She refers in her papers at this time again and again to conservations with Fischer. This epoch extends until about 1919.

Already in Erlangen about 1913 Emmy lectured occasionally, substituting for her father when he was taken ill. She must have been to Göttingen about that time, too, but I suppose only on a visit with her brother Fritz.

During the war, in 1916, Emmy came to Göttingen for good; it was due to Hilbert's and Klein's direct influence that she stayed. Hilbert at that time was over head and ears in the general theory of relativity, and for Klein, too, the theory of relativity and its connection with his old ideas of the Erlangen program brought the last flareup of his mathematical interests and mathe-matical production. To both Hilbert and Klein, Emmy was wel-come as she was able to help them with her invariant-theoretic knowledge. For two of the most significant aspects of the general relativity theory she gave at that time the genuine and universal mathematical formulation.

During World War I, Hilbert tried to push through Emmy

Noether's "Habilitation" in the Philosophical Faculty in Göttingen. He failed due to the resistance of the philologists and historians. It is a well-known anecdote that Hilbert supported her application by declaring at the faculty meeting, "I do not see that the sex of the candidate is an argument against her admission as Privatdozent. After all we are a university and not a bathing establishment." Probably he provoked the adversaries even more by that remark. Nevertheless, she was able to give lectures in Göttingen, that were announced under Hilbert's name. But in 1919, after the end of the War and the proclamation of the German Republic had changed conditions, her Habilitation became possible. In 1922 there followed her nomination as a "nichtbeamteter ausserordentlicher Professor"; this was a mere title carrying no obligations and no salary. She was, however, entrusted with a "Lehrauftrag" for algebra, which carried a modest remuneration.

During the wild times after the Revolution of 1918, she did not keep aloof from the political excitement, she sided more or less with the Social Democrats: without being actually in party life she participated intensely in the discussion of the political and social problems of the day.

She always remained a convinced pacifist, a stand which she held very important and serious.

In the modest position of a "nichtbeamteter ausserordentlicher Professor" she worked in Göttingen until 1933, during the last years in the beautiful new Mathematical Institute that had risen in Göttingen chiefly by Courant's energy and the generous financial help of the Rockefeller Foundation. I have a vivid recollection of her when I was in Göttingen as visiting professor in the winter semester of 1926–1927, and lectured on representations of continuous groups. She was in the audience; for just at that time the hypercomplex number systems and their representations had caught her interest and I remember many discussions when I walked home after the lectures, with her and von Neumann, who was in Göttingen as a Rockefeller Fellow, through the cold, dirty, rain-wet streets of Göttingen. When I was called permanently to Göttingen in 1930, I earnestly tried to obtain from the Ministerium a better position for her, because I was ashamed to occupy such a preferred position beside her whom I knew to be my superior as a mathematician in many respects. I did not suceed, nor did an attempt to push through her election as a member of the Göttinger Gesellschaft der Wissenschaften. Tradition, prejudice, external considerations, weighted the balance against her scientific merits and scientific greatness, by that time denied by no one. In my Göttingen years, 1930–1933, she was without doubt the strongest center of mathematical activity there, considering both the fertility of her scientific research program and her influence upon a large circle of pupils.

Her development into that great independent master whom we

admire today was relatively slow. Such a late maturing is a rare phenomenon in mathematics; in most cases the great creative impulses lie in early youth. Sophus Lie, like Emmy Noether, is one of the few great exceptions. Not until 1920, thirteen years after her promotion, there appeared in the Mathematische Zeitschrift that paper of hers written with Schmeidler, "Über Moduln in nicht-kommutativen Bereichen, insbesondere aus Differential- und Differenzen-Ausdrucken," which seems to mark the decisive turning point. It is here for the first time that the Emmy Noether appears whom we all know, and who changed the face of algebra by her work. Above all, her conceptual axiomatic way of thinking in algebra becomes first noticeable in this paper dealing with differential operators as they are quite common nowadays in quantum mechanics. In performing them, one after the other, their composition, which may be interpreted as a kind of multiplication, is not commutative. But instead of operating with the formal expressions, the simple properties of the operations of addition and multiplication to which they lend themselves are formulated as axioms at the beginning of the investigation, and these axioms then form the basis of all further reasoning. A similar procedure then remained typical for Emmy Noether from then on.

Emmy Noether had many pupils, and one of the chief methods of her research was to expound her ideas in a still unfinished state in lectures, and then discuss them with her pupils. Sometimes she lectured on the same subject one semester after another, the whole subject taking on a better ordered and more unified shape every time, and gaining of course in the substance of results. It is obvious that this method sometimes put enormous demands upon her audience. In general, her lecturing was certainly not good in technical respects. For that she was too erratic and she cared too little for a nice and well arranged form. And yet she was an inspired teacher; he who was capable of adjusting himself entirely to her, could learn very much from her. Her significance for algebra cannot be read entirely from her own papers; she had great stimulating power and many of her suggestions took final shape only in the works of her pupils or co-workers. A large part of what is contained in the second volume of van der Waerden's "Modern Algebra" must be considered her property. The same is true of parts of Deuring's book on algebras in which she collaborated intensively. Hasse acknowledges that he owed the suggestion for his beautiful papers on the connection between hypercomplex quantities and the theory of class fields to casual remarks by Emmy Noether. She could utter far-seeing remarks in her prophetic lapidary manner, out of her mighty imagination that hit the mark most of the time and gained the strength in the course of years; and such a remark could then become a signpost to point the way for difficult future work. And one cannot read the scope of her accomplishments from the individual results of her papers alone: she originated above all a new and epoch-making style of thinking in algebra.

She lived in close communion with her pupils; she loved them, and took interest in their personal affairs. They formed a somewhat noisy and stormy family, "the Noether boys" as we called them in Göttingen. Artin and Hasse stand beside her as two independent minds whose field of production touches on hers closely, though both have a stronger arithmetical texture. With Hasse above all she collaborated very closely during her last years. Richard Brauer and she dealt with the profounder structural problems of algebras, she in a more abstract spirit, Brauer, educated in the school of the great algebraist I. Schur, more concretely operating with matrices and representations of groups; this, too, led to an extremely fertile cooperation. She held a rather close friendship with Alexandroff in Moscow, who came frequently as a guest to Göttingen. I believe that her mode of thinking has not been without influence upon Alexandroff's topological investigations. About 1930 she spent a semester in Moscow and there got into close touch with Pontrjagin also. Before that, in 1928–1929, she had lectured for one semester in Frankfurt while Siegel delivered a course of lectures as a visitor in Göttingen.

In the spring of 1933 the storm of the National Revolution broke over Germany. The Göttinger Mathematisch-Naturwissenschaftliche Fakultät, for the building up and consolidation of which Klein and Hilbert had worked for decades, was struck at its roots. After an interregnum of one day by Neugebauer, I had to take over the direction of the Mathematical Institute. But Emmy Noether, as well as many others, was prohibited from participation in all academic activities, and finally her *venia legendi*, as well as her "Lehrauftrag" and the salary going with it, were withdrawn. A stormy time of struggle like this one we spent in Göttingen in the summer of 1933 draws people closer together; thus I have a particularly vivid recollection of these months. Emmy Noether, her courage, her frankness, her unconcern about her own fate, her conciliatory spirit, were, in the midst of all the hatred and meanness, despair and sorrow surrounding us, a moral solace. It was attempted, of course, to influence the Ministerium and other responsible and irresponsible but powerful bodies so that her position might be saved. I suppose there could hardly have been in any other case such a pile of enthusiastic testimonials filed with the Ministerium as was sent in on her behalf. At that time we really fought; there was still hope left that the worst could be warded off. It was in vain. Franck, Born, Courant, Landau, Emmy Noether, Neugebauer, Bernays and others—scholars the university had before been proud of—had to go because the possibility of working was taken away from them. Göttingen scattered into the four winds! This fate brought Emmy Noether to Bryn Mawr; she taught there for a short time and was also a guest at the Institute for Advanced Study in Princeton. She harbored no grudge against Göttingen and her fatherland for what they had done to her. She broke no friendship on account of political dissension. Even in the summer of 1934 she returned to Göttingen, and lived and worked there as though all things were as before. She was sincerely glad that Hasse was endeavoring with success to rebuild the old, honorable and proud mathematical tradition of Göttingen even in the changed political circumstances. But she had adjusted herself with perfect ease to her new American surroundings, and her girl students there were as near to her heart as the Noether boys had been in Göttingen. She was happy at Bryn Mawr; and indeed perhaps never before in her life had she received so many signs of respect, sympathy, friendship, as were bestowed upon her during her last one and a half years at Bryn Mawr.

I shall close with a short general estimate of Emmy Noether as a mathematician and as a personality. Her strength lay in her ability to operate abstractly with concepts. It was not necessary for her to allow herself to be led to new results on the leading strings of known concrete examples. This had the disadvantage, however, that she was sometimes but incompletely cognizant of the specific details of the more interesting applications of her general theories. She possessed a most vivid imagination, with the aid of which she could visualize remote connections: she constantly strove toward unification—she possessed a strong drive toward axiomatic purity.

Of her predecessors in algebra and number theory, Dedekind was most closely related to her. For him she felt a deep veneration. She expected her students to read Dedekind's appendices to Dirichlet's "Zahlentheorie" not only in one, but all editions. She took a most active part in the editing of Dedekind's works; here, the attempt was made to indicate, after each of Dedekind's papers, the modern development built upon his investigations. Her affinity with Dedekind, who was perhaps the most typical Lower Saxon among German mathematicians, proves by a glaring example how illusory it is to associate in a schematic way race with the style of mathematical thought. In addition to Dedekind's work, that of Steinitz on the theory of abstract fields was naturally of great importance for her own work. She lived through a great flowering of algebra in Germany, toward which she contributed much. Her methods need not, however, be considered the only means of salvation. In addition to Artin and Hasse, who in some respects are akin to her, there were algebraists of a still more different stamp, such as I. Schur in Germany, Dickson and Wedderburn in America, whose achievements are certainly not behind hers in depth and significance.

Two traits above all determined Emmy Noether's nature. There was first, the native productive power of her mathematical genius. She was not clay, pressed by the artistic hands of God into a harmonious form, but rather a chunk of human primary rock into which He had blown his creative breath of life. Second, her heart knew no malice; she did not believe in evil—indeed it never entered her mind that it could play a role among men. This was never more forcefully apparent to me than in the last stormy summer, that of 1933, which we spent together in Göttingen. The memory of her work in science and of her personality will not soon pass away.

As Weyl's biography states, Emmy Noether's greatness is found not only in her own research but also in her stimulating effect on other mathematicians and, above all, in the fact that "she originated a new and epoch-making style of thinking in algebra." As a tribute to that new mode of thought, we have already given much space to the discussion of modern abstract algebraic systems. We have explained the nature of groups, rings, integral domains, fields, vector spaces, linear algebras (hypercomplex number systems), and Boolean lattices. Our spiral scheme of organization permits us to proceed further in the treatment of any or all of these structures. But we shall backtrack and advance only in relation to two of Emmy Noether's specialties, namely, the theory of ideals and the theory of hypercomplex number systems.

Weyl tells us that she was a disciple of Dedekind and compares some of her research with that of Wedderburn and Artin. Let us therefore focus on some of the more elementary concepts which appear in her work, as well as in that of the other three mathematicians named. Since we have already discussed some hypercomplex systems in connection with Hamilton, we shall postpone enlargement of the subject to our second illustration and shall begin the present discussion by talking about *ideals*. We must show how an ideal in a ring is analogous to a normal subgroup in a group, a fact making Galois the inspiration for both Dedekind and Noether. We must also indicate how ideals enabled Dedekind to realize the objective of providing unique factorization into "primes" (actually *prime ideals*) for certain integral domains where unique factorization into "primes" is lacking.

Since an ideal is a special type of subring of a ring, we must recall the technical meaning of the term "ring." For a classic example, we return to the set of integers

$$S = \{ \ldots, -3, -2, -1, 0, 1, 2, 3, \ldots \}$$

Then the system $\{S, +, \times\}$ is a *ring*, that is, one can perform addition and multiplication within the system in such a way that traditional rules are satisfied. More exactly, the system is an *abelian group* with respect to addition, a *semigroup* with respect to multiplication, and multiplication is distributive with respect to addition.

If S is the set of all $n \times n$ matrices (Chapter 17), then the system $\{S, \oplus, \otimes\}$ where $\oplus$ and $\otimes$ are matrix addition and matrix multiplication, provides another example of a ring. This second instance is a more general type of ring since its multiplication is *not* commutative. Hereafter we shall refer to a ring with commutative multiplication as a *commutative ring*.

The ring of integers is specialized not only by the commutativity of its multiplication but also by the fact that one can carry out cancellation within the system, that is, if $ca = cb$, where a, b, and c are integers and $c \neq 0$, then $a = b$. Any ring having the two special properties described is called an *integral domain*. An additional example of an integral domain is the system $\{S, +, \times\}$ where S is the set of all numbers of the form $a + b\sqrt{2}$, where a and b are ordinary integers. By applying school algebra, the reader can demonstrate that all the required postulates are satisfied. To provide instances that are simpler for present purposes, let us return to "clock arithmetic," that is, to addition and multiplication of integers modulo m, where m is some fixed integer. Let us choose $m = 3$ and consider the following tables for the arithmetic of "residues" or "residue classes" modulo 3. The first tabulation repeats that on page 37. In the second table, the only fact that may call for review is $2 \otimes 2 = 1$. The reader must recall that $2 \otimes 2$ signifies the remainder or "residue" when the ordinary product, 2×2, is divided by the modulus 3.

Addition Modulo 3				*Multiplication Modulo 3*		
$\oplus$	0	1	2	$\times$	0	1	2
0	0	1	2	0	0	0	0
1	1	2	0	1	0	1	2
2	2	0	1	2	0	2	1

If $S = \{0, 1, 2\}$ is the set of residues modulo 3, then we have already shown (page 37) that those residues constitute an abelian group with respect to $\oplus$, addition modulo 3. The above multiplication table indicates that $\otimes$ is closed on the set S. The reader can readily verify that $\otimes$ is associative and commutative, also that it is distributive with respect to $\oplus$. But we shall presently demonstrate those special properties in a somewhat different way by showing that they must hold of necessity because they must "mirror" the corresponding properties of $\times$ and $+$, ordinary multiplication and addition of integers. At any rate, $\{S, \oplus, \otimes\}$, as defined by the tables above, is a *commutative ring*.

The *finite* modulo 3 ring is derived from the *infinite* ring of integers and has a similar structure. The two rings are *not* isomorphic however, since their elements are not in one-to-one correspondence. Then just how are the rings related? To explain this, one picture will be worth a thousand words. As a start, we reintroduce the number line (Figure 28.1) with the integers represented as equidistant

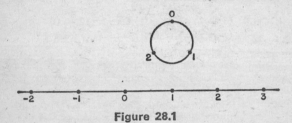

Figure 28.1

points on that line. Next, we wind the line around a circular "clock" of circumference 3 (Figure 28.1) so that the points 0, 1, 2, of the number line are superimposed on the same numbers on the "clock" and the rest of the number line is wound round and round in both directions forever. Then 3, 4, 5 will fall on the hours 0, 1, 2, respectively. Winding in the other direction will place $-1, -2, -3$, on 2, 1, 0, respectively, and members of the three residue classes

$$S_0 = \{\ldots, -6, -3, 0, 3, 6, \ldots\}$$
$$S_1 = \{\ldots, -5, -2, 1, 4, 7, \ldots\}$$
$$S_2 = \{\ldots, -4, -1, 2, 5, 8, \ldots\}$$

will fall on 0, 1, 2, respectively.

We have just mapped the whole world of integers onto the three points $\{0, 1, 2\}$ on the clock of Figure 28.1. The

associated mapping or function is a many-to-one correspondence, particularly impressive because it is an infinity-
to-one correspondence that telescopes an infinite structure
into a finite one. Although the mapping considered is not
one-to-one as in the Klein geometric transformations or in
the homeomorphisms of topology, a pertinent question
would once again ask whether any features of the original
picture remain *invariant*. The whole ring structure of the
integers is, in fact, invariant when the integers are projected
onto the modulo 3 system. This occurs because the *addition
and multiplication operations are preserved*. By this we
mean that $+$ corresponds to $\oplus$, $\times$ to $\otimes$, that the modulo 3
image of a sum of integers is the (modulo 3) sum of their
images, the modulo 3 image of a product of integers is the
(modulo 3) product of their images. For example, there are
the following features of the mapping:

$$5 \rightarrow 2$$
$$7 \rightarrow 1$$
$$(5 + 7) \rightarrow (2 \oplus 1) \text{ because } 12 \rightarrow 0$$
$$(5 \times 7) \rightarrow (2 \otimes 1) \text{ because } 35 \rightarrow 2$$

Since addition and multiplication of integers are preserved,
so are the ring properties of those operations. For example,
if a, b, c are any three integers, and a', b', c' are their images
under the mapping, then

$$[(a + b) + c] \rightarrow [(a' \oplus b') \oplus c']$$
$$[a + (b + c)] \rightarrow [a' \oplus (b' \oplus c')]$$

and hence

$$(a' \oplus b') \oplus c' = a' \oplus (b' \oplus c')$$

In other words, the associativity of addition of integers is
preserved in the modulo 3 map. The preservation of the
other properties of $+$ and $\times$ can be demonstrated in similar
fashion.

In more technical language, the type of mapping illustrated is called a *homomorphism* (not to be confused with
the homeomorphism of topology). A *homomorphism* or
homomorphic mapping of a ring is a mapping that preserves
sums and products. In general, a ring homomorphism is a
many-to-one correspondence, but includes, as a special case,
a one-to-one correspondence preserving sums and products,
namely, a ring *isomorphism*. Isomorphic rings, like other
isomorphic structures, are considered abstractly identical.

But in many cases one of two isomorphic models may be easier to handle than the other. For example, we have the case of analytic Euclidean geometry versus the isomorphic classic synthetic model.

The fact that a homomorphism may effect a substantial condensation without changing structure makes that type of mapping an extremely important tool, the more so since the ring is not the only algebraic system susceptible to such telescoping. A homomorphism can be applied to structures with fewer than two operations—groupoids, semigroups, groups—and to systems with two or more operations—vector spaces, linear algebras, etc. Since a homomorphic mapping preserves *all* operations, it maps groups onto groups, vector spaces onto vector spaces, etc.

In passing, let us point out that "preserving operations" has a meaning more subtle than that phrase indicates. Thus consider the mapping of the set of integers onto the set of integral powers of 2, as indicated below:

$$\begin{pmatrix} \dots, & -3, & -2, & -1, & 0, & 1, & 2, & \dots \\ \dots, & 2^{-3}, & 2^{-2}, & 2^{-1}, & 2^{0}, & 2^{1}, & 2^{2}, & \dots \end{pmatrix}$$

The first row is a group with respect to *addition;* the second row is a group with respect to *multiplication. Sums* in the first row are "preserved" as *products* in the second. For example, $(-3) + 2 = -1$ is mapped onto $2^{-3} \times 2^{2} = 2^{-1}$. Hence if S is the set of integers and T is the set of integral powers of 2, then the *group* $\{S, +\}$ is homomorphic, in fact isomorphic, to the group $\{T, \times\}$. The addition of the first group is preserved as multiplication in the second. In a homomorphism, all that is required is that there be matching of operations and results of operations in a system and its image.

For present purposes, let us concentrate on the group homomorphism where the additive group of integers is mapped onto the additive group of residues modulo 3. Then, by examining the classes S_0, S_1, S_2 (page 414), which are mapped onto 0, 1, 2, respectively, it will be seen that S_0 possesses special properties that are lacking in S_1 and S_2. It is easy to observe that $\{S_0, +\}$ is an abelian group, in fact a *normal subgroup* of the additive group of integers. But +, ordinary addition, is *not* even closed on S_1 (or S_2). Thus, for example, the sum of 1 and 4 (two elements of S_1) is 5, a member of S_2, and in S_2, $2 + 5 = 7$ (a member of S_1).

Hence S_1 and S_2 are not even semigroups under ordinary addition.

The special property possessed by S_0 illustrates a general theorem which states that, in *every* homomorphic mapping of one group onto another group, the set of elements mapped onto the identity of the second group constitutes a *normal subgroup* of the first group. There is also a converse theorem indicating that every normal subgroup of any group will lead to a homomorphism where the normal group and its cosets are the "residue classes," and the normal subgroup is mapped onto the identity of the image group. Since a group homomorphism is thus always associated with a *normal subgroup*, the latter is called the *kernel* of the homomorphism. In the case of finite groups, the index of the normal subgroup in the whole group (Chapter 16) gives the order of the image group and indicates the degree of condensation effected by the homomorphism. Thus the *maximal* proper normal subgroup of a group would offer the greatest opportunity for telescoping the group into a smaller group. Of course the whole group is an "improper" normal subgroup of itself, and if it is the kernel of a homomorphism, the whole group is mapped onto a single image element. That would represent condensation to the state of complete collapse, where a trivial picture results—a singleton group. At the other extreme, the group identity constitutes a normal subgroup, and if that is the kernel of a homomorphism, there are only single elements in the cosets or residue classes, and the homomorphic image is an isomorphic or abstractly identical group. This result is not a condensation but a duplication.

Let us now consider S_0 in relation to the *ring* of integers, where two operations, $+$ and $\times$, are involved. We have seen that S_0 is closed under $+$, ordinary addition. But now we observe that S_0 consists of all integral multiples of 3, and thus S_0 is also closed under $\times$, ordinary multiplication, since the product of any two multiples of 3 is a multiple of 3. Then, because S_0 is an abelian group under $+$ and closed under the associative multiplication operation $\times$, which is distributive with respect to $+$, the system $\{S_0, +, \times\}$ is a *ring*, in fact, a proper *subring* of the ring of integers.

In the homomorphic mapping of the ring of integers onto the modulo 3 ring, the class S_0 is still the kernel, that is, S_0 is mapped onto 0, the additive identity, and the role of $\{S_0, +\}$ as a special type of subgroup of the additive group of integers, namely, a normal subgroup, suggests that $\{S_0, +, \times\}$ may be a special type of subring of the ring of integers. Hence, let us search for special multiplicative properties of S_0. We readily see that if a member of S_0 is multiplied by *any integer whatsoever*, whether or not the integer is in S_0, the product is a member of S_0. Thus it is not surprising that $3(-6) = -18$, a member of S_0, since S_0 is closed under $\times$. But we also have $3 \times 4 = 12$, a member of S_0, $3 \times 5 = 15$, a member of S_0, although 4 and 5 are not members of S_0.

A subring possessing the property just described is called an *ideal*. In other words, a subset of a ring with a commutative multiplication is called an ideal if it is a subgroup of the additive group of the ring and if it contains all products of its elements by arbitrary elements of the ring. (In rings with a noncommutative multiplication, there are *left ideals* and *right ideals*.)

It can be proved that in any ring homomorphism, the set of elements mapped onto the zero (additive identity) of the image is an ideal of the original ring, and conversely, an ideal of a ring can be made the *kernel* of a homomorphic mapping. Then, as in the case of normal subgroups of a group, the ideals of a ring determine the ring homomorphisms and the possibilities for condensation. Again, if a ring has no ideals other than itself and the subset consisting of the additive identity, it has only "improper" homomorphisms.

What has just been said can be applied to showing that a *field*, the fundamental structure of arithmetic and algebra, cannot be properly condensed, that is, has no proper homomorphisms. For proof, one can consider a field as a special kind of ring and then show that it has no ideals except itself and the additive identity (zero). Suppose that a field has an ideal other than zero. Then that ideal contains at least one nonzero element, which we shall symbolize as a. Because $a \neq 0$, it has a multiplicative inverse, a^{-1}, in the field (Chapter 4). Now the product of a member of an ideal by any ring element whatsoever must belong to the ideal. Hence $aa^{-1} = 1$ is an element of the ideal and, by virtue of the property just applied, $b \cdot 1 = b$ belongs to the ideal, where b is any element whatsover in the field. Thus the ideal is identical with the whole field. In summary, in any field the field itself and the zero ideal are the only ideals, and the only homomorphisms are therefore either an isomorphism or a map onto a single element.

In the ring of integers, the set of all multiples of 3 constitutes an ideal, a fact which suggests that all multiples of any integer m will form an ideal and therefore be the kernel of a homomorphism onto the ring of residues modulo m. The reader can check that this is actually the case by studying homomorphisms of the ring of integers onto modulo 2, modulo 4, modulo 5, etc., rings and showing that the sets

$$(2) = \{\ldots, -2, 0, 2, 4, \ldots\}$$
$$(4) = \{\ldots, -4, 0, 4, 8, \ldots\}$$
$$(5) = \{\ldots, -5, 0, 5, 10, \ldots\}$$
$$(6) = \{\ldots, -6, 0, 6, 12, \ldots\}$$

constitute ideals in the ring of integers. The ideals we have symbolized by (2), (4), (5), and (6) are specialized in type because the membership in each case is made up of multiples of a singe element—2 or 4 or 5, etc. Such ideals are described as *principal*.

A *principal ideal* in a ring is an ideal whose elements are all the multiples of a single element a which is said to *generate* the ideal. In other words, the principal ideal (a) is the set of all elements xa, where a is a fixed member of the ring and x is any other member. It turns out that in the ring of integers *all* ideals are principal. But the same property need not obtain in more general rings. There may, for example, be an ideal "generated" by two elements. Such an ideal would be symbolized by (a, b) and, in a commutative ring with unit element (multiplicative identity), would consist of all elements $xa + yb$, where a and b are fixed members of the ring and x and y are *any* elements whatsoever in the ring.

The principal ideals (2), (3), (4), etc. are all subrings of the ring of integers, but one can go further by showing that some of these ideals are *subideals* of others. Thus, since multiples of 4, for example, 8, 12, 16, 20, etc., are obviously also multiples of 2, the ideal (4) is a subideal of the ideal (2). This fact can be symbolized as $(4) \subseteq (2)$, where $\subseteq$ is the standard symbol for "is contained in." Or using $\supseteq$ the symbol for "contains," one has $(2) \supseteq (4)$; that is, the principal ideal (2) contains the principal ideal (4) as a subideal. The reader can verify that $(3) \supseteq (6) \supseteq (12)$, $(2) \supseteq (10)$, $(5) \supseteq (10)$, etc. The illustrative examples suggest that if a and b are given integers, then $(a) \supseteq (b)$ if and only if a *divides* b, symbolized as $a|b$. Thus, in the case of principal ideals, the relation of class inclusion, $\supseteq$, and the relation of ordinary arithmetic divisibility, $|$, are apparently interchangeable.

Let us see how far the analogy between $\supseteq$ and $|$ can be pushed. We recall that an integer m is a prime if its only divisors are itself and the unit 1, that is, the only possible divisibility statements are $m|m$ and $1|m$. By analogy, the corresponding relations involving inclusion of ideals would be $(m) \supseteq (m)$ and $(1) \supseteq (m)$. (Note that (1) signifies the aggregate of multiples of the unit 1, in other words, the entire set of integers.) The inclusion statements define a *maximal ideal*, for they assert that (m) is a subideal only of itself and the entire ring, (1). Or one can say, by analogy with arithmetic, that (m) is "divisorless," that is, lacks proper divisors. At this point the analogy with elementary arithmetic begins to weaken since, in the very general rings of Dedekind's theory, being maximal (divisorless) is a sufficient but *not* a necessary condition for an ideal to be prime. According to Dedekind's definition, of which we shall give a sophisticated formulation later, if an ideal is maximal (divisorless), it is surely prime, but if it is prime, it need not be maximal.

If we continue with everyday questions of arithmetic divisibility and the associated decomposition of an integer into a product of other integers, for example, $6 = 2 \times 3$, we can inquire about the corresponding factorization of ideals. Thus, if (x) and (y) are principal ideals, their product, $(x)(y)$, is *defined by*

$$(x)(y) = (xy)$$

that is, the product of two principal ideals is generated by the product of the generating elements of the two ideals. Hence

$$(2)(3) = (2 \cdot 3) = (6)$$

which is the analogue of the arithmetic factorization cited above. As another example, the reader can verify that

$$1155 = 3 \cdot 5 \cdot 7 \cdot 11$$
$$(1155) = (3)(5)(7)(11)$$

Our illustrations suggest a complete parallel between factorization of integers and factorization of ideals, so that for the ring of integers (or for any ring all of whose ideals are *principal*) the analogy is perfect. But the trouble starts when more general integral domains are examined. For example, consider S, the set of all numbers, $a + b\sqrt{-5}$, where a and b are ordinary integers. Then $\{S, +, \times\}$ can be shown to be an integral domain, and in that domain, 6 is not only the product of 2 and 3 but also of $1 + \sqrt{-5}$ and $1 - \sqrt{-5}$, where $1 + \sqrt{-5}$, $1 - \sqrt{-5}$ can be proved to be "primes," that is, irreducibles of the integral domain. Euclid's fundamental theorem asserting unique factorization fails for this integral domain and for many others. But when Dedekind arrived at a definition of a *prime ideal* suitable for his purposes, he was able to show that (2), (3), $(1 + \sqrt{-5})$, $(1 - \sqrt{-5})$ are *not* prime ideals and can be broken down into prime ideal factors as follows:

$$(2) = (2, 1 + \sqrt{-5})(2, 1 - \sqrt{-5})$$
$$(3) = (3, 1 + \sqrt{-5})(3, 1 - \sqrt{-5})$$

Then, by Dedekind's definition, the *ideal* (6) does have a *unique* factorization into prime ideals

$$(6) = P_1 P_2 P_3 P_4$$

where $P_1 = (2, 1 + \sqrt{-5})$ and P_2, P_3, P_4, are the other ideals in the right members of the above equations for (2) and (3). Let us remind the reader of the exact meaning of an ideal with two generators, for example,

$$P_2 = (2, 1 - \sqrt{-5})$$

As stated on page 419, the ideal P_2 must consist of all the numbers $2x + (1 - \sqrt{-5})y$ where x and y are any numbers whatsoever in the domain, that is, any numbers of the form $a + b\sqrt{-5}$, with a and b ordinary integers. Thus, for example, $2(3 - 2\sqrt{-5}) + (1 - \sqrt{-5})(2 + \sqrt{-5}) = 13 - 5\sqrt{-5}$ would be a member of the prime ideal P_2. Also we must explain that the product of ideals with more than one generator can be defined in a manner illustrated by

$$(a, b)(c, d) = (ac, ad, bc, bd)$$

We shall continue discussion of the generalization of number-theory concepts through the theory of ideals after we have probed a little more deeply into some side-effects of ring homomorphisms. When a homomorphic mapping is not an isomorphism, it is a many-to-one correspondence, and as a result some algebraic properties that depend on the individuality of the ring elements may be lost. This may produce a representation that is more general or freer than the original system because it is bound by fewer laws. On the other hand, the fusion of elements into a single image by means of a many-to-one map may produce a type of blurring where the image has certain properties not present in the original. In that case the map is more specialized or less general than the system it represents. A homomorphic projection is like a shadow. Some features of the original system appear clearly, but some may be lost and others exaggerated. Both types of shadow effect are found in different modulo m maps of the ring of integers, as we shall now see.

In order to study a property that may be preserved in some homomorphic maps of the ring of integers and lost in others, let us start with the elementary problem of finding integral solutions of a quadratic equation like

$$x^2 + x - 6 = 0$$

Using Harriot's method (Chapter 5), we factor the left member and obtain

$$(x - 2)(x + 3) = 0$$

Harriot reasoned that each parenthesis represents a number that *must* be zero for the first parenthesis or for the second or for both parentheses because *the product of two numbers is zero only if at least one of the numbers is zero.* This fact seems obvious to us, but it is actually one of the laws governing the world of integers and *not* a characteristic of rings in general.

The application of this special law enables one to say that

$$x - 2 = 0 \quad \text{or} \quad x + 3 = 0$$

and

$$x = 2 \quad \text{or} \quad x = -3$$

so that there are two integers meeting the conditions expressed by the equation.

Let us now prove that the law assumed by Harriot in solving polynomial equations must hold in every ring that is an *integral domain* and can in fact be deduced from the *cancellation law* (Chapter 4), the property distinguishing an integral domain from more general commutative rings. We must show then that if a and b are elements of an integral domain such that

$$ab = 0$$

then

$$a = 0 \quad \text{and/or} \quad b = 0$$

Now either a and b are both equal to zero, or at least one of them is not equal to zero. Suppose then that $a \neq 0$. We would have

$$ab = 0 \quad \text{and} \quad a \cdot 0 = 0$$

so that

$$ab = a \cdot 0$$

In the last equation a may be cancelled to yield

$$b = 0$$

(Similarly, if we started by assuming $b \neq 0$, we could prove that $a = 0$. In any case, at least one factor must vanish.)

Conversely, if Harriot's law is assumed, the cancellation law follows. Thus, given

$$ab = ac, \quad a \neq 0$$

then

$$ab - ac = 0$$

or

$$a(b - c) = 0$$

By Harriot's law, either one factor or both factors must vanish. Since $a \neq 0$,

$$b - c = 0$$

and

$$b = c$$

so that the cancellation law has been deduced.

As stated in our chapter on symbolic logic, $p \Leftrightarrow q$ signifies that propositions p and q are logically equivalent. In the present instance, the cancellation law and Harriot's law are logically equivalent. For that reason, an integral domain is sometimes *defined* as a commutative ring in which Harriot's law is satisfied.

Let us now see whether the above equivalent properties of the ring of integers are preserved when that ring is mapped homomorphically on {0, 1, 2, 3}, the ring of residues (or residue classes) modulo 4, whose addition and multiplication tables are as follows:

Addition Modulo 4

$\oplus$	0	1	2	3
0	0	1	2	3
1	1	2	3	0
2	2	3	0	1
3	3	0	1	2

Multiplication Modulo 4

$\times$	0	1	2	3
0	0	0	0	0
1	0	1	2	3
2	0	2	0	2
3	0	3	2	1

To furnish ammunition, we now seek solutions of the first-degree equation

$$2 \otimes x = 0$$

in the modulo 4 ring, that is, when the domain of x is the set of residues {0, 1, 2, 3}. Our problem is equivalent to solving the congruence

$$2x \equiv 0 \pmod 4$$

(See Chapter 21). In any case,

$$x = 0 \quad \text{or} \quad x = 2$$

will solve either the equation or the congruence, since

$$2 \otimes 0 = 0 \quad \text{and} \quad 2 \otimes 2 = 0$$

or alternatively

$$2 \cdot 0 \equiv 0 \pmod 4 \quad \text{and} \quad 2 \cdot 2 \equiv 0 \pmod 4$$

Here the corollary to the fundamental theorem of algebra fails because a first-degree equation has two roots. This will not surprise us, because Chapter 21 indicated that this sort of thing may occur for congruences whose modulus is *not* prime. But we are more interested in showing that the failure of the fundamental theorem results from the fact that a particular homomorphic image of the ring of integers—namely, the modulo 4 ring—is *not* an integral domain. The modulo 4 multiplication table indicates that $2 \otimes 2 = 0$. Here a product vanishes although neither factor is equal to zero, and hence Harriot's rule is *not* a universal law for the modulo 4 ring. Then that ring will also lack a cancellation law. The modulo 4 multiplication table shows that $2 \otimes 3 = 2$ and $2 \otimes 1 = 2$. Therefore

$$2 \otimes 3 = 2 \otimes 1$$

Someone not aware that the cancellation law fails in the modulo 4 ring might cancel 2 from the last equation and thus arrive at the paradox, $3 = 1$.

In the statement $2 \otimes 2 = 0$, 2 is said to be a *divisor of zero*. Thus an integral domain is often described as a commutative ring in which there are no divisors of zero. For further examples of rings with divisors of zero, the reader can verify that in arithmetic on an ordinary clock, that is, in the modulo 12 ring, $2 \otimes 6 = 0$ and $3 \otimes 4 = 0$ so that 2, 3, 4, and 6 are all divisors of zero. It is readily seen that there are always divisors of zero in modulo m rings when m is *not* prime. Therefore, such homomorphic maps of the integers are rings but *not* integral domains.

It is in fact a theorem of modern algebra that a modulo m ring is an integral domain if, and only if, m is a *prime* number. Thus we may wish to avoid modulo 6, modulo 8, modulo 9, and modulo 10 systems, for example, since 6, 8, 9, and 10 are composite numbers. Suppose that we use as homomorphic images of the integers only the modulo m systems with $m = 3$ or 5 or 7 or 11 or some other prime number. Some parts of the theory of equations are safe, but will other aspects of the algebra of integers be blurred or distorted? The axioms defining a ring permit addition, subtraction (by means of additive inverses), and multiplication, but say nothing about division, that is, about multiplicative inverses. Every division question can be converted into one about multiplication. For example, $6 \div 2 = ?$ becomes $2 \times ? = 6$ or a matter of solving $2x = 6$. In the domain of integers the cancellation law permits us to cancel 2 if we write the last equation as

$$2x = 2 \times 3$$

and thus

$$x = 3$$

But suppose that we ask for an answer to $2 \div 5$, that is, seek a solution to $5x = 2$. Our world is that of the integers, and hence we cannot solve this problem in that domain. No integer can properly fill the blank in $(5)(\ ) = 2$, nor can we carry out an integral factorization of the right member of $5x = 2$ that will permit cancellation of 5 from both members. Infinitely many other equations of the form $ax = b$, where a and b are integers, are impossible to solve within the integral domain.

Since 3 is a prime number, the modulo 3 ring is an integral domain and does not present special difficulties with respect to cancellation or divisors of zero. But if the integers are mapped on the modulo 3 system, does that map reflect the impossibility of performing division with certain pairs of integers? Suppose that $1 \oslash 2$ is called for, that is, the solution in the modulo 3 system of $2 \otimes x = 1$. The answer is $x = 2$ because $2 \otimes 2 = 1$ in the modulo 3 ring. In other words, $1 \oslash 2 = 2$ in that ring, and this fact does not reflect the impossibility of carrying out in the original aggregate of integers the following combinations (and an infinite number of others) of which $1 \oslash 2$ is the image: $1 \div 2$, $4 \div 11$, $13 \div 5$, $22 \div 17$. What has happened is that these division combinations, impossible in the domain of integers, have become fused with the possible combinations projected onto $1 \oslash 2$. Some of the latter are $4 \div 2$, $25 \div 5$, $16 \div 8$, $88 \div 11$. In the modulo 3 ring, except for division by zero, which is always excluded in arithmetic, all division combinations can be carried out, because the modulo 3 ring is in fact a *field*.

To prove that a commutative ring is a field, one must show that it has a unit element (multiplicative identity) and that every element except zero has a multiplicative inverse (Chapter 4). If we examine the modulo 3 multiplication table (page 413), we can see that 1 is a multiplicative identity because its product with any element of the ring leaves that element unchanged. The table also shows that 1 and 2 have themselves as multiplicative inverses since $1 \otimes 1 = 1$, $2 \otimes 2 = 1$. Hence the modulo 3 ring is a field.

It can be proved that every modulo p ring where p is a prime number is a field and thus that the homomorphism of the integers onto such modulo p fields leads to a representation with additional properties not present in the original system. Here the shadow distorts the original structure so that it assumes a more specialized form. This mapping effect is opposite in type to that in the case of the modulo

4, modulo 6, modulo 8, etc. images, which remove original properties and present a more general picture than the original domain of integers.

In homomorphisms of the ring of integers, the images are either fields or else commutative rings that are not even integral domains, and there is no middle ground where the image is an integral domain but not a field. But in homomorphic mappings of integral domains more general than the set of integers, the intermediate result may occur, namely, preservation of the property of being an integral domain without distortion into a field. That fact is used in one modern definition of Dedekind's conception of a *prime ideal*: An ideal in an integral domain is said to be prime if, when the ideal is the kernel of a homomorphic mapping, the image is an integral domain. If the image satisfies the stronger condition of being a field, the ideal is not only prime but divisorless (maximal).

Our exposition of the nature of rings and ideals, homomorphisms of rings and other algebraic structures, would make it possible for a reader to examine one of Emmy Noether's most important research papers, namely, her 1926 *Abstrakter Aufbau der Idealtheorie*. A year after that memoir was published she was collaborating with Richard Brauer (today one of the leading American algebraists) in a different but not entirely unrelated area of abstract algebra. Then, in 1929, she began her advanced research on hypercomplex number systems. Although we shall not discuss her particular contributions to that subject, we shall honor her once again by explaining the background material that motivated her research, and by quoting the ideas and opinions of those whose fields of investigation were closest to her own.

For example, there is Emil Artin (1898–1962), about whom Hermann Weyl wrote, "He is in some respects akin to Emmy Noether." In a biographical eulogy of Artin in the January 1967 *Bulletin of the American Mathematical Society*, Richard Brauer says, "Whatever standards we use, he was a great mathematician." Brauer, describing Artin's manifold contributions to number theory, field theory, topology, and other mathematical subjects, offers the characterization, "For Artin to be a mathematician meant to participate in a great common effort, to continue work begun thousands of years ago, to shed new light on old discoveries, to seek new ways to prepare the developments of the future."

Let us see how Artin shed new light on the algebraic discoveries which preceded Emmy Noether's work and his own. The ideas he elucidated were those of the Scottish-American Joseph Henry Maclagen Wedderburn (1882–1948). Artin wrote:

> To give a really exhaustive account of the influence of Wedderburn on the development of modern algebra would require years of preparation. In order to present at least a modest account of this influence it is necessary to restrict oneself rather severely. If we were to mention all the consequences and applications of his theorems we could easily fill a whole volume. . . . For the understanding of the significance that Wedderburn's paper *On hypercomplex numbers* (1907) had for the development of modern algebra it is imperative to look at the ideas his predecessors had on the subject.*

It seems advisable to obey Artin's injunction, and consider the notions that paved the way for the 1907 memoir, *On hypercomplex numbers*. The date of the earliest hypercomplex numbers was 1843. These were the quaternions (Chapter 4), created by Hamilton when he was seeking to formulate an algebra of vectors in three-dimensional space that would be analogous to the algebra of 2-dimensional vectors, or their pure mathematical representation, the ordinary complex numbers $a + bi$, where a and b are real numbers and $i = \sqrt{-1}$ is the imaginary unit or the "normal" unit vector. From the point of view of modern mathematics, the most significant fact about the ordinary complex numbers is that they illustrate what Artin and other algebraists today term a *linear associative algebra* or, more briefly, an *algebra*, a system $\{S, \oplus, \otimes, \circ\}$, which can be described as a *ring* with an additional operation $\circ$, called an "external" or "scalar" multiplication in contrast to the ring multiplication, $\otimes$. Alternatively, as indicated at the close of Chapter 4, and also on page 92, an algebra can be considered to be a special type of *vector space*, one for which a binary vector multiplication $\otimes$ is defined, in addition to the unary scalar multiplication $\circ$ which every vector space must possess.

One can think of an ordinary complex number like $5 + 4i$

* Emil Artin, "The Influence of J. H. M. Wedderburn on the Development of Modern Algebra," *Bulletin of the American Mathematical Society*, Vol. 56, No. 1, Part 1 (January 1950).

as a vector with components (5, 4). Hence the algebra of such complex numbers or vectors is a set of rules for combining or operating on such number pairs. But to explain the adjective *linear* one can use the alternative form $a + bi$ which indicates any complex number as a linear combination

$$a \cdot 1 + b \cdot i$$

of the two basic elements or unit vectors 1 and i, where the coefficients a and b are numbers in the real number field. As for the term *associative*, it refers to the postulate that the ring multiplication obeys an associative law. Again, we have seen (Chapter 4) that any real quaternion is a linear combination of the "units" 1, i, j, k.

A *hypercomplex* number of *order* or *dimension* n can be thought of either as an ordered n-tuple $(a_1, a_2, a_3, \ldots, a_n)$, or else as a linear combination

$$a_1e_1 + a_2e_2 + a_3e_3 + \cdots + a_ne_n$$

of n "independent" elements of unit length, namely, the *unit vectors* $e_1, e_2, e_3, \ldots, e_n$, where the coefficients $a_1, a_2, a_3, \ldots, a_n$ are numbers in some *field*, called the scalar or external field. Note that in our description, we have, for the sake of simplicity, used $+$ instead of $\oplus$ (to signify vector addition) and have omitted the symbol o for scalar multiplication, merely employing a juxtaposition like a_1e_1 or a_2e_2, etc. instead of $a_1 \circ e_1$ or $a_2 \circ e_2$. We shall continue such simplified notation in the pages ahead.

This concept of hypercomplex numbers and their algebras was initiated by Hermann Grassmann (1809–1877), a German geometer, who formulated the notion in his *Ausdehnungslehre* (Theory of Extension) published in 1844, just a year after Hamilton presented his quaternions. As we shall see, Hamilton's algebra is just a special instance of the broader Grassmann concept, which embraces even the tensor algebra of general relativity. The German's ideas were overlooked in the main during his lifetime, and their greatness was not recognized until the twentieth century.

In any Grassmann linear algebra the addition operation and the external or scalar multiplication are defined much as one might expect by analogy with elementary algebra. But the distinguishing feature of the different algebras, in addition to dimension, is the definition of the ring (or vector) multiplication. Thus the sum of

$$a_1e_1 + a_2e_2 + \cdots + a_ne_n$$

and

$$b_1e_1 + b_2e_2 + \cdots + b_ne_n$$

is taken to be

$$(a_1 + b_1)e_1 + (a_2 + b_2)e_2 + \cdots + (a_n + b_n)e_n$$

which is just a generalization of such facts of elementary algebra as $(4 - 5i) + (-3 + 2i) = 1 - 3i$. Again, *scalar* multiplications like $6(-7 + 4i) = -42 + 24i$ are generalized to

$$k(a_1e_1 + a_2e_2 + \cdots + a_ne_n) = ka_1e_1 + ka_2e_2 + \cdots + ka_ne_n$$

where k is any number of the external or scalar field.

Suppose that the ring (or vector) multiplication is to be defined in an algebra of order 2. Then

$$(a_1e_1 + a_2e_2)(b_1e_1 + b_2e_2) = a_1b_1e_1^2 + a_1b_2e_1e_2 + a_2b_1e_2e_1 + a_2b_2e_2^2$$

must be a hypercomplex number of the ring and therefore a linear combination of e_1 and e_2. To make this possible, e_1^2, e_1e_2, e_2e_1, e_2^2 must each be such a combination, and it suffices to postulate a multiplication table for these basic vectors or units. (Observe that we have been using juxtaposition to abbreviate *vector multiplication*. Thus e_1^2 signifies $e_1 \otimes e_1$, and e_1e_2 signifies $e_1 \otimes e_2$, etc.)

In the algebra of ordinary complex numbers where $e_1 = 1$ and $e_2 = \sqrt{-1}$, the table is

$\otimes$	e_1	e_2
e_1	e_1	e_2
e_2	e_2	$-e_1$

which can be read $e_1e_1 = e_1^2 = e_1$, $e_1e_2 = e_2$, $e_2e_1 = e_2$, $e_2e_2 = e_2^2 = -e_1$. By substituting 1 for e_1 and $\sqrt{-1}$ for e_2, the reader can verify that this table agrees with the facts of algebra as learned at school.

But the above is not the only algebra of second order. If one attaches no concrete meanings to e_1 and e_2, but treats them as pure abstractions, it is permissible to postulate many different multiplication tables. For example, let us assume the table below:

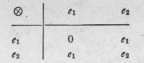

$\otimes$	e_1	e_2
e_1	0	e_1
e_2	e_1	e_2

From the table one obtains $e_1e_1 = e_1{}^2 = 0$, $e_1e_2 = e_1$, $e_2e_1 = e_1$, $e_2e_2 = e_2{}^2 = e_2$. The multiplication is commutative since $e_1e_2 = e_2e_1$.

It can be observed that the ring of complex numbers so defined is *not* an integral domain, because $e_1e_1 = 0$, that is, e_1 is a divisor of zero because the product in question is zero, although neither factor e_1 is zero. In fact, e_1 is a *unit* vector. To introduce some of the vocabulary associated with linear algebras, the element e_1 would be called *nilpotent* in the present case because, although it is not itself zero, one of its powers (in this case, the second) is zero. Such an element will be called *properly nilpotent* if its product with every hypercomplex number of the algebra is nilpotent. Thus, in the algebra under consideration it is possible to prove that the product e_1 with *any* hypercomplex number $a_1e_1 + a_2e_2$ is

$$e_1(a_1e_1 + a_2e_2) = a_1e_1{}^2 + a_2e_1e_2 = 0 + a_2e_1 = a_2e_1$$

and the second power of $a_2e_1 = a_2{}^2e_1{}^2 = a_2{}^2(0) = 0$ so that the product is nilpotent, and hence e_1 is *properly nilpotent*.

In the Wedderburn theorems, and in other major results on linear associative algebras, the *properly nilpotent* elements play an important part. If *all* the elements of an algebra are properly nilpotent, it is called a *nilpotent algebra*. If not, some of its elements may be properly nilpotent and the aggregate of these can be shown to be a *subalgebra*. All of this is the starting point of Wedderburn's theories. If one follows the further consequences of nilpotency, it is revealed that the study of linear associative algebras reduces itself to the consideration of three types called *nilpotent* algebras, total *matric* algebras, and *division* algebras.

Our brief discussion of nilpotency has given some idea of how elements in a nilpotent algebra may behave. A total matric algebra was in fact illustrated in Chapter 17, where definitions of matrix operations were given. When matrix addition, multiplication, and scalar multiplication are limited to the set of all 2×2 or 3×3 or . . . $n \times n$ matrices with entries from a specified field, the resulting system is a linear associative algebra often described as a *total matric algebra* of order 2^2 or 3^2 or . . . n^2. There remains the problem of illustrating the third type of algebra, the *division algebra*.

Whether one conceives of an algebra as a ring with a supplementary scalar multiplication or as a vector space with a supplementary vector multiplication, the fact is that one *cannot* invert vector multiplication, that is, carry out division, in a general linear associative algebra. Hence there is specialization in a *division algebra*, one in which it is possible to carry out division by any element except zero. The algebra of the ordinary plane complex numbers is such an algebra. The other 2-dimensional algebra cited above has a commutative multiplication, but it is *not* a division algebra, as one can realize from the fact that it is not even an integral domain where cancellations can be performed. We shall emphasize the fact by showing that it would not be possible, for example, to carry out the division

$$\frac{6e_1 + 2e_2}{2e_1}$$

If some complex number $xe_1 + ye_2$ of the algebra were an answer, then

$$xe_1 + ye_2 = \frac{6e_1 + 2e_2}{2e_1}$$

and

$$2e_1(xe_1 + ye_2) = 6e_1 + 2e_2$$

$$2xe_1^2 + 2ye_1e_2 = 6e_1 + 2e_2$$

$$0 + 2ye_1 = 6e_1 + 2e_2$$

which is impossible. Even if one selects $y = 3$, the last equation above leads to $2e_2 = 0$, which is false, since e_2 is a unit vector and $2e_2$ signifies a vector of magnitude 2 and the same direction as e_2.

For still other second-order algebras one might assign multiplication tables like

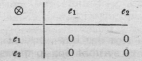

$\otimes$	e_1	e_2
e_1	0	0
e_2	0	0

and

$\otimes$	e_1	e_2
e_1	e_1	e_2
e_2	0	0

The first of these might be said to describe a *zero algebra* of order 2 since the product of any two complex numbers would be zero, because

$$(a_1e_1 + a_2e_2)(b_1e_1 + b_2e_2) = a_1b_1e_1^2 + a_1b_2e_1e_2 + a_2b_1e_2e_1 + a_2b_2e^2$$

and each real coefficient in this result is thus to be multiplied by zero, in accordance with the multiplication table.

The reader can verify that the second multiplication table above indicates that the unit e_2 is nilpotent and that the ring is *not* an integral domain, since $e_2e_1 = 0$ and $e_2e_2 = 0$ where none of the factors is zero. Since it is not an integral domain, the algebra is *not* a division algebra, a fact which can be further illustrated by attempting to find a meaning, within the algebra, for the "quotient," $(3e_1 - 1e_2)/e_2$. What we wish to stress above all is that this second algebra is *noncommutative*, because its multiplication table indicates that e_1e_2 is *not* equal to e_2e_1. Therefore, to show the impossibility of carrying out any kind of division above, the reader should consider *two* cases, namely, $e_2(xe_1 + ye_2) = 3e_1 - 4e_2$ and $(ze_1 + we_2)e_2 = 3e_1 - 4e_2$.

One might continue to postulate arbitrary multiplication tables for algebras of order 2—with the purpose of seeing what variety is possible, what the effect of changing the scalar field may be, whether any 2-dimensional algebra other than that of the ordinary complex numbers is a division algebra, and whether the abstract complex numbers $a_1e_1 + a_2e_2$ of the particular algebras of order 2 can be provided with geometrical or physical interpretations. Instead of mere enumeration or trial and error, perhaps some *theorems* on all such algebras should be sought. The last idea would have been typical of Wedderburn's thought, for he always sought general "structure theorems" to put an end to the enumeration of more and more particular instances of algebras with or without specified properties.

In the present case, some of the questions just raised can be answered by an earlier structure theorem, proved both by the German G. Frobenius (1849–1917) and by Charles

Saunders Peirce (1839–1914), who was the son of the better known Harvard mathematician Benjamin Peirce (1809–1880). The younger Peirce was granted recognition posthumously, but some of his contributions to pure mathematics are still overlooked, possibly because his influence on logic and philosophy was so much greater (Chapter 6). The Peirce-Frobenius structure theorem reveals that if the scalar or coefficient field is the system of real numbers, then the ordinary complex numbers constitute the *only* division algebra of order 2, and that if one proceeds to higher orders, there will be one more division algebra, of order 4, that of the quaternions with real coefficients. Morever, there are no other division algebras with real coefficients except that of the real numbers themselves (an algebra of the first order with the single basic unit 1). The structure theorem in question indicates what a time-saver such a proposition can be. It makes unnecessary the examination of the tremendous variety of multiplication tables one could postulate for algebras of each order, for example, the different rules for

$$e_1{}^2, e_1e_2, e_1e_3, \ldots, e_1e_5, e_2e_1, e_2{}^2, e_2e_3, \ldots, e_5e_1, e_5e_2, \ldots, e_5{}^2$$

in an algebra of the fifth order. The Peirce-Frobenius theorem tells us that, with *all* such tabulation, *forever*, no division algebras would be found, after the particular one of the fourth order discovered by Hamilton.

In 1961, the algebraic topologists J. F. Adams, R. H. Bott, M. A. Kervaire, and J. W. Milnor arrived at a more general theorem than that of Peirce and Frobenius by proving that the real *nonassociative* case provides only one more division algebra, namely, that of the Cayley 8-tuples discussed in Chapter 4.

The multiplication table for the quaternions of Hamilton appears in Chapter 4. We shall apply that table in showing that it is always possible to divide by any quaternion except zero. We shall employ a method similar to that learned at school for carrying out divisions with ordinary complex numbers where divisors are multiplied by conjugates, thus:

$$\frac{3-i}{4+2i} = (3-i)\left(\frac{1}{4+2i} \cdot \frac{4-2i}{4-2i}\right) = (3-i)\left(\frac{4-2i}{16-4i^2}\right) =$$

$$(3-i)\left(\frac{4-2i}{20}\right) = \frac{12-10i+2i^2}{20} = \frac{10-10i}{20} = \frac{1}{2} - \frac{1}{2}i$$

If the quaternion divisor (denominator) is $a_1 + a_2i + a_3j + a_4k$, we shall thus convert the division into multiplication by

$$\frac{1}{a_1 + a_2i + a_3j + a_4k}$$

Then, either left or right multiplication of the numerator and denominator of this fraction by the *conjugate* $a_1 - a_2i - a_3j - a_4k$ yields

$$\frac{a_1 - a_2i - a_3j - a_4k}{a_1{}^2 + a_2{}^2 + a_3{}^2 + a_4{}^2}$$

where the new denominator will be a positive real number, a scalar which we shall symbolize by r. Hence instead of dividing by the above quaternion, one can multiply by the quaternion

$$\frac{a_1}{r} - \frac{a_2}{r}i - \frac{a_3}{r}j - \frac{a_4}{r}k$$

The algebra of quaternions can be used to illustrate some of the questions raised about algebras in general. In the first place, if the field of the coefficients or scalars is changed, an algebra may cease to be a division algebra. In the second place, quaternions do have geometric and physical significance. If the field of the quaternion coefficients is that of the ordinary *complex numbers*, the method used above will indicate that division may not always be possible, for as we shall now show, r may turn out to be zero in many cases, and then

$$\frac{a_1}{r} - \frac{a_2}{r}i - \frac{a_3}{r}j - \frac{a_4}{r}k$$

would be meaningless. We recall that $r^2 = a_1{}^2 + a_2{}^2 + a_3{}^2 + a_4{}^2$. If we seek to divide by the quaternion $(\sqrt{-4} + 3i - 2j + \sqrt{-9k})$, then $a_1 = \sqrt{-4}$ and $a_1{}^2 = -4$, $a_2 = 3$ and $a_2{}^2 = 9$, $a_3 = -2$ and $a_3{}^2 = 4$, $a_4 = \sqrt{-9}$ and $a_4{}^2 = -9$, and

$$-4 + 9 + 4 - 9 = 0$$

Hence division by the given quaternion is impossible. The reader can provide other examples where division fails, if he will choose figures similar to the above—say, division by $1 + \sqrt{-25}i + 5j + \sqrt{-1}k$.

The application of quaternions to physics arises from Hamilton's efforts to design them for such a purpose. We may recall (Chapter 4) that he was seeking to extend a 2-dimensional vector algebra to three dimensions. A 2-dimensional vector may be symbolized by (a_1, a_2) or by the Gaussian $a_1 + a_2\sqrt{-1}$ where a_1 and a_2 are the vector components in the directions of the X- and Y-axes. Then a 3-dimensional vector, (a_1, a_2, a_3), was considered by Hamilton to be the quaternion $0 \circ 1 + a_1 i + a_2 j + a_3 k$. The product of two 3-dimensional vectors (a_1, a_2, a_3) and (b_1, b_2, b_3) was defined by Hamilton to be the product of the corresponding quaternions, that is,

$$(0 \circ 1 + a_1 i + a_2 j + a_3 k)(0 \circ 1 + b_1 i + b_2 j + b_3 k)$$

If the reader will find this product in accordance with the quaternion multiplication table, he will obtain the result

$$-(a_1 b_1 + a_2 b_2 + a_3 b_3) + i(a_2 b_3 - b_2 a_3) + j(a_3 b_1 - b_3 a_1) \\ + k(a_1 b_2 - b_1 a_2)$$

The trinomial $a_1 b_1 + a_2 b_2 + a_3 b_3$ is a *scalar* and may be given many physical interpretations, for example, as *work, electromotive force, circulation* in a fluid. For one geometric interpretation of this scalar, take the case where a quaternion is multiplied by itself or squared. Then $a_1 = b_1$, $a_2 = b_2$, etc., and the above trinomial becomes $a_1{}^2 + a_2{}^2 + a_3{}^2$, whose square root represents the magnitude (length) of the vector, just as in two dimensions $\sqrt{a_1{}^2 + a_2{}^2}$ is the length or magnitude (Chapter 4) of a vector with components a_1 and a_2. As for the coefficients of i, j, and k in the product above, it can be shown that they are the components of a vector whose magnitude is equal to the *area of the parallelogram* whose adjacent sides are the vectors (a_1, a_2, a_3) and (b_1, b_2, b_3).

Broad as Grassmann's concept of hypercomplex numbers was, his algebras did not include all possible multiplication tables, but only those satisfying the conditions

$$e_1{}^2 = 0,\ e_2{}^2 = 0,\ e_3{}^2 = 0,\ \ldots,\ e_n{}^2 = 0$$

$$e_1 e_2 = -e_2 e_1,\ e_1 e_3 = -e_3 e_1,\ \ldots,\ e_r e_s = -e_s e_r$$

It is the second set of conditions which makes Grassmann's algebras noncommutative, and the requirements $e_1{}^2 = e_2{}^2 =$

$e_3^2 = \cdots = e_n^2 = 0$ show that each of the basic units is *nilpotent*.

In fact, every element of a Grassmann algebra is nilpotent. That this is so can be inferred indirectly by realizing that Grassmann's work was "space analysis," where products had geometric interpretations. Thus, in 3-dimensional space, $a_1e_1 + a_2e_2 + a_3e_3$ is a *vector*, $Ae_1e_2 + Be_2e_3 + Ce_3e_1$ is an *area*, $Ke_1e_2e_3$ is a *volume*, and the product of any *four* units or basic vectors, for example $e_1e_2e_3e_1$ must be equal to zero, since a 4-dimensional entity is meaningless within a 3-dimensional space. One can prove directly, of course, that

$$e_1e_2e_3e_1 = e_1e_2(-e_1e_3) = e_1(-e_2e_1)e_3 = e_1(e_1e_2)e_3 = e_1^2e_2e_3$$
$$= 0(e_2e_3) = 0$$

and similarly that any other product of four units, for example, $e_3e_2e_1e_3$, must also be equal to zero. Therefore if the second or third power of an element of a 3-dimensional Grassmann algebra is not equal to zero, its fourth power must surely vanish, and hence, as stated above, every element is *nilpotent*.

In passing, a word about Grassmann himself. He came from a family of Protestant ministers, and it was therefore natural for him to specialize in theology at the University of Berlin. He was also greatly interested in philology, but his mathematical study was more of a sideline or hobby, and his first published work on a mathematical subject (the theory of tides) appeared in 1839, when he was thirty. In the interim he had done some teaching, and in 1842 he settled down to a career as a mathematics teacher at the *gymnasium* of the Baltic port of Stettin, his native city. He continued in this position all his life, and never attained the rank of a university professor. As stated previously, his mathematical stature has been recognized only in recent times. Before that he was considered something of a dilettante, who dabbled in politics, church affairs, music and art, and who placed his Sanskrit dictionary for the *Rig Veda* (one of the Hindu sacred writings) in the same category as his creation of hypercomplex numbers.

But to return to the ultimate development of Wedderburn's algebraic ideas, they are incorporated in the Wedderburn structure theorems:

Every algebra without properly nilpotent elements is uniquely expressible as the "direct sum" of algebras without proper ideals, and conversely.

Every algebra without proper ideals is the "direct product" of a division algebra and a total matric algebra.

The Wedderburn theory reveals the abstract structure of any linear associative algebra whatsoever as follows. First the properly nilpotent elements are removed. Then to the "difference" algebra that remains, the first of the above structure theorems applies, and that difference algebra is expressible in terms of algebras without proper ideals. These in turn are expressible, according to the second theorem above, in terms of division algebras and total matric algebras.

Thus the structure of *any* algebra is revealed by studying (1) the set of properly nilpotent elements initially removed (it can be proved that they form an algebra, hence a *nilpotent* subalgebra of the given one) and (2) the division and total matric algebras in terms of which the "difference algebra" is expressible. In this way the *infinite* variety of linear associative algebras or hypercomplex number systems was reduced by Wedderburn to a *finite* study of only three types of algebra, the nilpotent, division, and total matric types.

Within the mathematical world, Wedderburn's worth is fully recognized, but unfortunately hardly a single man in the street has ever heard of him. Therefore the reader should find the following biography of particular interest. It was written by Professor Hugh S. Taylor, Chairman of the Chemistry Department and Dean of the Graduate Division of Princeton University, and many of the facts included were provided by other associates and friends of Wedderburn, both at Princeton and at the Institute for Advanced Study.[*]

Wedderburn was born in 1882, in Forfar, Scotland, the tenth child in a family of fourteen children, which included seven brothers and six sisters. His father was Alexander Stormonth Maclagen Wedderburn, M.D., of Pearsie. His mother was Anne Ogilvie. On his father's side his grandfather was Parish Minister of Kinfauns and Professor of Exegesis in the Free Church College of Aberdeen. His paternal great-grandfather was Parish Minister of Blair Atholl and a Chaplain in the Black Watch. On his maternal side his grandfather was a lawyer in Dundee, as had been true of the family for several preceding generations. The detailed history of the Wedderburn family has been recorded in the *Wedderburn Book*. Of his many brothers and sisters only two sur-

[*] Royal Society of London, *Obituary Notices of Fellows*, Vol. 6, No. 18 (November 1949), pp. 618 ff.

vived him, a brother, Ernest Wedderburn of Edinburgh, Scotland, and a sister, Miss Elizabeth Wedderburn, of Paris, France.

Wedderburn's early school years were spent at the Forfar Academy from 1887 to 1895. In the latter year he transferred for the last three years of his school education to George Watson's College in Edinburgh, 1895–1898. From this college at the age of sixteen and a half years he obtained the leaving scholarship and entered Edinburgh University in the autumn of 1898. After five years as a student in this university he obtained, in 1903, the M.A. degree with First-Class Honours in Mathematics. His first research "On the isoclinal lines of a differential equation of the first order" was published in the *Proceedings of the Royal Society of Edinburgh* in the same year, when the author had just reached his twenty-first year. Two other communications to the Royal Society of Edinburgh date from the same year. During the year 1902–1903 Wedderburn had served as Nichol Assistant in the Physical Laboratory of the University.

In the following year Wedderburn pursued postgraduate studies in Germany. In the winter semester of 1903–1904 he attended the University of Leipzig; in the summer semester of 1904 he was at work in the University of Berlin. Appointed Carnegie Fellow for the year 1904–1905 he proceeded to the United States where the American phase of his scientific career began in postgraduate study at the University of Chicago. Two papers stem from this period, one "On the structure of hypercomplex number systems" and a second entitled "A theorem on finite algebras."

Following the year in the United States was a period of four years, 1905–1909, once more in Edinburgh as Lecturer in Mathematics and assistant to Professor George Chrystal. Communications to the Royal Society of Edinburgh, to the Edinburgh and London Mathematical Societies, to the *Annals of Mathematics* and, in collaboration with Oswald Veblen, to the *Transactions of the American Mathematical Society* characterize these years as a creative scientist. His joint authorship with Veblen stemmed from the year in Chicago and was an advance notice of a future association of both in Princeton University in the years ahead. Meanwhile the researches already accomplished earned for Wedderburn the degree of Doctor of Science in Edinburgh University in 1908. From 1906 to 1909 he served as editor of the *Proceedings of Edinburgh Mathematical Society*.

Wedderburn entered on the Princeton phase of his life's work in the autumn of 1909. He was called to Princeton as Preceptor in Mathematics, joining a goodly company of distinguished members of the Princeton faculty. The "preceptor guys" as several generations of Princeton students have labelled them, not without deep affection and esteem, were the creation of Woodrow Wilson in his reorganization of the Princeton Faculty. That revolution "required a large scale infusion of new blood, of scholars who would assume an intimate personal relation with small groups of undergraduates and impart to them something of their own enthusiasm for things of the mind." To Wilson, the preceptorial system seemed "the only effectual means of making university instruction the helpful and efficient thing it should be." With a body of fifty preceptors which he brought to Princeton in 1905 he planned to "transform the place where there are youngsters doing tasks to a place where men are doing thinking."

It was thus that L. P. Eisenhart and Oswald Veblen, Gilbert A. Bliss, George D. Birkhoff and Joseph H. M. Wedderburn joined the preceptors of mathematics in Princeton in the years 1905 to 1909. Bliss left after three years to pursue his distinguished career in Chicago. Birkhoff stayed three years and proceeded to Harvard to become there eventually leader in mathematics and Dean of the Faculty of Arts and Sciences. Eisenhart, Veblen and Wedderburn stayed on at Princeton, building up its standards and traditions in mathematical research. Veblen left Princeton University in 1932 to establish, by a process of fission from the Department of Mathematics in the University, a Department of Mathematics in the newly organized Institute for Advanced Study also located in Princeton. Veblen, Alexander and von Neumann made the transition. Eisenhart and Wedderburn stayed behind.

Five happy years as preceptor at Princeton were succeeded by the five grim years of World War I. Wedderburn responded immediately to the call to arms. In view of his already great scientific achievements it would not have been difficult at all for him to have obtained a commission in the British Army at the outset of hostilities. He had already seen service in the Territorial Forces before the war. It is altogether characteristic of the man and of his exceptional modesty that he volunteered at the beginning of hostilities as a private. The Princeton records show that he was the first resident of Princeton to leave for the war on the outbreak of hostilities, and had the longest war service of any member of the University or resident of the town. By November 1914, he had obtained his commission as Lieutenant in the 10th Battalion of the Seaforth Highlanders, receiving his Captaincy in January 1915. From 1915 to February 1918 he continued as Captain in the Seaforth Highlanders but transferred then to the Royal Engineers as Captain in the 4th Field Survey Battalion. In this capacity he saw service in France from January 1918 to March 1919. To this service he brought his exceptional gifts as mathematician and physicist taking an active part in the development of sound-ranging techniques on the field of battle. His services were mentioned in despatches from the British Army in France.

Wedderburn returned to Princeton after the conclusion of the war still in the capacity of preceptor. In 1920–1921 he was Assistant Professor of Mathematics, and was promoted in the spring of 1921 to an Associate Professorship on permanent tenure. Seven years later he was promoted to Professor of Mathematics, a position which he held until his retirement in 1945, with a continuous faculty record of thirty-seven years of service.

His colleagues among the Princeton preceptors recall with enthusiasm the rich human qualities of Wedderburn. They recall his passion for play as well as for work, his desire for companionship and association with men. He loved the out-of-doors, found deep satisfaction in the wilderness, in the woods, canoeing along rivers and streams in the company of thoughtful men. As in his scientific work, he brought to the construction of the camp-site, the erection of the tent, the paddling of the canoe up- and down-stream the qualities of a complete perfectionist. In the wilds of Northern Canada, with congenial men, he found complete happiness. In the tasks of leisure hours he utilized the same resources of knowledge in mathematics, mechanics and physics that marked him out among his scientific colleagues in the class-room and the mathematics seminar. His taste in literature ran to books of travel and he accumulated a large library of travel. He admired John Buchan both for his native Scottish background and his appreciation of the open spaces of the earth.

While Wedderburn had a broad and comprehensive knowledge of pure and applied mathematics, his research work was done exclusively in algebra. Indeed, algebra was his all-embracing scientific passion and it is in algebra that he made his eminent contributions, distinguished no less by their originality than by their depth. It was these characteristics which earned for him, from the Royal Society of Edinburgh, his first major distinction, the award to him in 1921 of the MacDougall-Brisbane Gold Medal and Prize for the period 1918–1920, in recognition of his investigations on hypercomplex numbers. The Royal Society of London, in 1933, elected him Fellow, also by reason of his distinction in the field of algebra.

His mathematical discoveries include two famous theorems which bear his name, frequently quoted by mathematicians. One of his Princeton colleagues in mathematics has said:

"Before Wedderburn began his investigations, the classification of the semi-simple algebras was done only if the ground field was the field of real or complex numbers. Interesting as this investigation was, it did not lead to a deeper insight into the nature of the hypercomplex numbers. Wedderburn attacked the problem in full generality and introduced new methods. This led to a complete understanding of the structure of semi-simple algebras over any given ground field. He showed that they are a direct sum of simple algebras and finally proved the celebrated theorem that a simple algebra consists of all matrices of a given degree with elements taken from a division algebra. These results were found in 1907 and stated in his famous paper entitled 'On hypercomplex numbers.' This paper contains many other results and ideas and was the beginning of a new era in the theory.

"The second important contribution concerns the investigation of skew fields with a finite number of elements. The commutative case had been investigated before by E. H. Moore and had led to a complete classification of all commutative fields with a finite number of elements. Since a non-commutative finite field had never been found one could suspect that they do not exist. It was Wedderburn who showed in 1905 that this is indeed the case.

"This second theorem gives at once the complete classification of all semi-simple algebras with a finite number of elements. But it also had numerous other applications in number theory and in projective geometry. It gave at once the complete structure of all projective geometries with a finite number of points and showed the interesting fact that in all these geometries the theorem of Pascal is a consequence of the theorem of Desargues."

It is of the article "On hypercomplex numbers" that Hermann Weyl, in his book *The classical groups*, remarks "of paramount importance for the modern development is Wedderburn's paper of the year 1908, where he investigates associative algebras in an arbitrary number field k."

After the war period and during the 1920's came a group of papers dealing with other aspects of modern algebra. Wedderburn's greatest contributions were made prior to 1930, and his most important publication thereafter was undoubtedly his book *Lectures on Matrices* (1934). The work is a synthesis that is Wedderburn's own. It contains a number of original contributions to the subject. Though he did not follow the abstract point of view that had just become dominant, neither did he commit the error made by others of treating matrix theory as an art of juggling elements in an array. The important ideas of linear transformations, vector spaces, bilinear forms, appear in Wedderburn's book. Also, as in his best work, one finds here some neat and suggestive algebraic devices that make the book a very valuable reference book, even at the present time.

Of the papers that Wedderburn published after 1930, the best one was *Non-commutative domains of integrity* (Crelle 1931). In this paper the author gave an improvement and extension of known results on reducing a matrix with elements in a Euclidean domain to diagonal form. This stimulated further work on this problem and led to a complete solution a few years later. Also Wedderburn considered in this paper the important problem of imbedding a non-commutative domain in a division ring. He showed that this can be done if common multiples exist. This result was found independently by Oystein Ore.

Towards the close of the 1920's Wedderburn suffered what some of his friends considered a mild nervous breakdown. More and more he withdrew from normal companionships, turned away from such leisurely pursuits and distractions as he had hitherto enjoyed. He followed an increasingly solitary life, dining alone at his club, making no effort to seek out his friends. Even on holidays in the Berkshire Mountains he would spend long intervals in solitude and silence. Those who deliberately penetrated beyond this self-imposed barrier found the same friendly human person that his earlier preceptor colleagues had known, with the same intellectual vigour, originality, depth of understanding and quality of effort that characterized all his scientific work. To one such visitor he occasionally remarked that he "lived too much alone." To reverse the trend seems, however, to have been beyond his capacities if not his desires. In the last years his solitariness increased so that a new generation of undergraduates and research scholars saw less and less of him. He was made Professor Emeritus in 1945 and spent the remaining three years of his life, seeing little of colleagues and friends. It was possible occasionally to break down the barriers of his reserve as, for example, on the occasion of the Princeton Bicentennial Celebrations; at the conference on the physical sciences, when, as it happened, a dozen or so of the Fellows of the Royal Society were at one time in town he accepted an invitation to meet with them at tea. But these were rare and exceptional occasions, less and less frequent as the years passed, and in October 1948, Wedderburn was found dead in his residence at Princeton, where for many years he had lived alone.

He had suffered a heart attack, and no one was present to cheer his last moments.

Wedderburn's work has been presented in order to indicate the nature of the ultimate generalization of elementary arithmetic. In addition, the discussion of linear algebras supplements the general treatment of abstract algebra by providing specific details of the subject matter in one very important area.

Chapter 29

Twentieth-Century Vistas— Logic and Foundations

Having probed some of the heights and depths of modern algebra, we now proceed to our third sample of recent mathematical activity, namely, the attempt to place all mathematical reasoning on a firmer foundation. Various foundational "crises" arose in the course of mathematical history but were, as we have seen, successfully resolved. In the earliest instance, Eudoxus showed how subtle assumptions and definitions would handle the problem of the incommensurable, the issue which confronted the Pythagoreans when they encountered $\sqrt{2}$. Much later, Lobachevsky settled the matter of the parallel postulate and his solution led to the definite formulation of the modern axiomatic method (Chapter 3). By substituting rigorous arithmetic procedures for geometric intuition, Cauchy and Weierstrass liquidated the classical analytical monstrosities (Chapter 22). More recently Kurt Gödel and Paul Cohen tangled with set-theory foundations and, among a number of brilliant results, provided an elegant answer to the challenges raised by the continuum hypothesis and the axiom of choice (Chapter 24). Some of the paradoxes associated with Cantor's theory of infinite sets had, in fact, been accorded a partial resolution in the Whitehead-Russell theory of types (Chapter 24) and in the gradual building of a restrictive foundation for pure (abstract) set theory by Zermelo, Fraenkel, von Neumann, Bernays, and others.

All such solutions to critical problems can be considered triumphs of the axiomatic method. Even the answers to lesser questions have been related to special properties of the postulate systems forming the bases of mathematical sciences. Thus, *completeness* was seen to be desirable in Euclidean geometry (Chapter 3) if one wished to be able to decide whether or not every triangle is isosceles or, more generally, to be able to prove or refute any statement involving permissible (defined or undefined) terms of Euclidean geometry. Completeness, then, might be desirable in other deductive systems as well, or even in a system of logical reasoning whose purpose would be the deduction of *all* of mathematics.

From what we have said, it might seem that if one were careful enough in the selection of the basic assumptions serving as the foundation of mathematics, then all paradoxes could be avoided and all problems could be solved. That this is *not* the case was indicated in 1931 by a devastating discovery, namely, Gödel's "metamathematical" *incompleteness theorem,* whose background we shall now present prior to considering the content of the theorem itself. It can come as no surprise that Gödel is the author of the most revolutionary result in modern mathematical philosophy, since his name has occurred previously in our story whenever some recondite issue of mathematical foundations was discussed (Chapters 3 and 24).

After Lobachevsky's day, the axiomatization of various parts of mathematics and logic was eminently successful and reached a peak of purification (abstractness) in Hilbert's *formalist* school of thought. Hilbert held that "mathematics is a game played according to certain simple rules with meaningless marks on paper." In a Hilbertian *formal system* one has a collection of symbols, along with rules for combining these symbols into "well-formed" formulas. Some of these formulas are the initial postulates and some are "derived" or "deduced" from the postulates by rules of proof. Since the symbols are devoid of meaning, the manipulations with them might turn out to be utterly senseless, that is, might ultimately lead to *contradictions* unless *consistency* of the whole system of rules can be established.

In relation to consistency proofs, Hilbert introduced the idea of *metamathematics,* a theory which studies the properties of formal axiomatic systems. Metamathematics is, in a sense, *external* to all formal systems, that is, outside or beyond Hilbert's "game with meaningless marks." Then metamathematical statements are *not* among the formulas of the "game" but, instead, are *meaningful* assertions about the properties and relations of symbols, axioms, theorems, etc. in a formalized system. Thus the following four formulas might occur *within* some formalization of arithmetic:

$$1 + 1 = 2$$
$$1 + 1 = 3$$
$$y > 2$$
$$3 > 2$$

On the other hand, the following five examples would be *metamathematical* statements about the system:

"*y*" is a variable

"2" is a numeral

The formula "3 > 2" is obtained from the formula "*y* > 2" by substituting the numeral "3" for the variable "*y*."

"1 + 1 = 3" is a formula but *not* a theorem of the system.

The formal arithmetic system is consistent.

How can one prove or refute the last metamathematical statement illustrated above? In general, as we have already stated, consistency is the essential problem of Hilbert's formalist philosophy. Now, in Chapter 3, we indicated that the method of *models*, that is, interpretations, is the usual technique for establishing the consistency of a set of postulates. But, if one uses that method, one furnishes only a *relative* proof of consistency. Thus one may establish the consistency of Lobachevskian or Riemannian geometry by using parts of Euclidean geometry as models, and the consistency of Euclidean geometry by using Cartesian geometry as a model. But then how is Cartesian geometry to be proved consistent? One might interpret that in terms of algebra (arithmetic). But then all such models merely shift the responsibility for consistency from one branch of mathematics to another and thus would require that, ultimately, the consistency of some system (usually arithmetic) be *assumed*. This idea seemed unsatisfactory to Hilbert, and hence he sought "absolute" (*not* relative) consistency proofs, above all, for the formal system on which the consistency of other parts of mathematics rests, namely the arithmetic of the whole numbers. An *absolute* consistency proof is one that does *not* assume the consistency of some other system. To indicate what such a proof requires, let us form a crude and oversimplified analogy. Thus one knows *directly* from the rules of poker that a hand can contain four aces but cannot possibly contain five aces. On a higher level, Hilbert hoped to be able to formalize mathematical systems so that direct examination of the rules of those "games" and the inevitable consequences of the rules would indicate the impossibility of deducing as theorems *both* a well-formed formula and its formal negation.

Hilbert, Bernays, and their followers were able to provide absolute proofs of consistency for certain limited formal systems, for example, a formalized additive (but not multiplicative) arithmetic of the whole numbers. Again, when the truth-table logic of Chapter 6 is properly formalized, it is not difficult to give an absolute proof of its consistency (as well as its completeness). It was hoped, therefore, that an absolute proof of the consistency of the arithmetic (additive and multiplicative) of the whole numbers would soon be found, but all efforts in that direction failed. Hilbert's most serious troubles arose in attempting to construct an absolutely consistent, complete formal system for the derivation of *all* of classical mathematics including arithmetic). Then, in 1931, the twenty-five-year-old Kurt Gödel delivered the body blow to the formalist program by proving that Hilbert's formalization or, in fact, *any* formal system equivalent to the Russell-Whitehead *Principia Mathematica* must, of necessity, be incomplete. What Gödel did was show that there must be "undecidable" statements in *any* such system, that is, propositions which can neither be proved nor refuted using the rules of the system, and that *consistency* is one of those *undecidable* propositions. In other words, the consistency of an all-embracing formal system can neither be proved nor disproved within the formal system itself. Thus Gödel's "incompleteness theorem" put an end to Hilbert's dream of providing for all of mathematics a formal axiomatization that is both complete and absolutely consistent.

Gödel's proof that one cannot establish the consistency of any formalization of elementary number theory is a consequence of his and Hilbert's use of "finitistic" constructive methods. Naturally, if one is "playing a game" part of which is to make an exhaustive examination of relations among the formulas of that "game" in order to search for possible contradictions producing inconsistency, he will have to limit himself to formulas with a *finite* number of symbols and to *finite* sets of properties or relations (unless he makes a "permissible" induction by "construc-tive" procedures). Also, "finitistic" techniques avoid the type of crisis which, as we have seen, may occur in reason-ing with infinite sets. But if one is fearless, he may proceed in the fashion of the German logician, Gerhard Gentzen, who, in 1936, gave a proof for the consistency of arithmetic by using transfinite induction up to a sufficiently large transfinite ordinal (Chapter 24). Thus his demonstration was *not* a "finitistic" absolute proof within formal arithmetic itself.

Gödel's 1931 discovery was revolutionary in the same negative fashion as Galois' proof of the impossibility of finite solvability for polynomials of degree higher than 4 (Chapter 16) and Hamilton's relinquishment of commutative multiplication (Chapter 4). But Gödel's incompleteness the-orem and its corollary concerning consistency are even more destructive, for they attack the very *foundation* of *all* pure mathematics. Although Gödel's later work has also been revolutionary (Chapter 24), no other one of his contribu-tions is so *final* for mathematical methodology as the 1931 theorem. As recognition of that achievement, he was made a permanent member of the Institute for Advanced Study at Princeton in 1938, and was awarded an honorary degree at Harvard University in 1952.

Apropos of one of Hilbert's major discoveries, the alge-braist P. Gordan (1837–1912), one of Emmy Noether's teachers, proclaimed, "This is not mathematics; it is theol-ogy!" Perhaps Gordan's statement would be more applicable to Gödel's theorem for, if one insists on *absolute* consistency proofs, and if these are unattainable, then consistency be-comes a matter of *faith* rather than a question of logical reasoning.

Gödel's proof is highly technical and employs a novel methodology. Nevertheless, since the work is a modern classic, we shall outline his demonstration and feature its high points. But first, let us remark that his famous argu-ment is patterned, in part, on a logical paradox formulated by the Frenchman Jules Richard in 1903. The Richard paradox arises as follows. Suppose that one wishes to list a sequence of properties of the whole numbers, characteristics with descriptions like "prime" or "even" or "perfect square" or "multiple of 4." Having formulated definitions, one will require some criterion for ordering them. Thus, observing that each definition contains a finite number of words each containing a finite number of letters, we can pick out the definition containing the smallest number of letters and assign to it position (1) in the serial order. The next shortest definition can then be given position (2), and so on. If two definitions contain the same number of letters, we can place them on the basis of the alphabetical order of the letters in each. Thus each definition will have its own order number.

Now we note a certain possibility. Perhaps a particular order number may possess the characteristic described in the definition to which it corresponds. Thus it might possibly occur that 19 has been assigned to the property of "being prime," whose definition has been formulated, as "*x*, a whole number, is prime if and only if it is not exactly divisible by any natural number except itself and 1." Observe that 19 actually has the property described. By contrast, the order number 12 may have been assigned to the property of "being odd," whose definition is "*x*, a whole number, is odd if and only if it leaves a remainder 1 when divided by 2." Note that 12 does *not* have the characteristic defined. An order number like 12 that does *not* possess the property described in the definition to which it corresponds is called *Richardian*. A number like 19, then, is *not* Richardian.

But consider the property of being Richardian. When that is carefully defined, its definition will contain a certain number of letters of the alphabet and hence can be assigned a position in our sequence of definitions. Let us symbolize the number assigned by the letter *n*. Our challenge now arises: *Is the number n Richardian?* If the answer should in fact be affirmative, then *n* cannot possess the property to which it corresponds (thus, the property of being Richardian). In other words, if we assume that *n* is Richardian, then we must conclude that it is not Richardian. Let us start anew and this time assume that *n* is not Richardian. Then *n* must possess the property to which it corresponds (thus, the property of being Richardian). In the present case, the hypothesis that *n* is not Richardian leads to the conclusion that it is Richardian. In summary, we have a *paradox* because there are only two possible answers to the question raised and either one leads to the conjunction of a statement R and its negation $\sim R$. The situation violates the law of contradiction, $\sim (p \wedge \sim p)$ (Vol. I, page 176), which asserts that a statement and its negation cannot both be true.

Now one refutation* of the Richard paradox argues that "being Richardian" is a notational property depending on *metamathematical* concepts like the number of letters in a sentence, etc. and hence that its definition does *not* belong on a list of purely arithmetic properties. If the said definition is deleted from our list (or, at any rate, transferred to some metamathematical theory about that list), then there can be no argument like the one presented above and hence the paradox is resolved.

Although Gödel may have patterned his proof on the Richard paradox, he avoided pitfalls by *arithmetizing* metamathematical statements, that is, by translating them into arithmetical formulas which properly belong in a list of such formulas. What he did was to construct a formal system for elementary number theory, that is, for the higher arithmetic of the whole numbers. Then he provided a scheme (*not* lexicographic) of assigning a different natural number (called a Gödel number) to each entity of his formalized system. Thus there are Gödel numbers for his basic meaningless symbols, for his well-formed formulas, in particular for his postulates and his theorems, and also for his proofs (finite sequences of formulas derived by his rules for deduction). Every Gödel number is a natural number, but the converse is false. Not every natural number is a Gödel number. For example, in Gödel's original scheme, the number 4 is not assigned to any entity of the formal system. At any rate, Gödel's numbering *maps* his formalized number theory (and the part of *Principia Mathematica* essential to his formal logical procedures) onto a proper subset of the natural numbers. Then, given a formula or a proof, its Gödel number can be computed. In reverse, given a natural number, one can first determine whether or not it is a Gödel number. Then, if it is actually the Gödel number of a formula or proof, that formula or proof can be reconstituted (by factorization of the Gödel number into primes, a familiar procedure of number theory). Finally, metamathematical statements are "mirrored" by arithmetic equivalents, that is, they are mapped isomorphically, as it were, onto statements about ordinary arithmetic relations, and then the latter statements are formalized, or given representation by the "meaningless" symbols of the formal system. Hence,

---

* See, for example, E. Nagel and J. R. Newman, *Gödel's Proof*, New York University Press, New York, 1958, p. 63.

whereas in the Richard paradox a number n is associated with a metamathematical statement, in Gödel's proof n is associated with a pure arithmetical formula whose intuitive content or interpretation is the metamathematical statement.

We shall now sketch in broad outline, in *non*rigorous, informal (nonsymbolic) fashion, the main argument in Gödel's original proof of the incompleteness theorem. Our presentation will follow virtually what Gödel himself said at the very beginning of his 1931 paper—prior to his formal proof, which required 46 preliminary definitions and several preliminary theorems, all expressed symbolically, as the background for his ultimate demonstration. At one point in his introduction, Gödel asserted that his method of proof can be applied to *every* formal system in which the concept of "provable formula" is defined and in which every provable formula is "true." If this last statement puzzles the reader, he can think of "provability" as a notion formalized *within* the system, and of "truth" as an idea associated with models (interpretations), hence *outside* the system, thus metamathematical.

In the case of the Richard paradox, there was a sequence of definitions with a corresponding sequence of natural numbers. If we think of the definitions as open sentences, "x is . . . ," where the domain, or replacement set, for x is the aggregate of whole numbers, then the typical terms of the two sequences can be pictured as

Natural Number	Open Sentence
k	x is . . .

To test whether or not k is Richardian, one substitutes k for x in the open sentence corresponding to k, to yield the statement "k is . . . ." When k does *not* have the property described, k is Richardian. Next, a certain natural number n corresponds to "x is Richardian." Substitution of n for x produces "n is Richardian," and our previous argument leading to the Richard paradox follows.

Gödel's procedure is roughly analogous to the above. To make the analogy closer, we shall use the term "troublesome" to correspond to "Richardian" and claim that a number in Gödel's sequence is "troublesome" if and only if it *cannot* be *proved* to have the property to which it corresponds. More exactly, Gödel considers only those formulas of his system that are open sentences in a single variable x, where the domain of x is the set of Gödel numbers. Those open sentences can be ordered as a sequence corresponding to the increasing magnitude of their Gödel numbers. Next, the sequence of Gödel numbers is subdivided into two complementary subsets T and $\overline{T}$, containing "troublesome" and "nontroublesome" Gödel numbers of the sequence, respectively. The Gödel criterion is: A number k of the sequence belongs to T (in our popularization, is "troublesome") if and only if its substitution for x in the open sentence corresponding to k results in a formula that is *unprovable*. Thus we have

Gödel Number	Open Sentence
k	$\ldots x \ldots$

and k belongs to T or is "troublesome" if and only if "$\ldots k \ldots$" is an *unprovable* formula. If the formula is provable, k belongs to $\overline{T}$ or is "nontroublesome."

Now we shall give the intuitive content of one of Gödel's open sentences but, instead of computing its Gödel number, shall merely symbolize that number by n. Thus

Godel Number	Open Sentence
n	x is a member of T, that is, x is troublesome.

Next, imitating the procedure that leads to the Richard paradox, we must substitute n for x in the open sentence to produce a proposition which, expressed informally, is

$$G = n \text{ is a member of } T, \text{ that is, } n \text{ is troublesome}$$

We have labeled this proposition with the letter G in honor of Gödel. Here G is a proposition whose formal counterpart is *undecidable* within the formal system. For if G were assumed to be provable, then it would be "true" and by its *valid* content would reveal that n is "troublesome." This would mean (by definition) that the proposition which results from substituting n for x in the open sentence to which n corresponds, namely, the *proposition G itself*, would be *unprovable*. Thus the assumption that G is provable leads us to the conclusion that it is not provable, a *contradiction*, and hence we must relinquish the assumption.

Suppose, on the other hand, that the negation

$$\sim G = n \text{ is } not \text{ a member of } T$$

is provable, hence "true." Then by what $\sim G$ validly asserts, n would belong to $\overline{T}$. In other words, n would be a "nontroublesome" Gödel number, and the result of its substitution in the formula to which it corresponds, namely, the proposition G, would be *provable*. Thus the assumption that $\sim G$ is provable leads to the conclusion that G is provable, an impossibility in a *consistent* system because in such a system a proposition and its negation cannot both be provable. We remark in passing that a *formal* proof of Gödel's theorem makes use of a more stringent condition, called ω-consistency. In conclusion, the argument in this paragraph and the one preceding it shows that if the formal system is consistent, neither G nor $\sim G$ is provable. Hence G is *undecidable* and the system is *incomplete*.

Let us digress briefly to comment on certain side-effects of Gödel's proof. If the reader will return to the paragraph before the last, he will observe that our lengthy analysis of the content of the proposition G boils down to the conclusion that what G actually asserts is "G is not provable." Gödel points out that here we have an analogy with the "liar paradox" (Chapter 24), namely, a proposition referring to itself, in particular, to its own unprovability. But G is *not* circular since, in the proof itself, G asserts the unprovability of a very definite formula, the one that will result if there is a permissible substitution in the formula with number n. Only *subsequently*, almost accidentally, does it turn out that the resulting formula will be G itself. At any rate, the situation caused Gödel to say that Russell and Whitehead were too drastic when they sought to solve the "liar paradox" by forbidding a proposition to talk about itself. Gödel remarked that it is even possible to construct, for *any* metamathematical property that has a symbolic counterpart in his formal system, a proposition which says of itself that it has this property. Again, we must reveal that neither the Richard paradox nor the "liar paradox" need be used as the pattern for Gödel's proof. Many other antinomies would serve equally well. As a final point in our digression, we should like to point out another remarkable feature of Gödel's proof, namely, that since, *metamathematically* speaking, G asserts its own unprovability, G is *true* because it is indeed unprovable (in fact, undecidable). Hence the proposition G, undecidable *within* Gödel's formal system, can be decided by metamathematical arguments.

In our original discussion of completeness (Chapter 3) we pointed out how the undecidability of a proposition can be removed by adding supplementary axioms to the postulate set of a deductive system. In particular, one can add as an assumption either the undecidable proposition or its negation. Hence, in the present instance one could make G decidable by postulating either G or $\sim G$. Let us do so, and call the additional postulate G_0. But then Gödel's proof indicates how, on the basis of the enlarged postulate system, a *new* undecidable formula can be constructed. One can then add either that formula or its negation as a supplementary postulate, G_1. Now Gödel's process can be repeated again and again indefinitely so that the addition of a sequence of supplementary postulates, $\{G_0, G_1, G_2, G_3, \ldots\}$, will *not* complete the system. It is *essentially* incomplete.

Thus Gödel demonstrated that *every* "finitistic," consistent, formal system must always have some undecidable formula F. (Note that we use the symbol F instead of G so as not to confuse the reader, since the previous paragraph suggests that our original undecidable G may have been added as a postulate.) Now we proceed to Gödel's all-important corollary for a system like the one just described. He proved the corollary by first mapping the metamathematical statement "The system is consistent" onto a formula C within the system. Next he demonstrated the validity of the implication,

$$(F \text{ is not provable}) \rightarrow (C \text{ is not provable})$$

But "F is not provable" is true, since F is undecidable. Hence, by the rule of detachment (Chapter 6), "C is not provable" is true. Thus, even though the formal system is consistent (as assumed in the first sentence of the present paragraph), its consistency cannot be proved *within* the system.

Gödel's incompleteness theorem and its corollary, the impossibility of absolute consistency proofs, represent a genuine crisis in mathematical foundations, one which cannot be resolved if one demands *finitistic* foundations for *all* of *pure* mathematics. Why "finitistic" foundations? Does "finitistic" mean something other than finite? These questions arose out of an earlier crisis whose nature will now be explained.

Let us now turn back from Gödel today to Kronecker, who, in the late nineteenth century, had objected to the analytic methods of Cantor, Dedekind, and Weierstrass, saying that the definitions they employed, particularly those for infinite classes, did not make it possible in every case to decide whether an entity meets the conditions specified.

L. E. J. Brouwer (1881–1967) developed this iconoclastic point of view further, his *bête noire* being the law of the excluded middle, which he refused to accept in reasoning with infinite sets. We recall that this law is the logical tautology $p \lor \sim p$, and that it corresponds to the Boolean identity $P \cup P' = I$. It states that for any proposition p, either the statement itself or its negation must be true. If p is the proposition "Every member of a set S has a specified property," then $\sim p$ is the proposition "At least one member of the set S lacks the specified property." In the case of *finite* sets one would be able to examine the individual members and decide between the alternative propositions. *Direct* verification for p would *not*, of course, be possible in the case of an infinite set, but p might be true by definition or by logical inference from other propositions. If, on the other hand, inference shows p to be false, Brouwer would *not* permit us to say, automatically, that $\sim p$ is true. He would require us to find a member of the infinite set actually lacking the property in question. This might put us in a quandary, since examination of a trillion or more members might fail to reveal such a member and our only hope would be to search on and on.

For further examples of difficulties in reasoning with infinite sets, in particular with applying the law of the excluded middle to them, for Brouwer's notion of *constructive proof*, for his belief that mathematics is prior to logic, and for a contrast between his point of view and Hilbert's formalism, we can do no better than refer the reader to an explanation by Rolin Wavre* (1896–1940), noted modern logician, philosopher, and disciple of Brouwer.

"Men do not understand each other because they do not speak the same language and because there are languages which are not learned."

In saying that, Poincaré sought to describe the irreconcilable nature of that clash of temperament manifested in the very heart of mathematics at the appearance of Cantorian ideas. The clash has taken form under various captions. Du Bois-Reymond called the divergent tendencies empiricist and idealist; Poincaré, pragmatist and realist; Brouwer, *intuitionist* and formalist. We shall here use intuitionist for the one, but according to circumstances, idealist, formalist, or even realist for the other.

The intuitionist is at present identified by his extreme caution.

* Rolin Wavre, "Is There a Crisis in Mathematics?" *American Mathematical Monthly*, Vol. 41, No. 8 (October 1934), pp. 488 ff.

Being anxious to attain the greatest intelligibility and clarity, he challenges such propositions as Zermelo's axiom of selection* or such reasoning as does not seem rigorous. The idealist claims to depart in nothing from the rigor which the intuitionist rightly demands, and this without evidencing the least distrust with regard to those modes of reasoning—even on the contrary conceding their perfect legitimacy and applying them literally and without restriction. Russell, Hilbert, Zermelo, and Hadamard are idealists; Lebesgue, Borel, and Baire are intuitionists.

The clash is very much more evident now than in the past, as a result of the several publications, on the one hand of Brouwer and Weyl, two new and undeniably revolutionary intuitionists, and on the other of Hilbert. We should like to summarize here the essence of these publications and show how clearcut the clash becomes in connection with the notion of existence and a doubtful application of the law of excluded mean.† We shall see in particular why, and in what system of definition, the intuitionist denies us the right to say:

Two mathematical points are either coincident or distinct.

Two functions defined for the same values of the independent variable coincide for all those values or else there exists one for which they do not coincide.

That the intuitionist formulates such paradoxes in the name of truth seems curious. But the paradox is bound up with the words and not with the ideas.

Weyl, however, believes he has discerned at the basis of the theory of real numbers a vicious circle which endangers its value, and that he should therefore declare that mathematics is undergoing a crisis. Brouwer and Weyl have attempted to reconstruct the theory of sets and that of functions on new foundations, carefully avoiding the suspected law and vicious circle. In this they have carried distrust as to certain modes of reasoning, whose legitimacy has created no doubt for three centuries, further perhaps than the French school of the theory of sets.

Hilbert is not of the opinion that it is the turn of mathematics, after physics, to go through a revolution. Observing that the consequences of the idealistic attitude would never lead to the slightest contradiction, however far they be pushed, he considers that the principles suspected by the intuitionists, although not having perfect evidence, are nevertheless legitimate. Unlike Brouwer and Weyl, Hilbert does not believe in the necessity of reconstructing the foundations of mathematics, for he prescribes a radical remedy in order to prevent the crisis and to legitimate a frankly idealistic

---

* We have seen in Chapter 24 how Cohen has given a definitive answer to that challenge.

† Wavre calls the disputed principle the "law of the excluded mean," but we have employed the more usual terminology, "law of the excluded middle."

attitude. This means is the axiomatic method. In substance he does this: to the axioms accepted by the intuitionists, he adjoins a new proposition called the axiom of the transfinite which contains in itself all the doubtful principles united. And from this would be deduced the doubtful applications of the law of excluded mean. But to justify such a procedure, it must be demonstrated that this total system of axioms does not imply contradiction. By this artificial union of its idealistic foundations present-day mathematics would not forfeit the renown of being the discipline whose truth is above suspicion.

I do not conceal the difficulty encountered in trying to express the exact meaning of the relation Brouwer establishes between mathematics and logic. However, I shall try to set off the essentials in the thought of the great Dutch mathematician. In 1907 Brouwer made bold to reverse the roles which Russell would have had mathematics and logic play. Instead of its being the second which accounts for the first, it is on the contrary the part of mathematics to comprise logic, even traditional. The Aristotelian logic, born of natural classification, would be adequate to the theory of finite collections and would not go beyond it; it would be concerned exclusively with the relations of whole and part. *Its complete self-evidence is the cause of the a priori character conferred on it; but, taken in by this a priori character, we would have called traditional logic to a function it is incapable of exercising.*

Traditional logic can at most claim to conform discourse to rules, but language itself becomes more and more inadequate to the genuine understanding of the facts of present-day mathematics; thus the word "all," for example, despite the subtle distinctions of Russell, has an unprecise meaning as soon as one is concerned with "all" the objects of an infinite collection. The mathematical intuition is, on the contrary, guarantee of the autonomy of this science, and is not bound to respect always and everywhere in its translation into discourse the rules of syntax which traditional logic prescribes. Logic, on the other hand, would be only the algebra of the *language* by which the reasoning is translated. But a logical construction of mathematics independent of the mathematical intuition is impossible, according to Brouwer, because one would obtain thereby only a verbal construction irrevocably divorced from the science. Further, this would be a vicious circle, *for logic itself requires the fundamental intuition of mathematics.*

According to Brouwer the field of application of traditional logic would be limited to finite collections. The crux of the issue then is the right to reason on finite and infinite sets in the same manner. For Brouwer does not admit the law of excluded mean, expressed *in abstracto* and *universally* in the form: "A thing either is or is not" or "A proposition is either true or false."

The laws of contradiction and of excluded mean express two

fundamental relations between an attribute A and its contradictory, *non-A*, both well defined relatively to the same object, such as even and odd for an integer. The law of contradiction forbids attribution of A and *non-A* at the same time to the same object. The law of excluded mean compels assertion of one or the other. They can be regarded as defining the words "well-defined attribute" or "attribute *non-A*" or simply negation; bound up as they are with the definitions, there can be no question of doubting them. *The sole question at issue is to know when they are applicable and to what attributes.* In more precise terms, it is a matter of recognizing whether two distinct attributes A and B are such that one is entitled to make one the logical equivalent of the negation of the other. It is a matter of knowing, for example, whether for an integer the attribute of being factorable is well defined and whether the attribute of being prime is by definition equivalent to non-factorable. If it is by definition, these laws would apply with full right; if not, a special examination of the two attributes becomes necessary, and it is only in virtue of an indirect evidence that the laws do apply. In the numerous examples which mathematics furnishes of well-defined attributes, or which one considers as such, *only an intuitive, extra-logical evidence permits us to consider two attributes A and B as the negation one of the other*.

The following example is suggestive and of great importance in the present issue: Let us call a *fundamental aggregate a sequence of integers:* 1, 3, 4, 5, 7, for example. Are the following propositions, which state an attribute of the sequence, related as A and *non-A*?

a. All the numbers of the sequence are odd.

b. There exists in the sequence an even number.

No one doubts that they are so related, but that is in virtue of direct evidence. I run through the sequence; this done, at some determinate position I either have or have not encountered an even number, and I cannot at the same time have found and not found one. I then have the right, from the point of view of their logical function, to assimilate *a* to *non-b* and *b* to *non-a*. The formalist makes "there exists" equivalent by definition to "not all." That is his right. But in doing so, he introduces a new axiom or a new definition.

To the question: Does there exist an even number in the sequence?, whether I refer to the intuitive sense of the word "exist" or to its logistic sense, I cannot refuse to answer with yes or with no; yes, if I affirm *b*, no, if I affirm *a*. Generalized, this becomes: (1.) *To the question: Does there exist in a fundamental aggregate a number having a well defined attribute A?, I can only reply with yes or no.* This is the application of the law of excluded mean which we had in mind.

Likewise the following undoubted proposition, "The numbers

of the sequence 1, 3, 4, 5, 7, which are odd form a new set 1, 3, 5, 7," becomes when generalized: (2.) In a fundamental aggregate, a well defined attribute A suffices to characterize a sub-class of the elements which possess it. With Brouwer, we call this principle (2) Zermelo's axiom of inclusion. It states that in a sequence of integers a definition by intension is equivalent to a definition by extension.* *The formalists believe that they have the right to apply principles 1 and 2 without any restriction to the case where the fundamental aggregate is composed of an infinity of elements, such as the natural series of positive integers. The intuitionists refuse this right.*

In exposition of the arguments for the respective positions, consider the following imaginary dialogue:

The Idealist: Either there exists a factorable number in the sequence $m_n = 2^{2^n + 38} + 1 (n = 1,2,3, \ . \ . \ .)$ or else one such does not exist. (This is the sequence 2^{239}, 2^{240}, 2^{241}, etc.)

The Intuitionist: I can only say one exists by exhibiting such a number, say m_{1000}, which is factorable; and I can only deny it by deducing from the definition of the numbers m_n that they are all prime. But I do not see that the rejection of one of the parts of the alternative compels me to affirm the other; as I cannot exclude *a priori* every *tertium*, I refuse to be reduced to your alternative.

The Idealist: Suppose I take successively the numbers 1, 2, 3, . . ; then either I shall or shall not come across a number n giving rise to a factorable number m_n. My encounter either will or will not occur.

The Intuitionist: To deny that all the numbers m are prime does not imply that there exists a determinate one, e.g., m_{268}, which is factorable. And in order to be certain of not having met one, you must have exhausted the series of integers, and that you will never do. You will take several steps in the series, and can perhaps say one exists, but you will never take enough to make a denial. *I should not deny that the number does or does not exist if the existence of an object in an infinite set were a well defined attribute of the set; but existence is not a well defined attribute. There are perhaps several modes of existing.*

Let us introduce the two following propositions which state two attributes of the fundamental aggregate:

a. All the numbers of the aggregate possess the attribute A.

b. There exists a number of the aggregate possessing the attribute non-A.

As soon as an infinity of objects is concerned, the word "all" is suspect to the intuitionist. The proposition a can only have the precise meaning which its demonstration confers on it. This

* This corresponds to what we have said many times, namely, that a subset of a universal set can be specified by a defining property or, in the finite case, by roster.

meaning will vary according to the demonstration. The most complete meaning would be such that it would follow just from the definition of the numbers of the set that they all have the attribute A. The "there exists" can only have meaning if the object said to exist is actually found. "There exists a number having such an attribute" signifies for the intuitionist: "Here is a number possessing this attribute." "All" from the formalist point of view means: and this, and this, . . . and this. Likewise, "there exists" means: or this, or this, . . . or this. They are logical product and sum. But if the fundamental aggregate is infinite, the handling of such product and sum requires precautions as to convergence analogous to those with the infinite products and series of analysis. Intuitionists (such as Weyl) seem to confer meaning only on the implication b implies *non-a*, which suffices to establish that propositions a and b cannot both be affirmed. But as the inferences *non-b* implies a and *non-a* implies b, maintained by formalists, are doubtful or no longer meaningful, they see no need of their being related by the law of excluded mean. Consider the intuitionist meaning of general and existential demonstrations and the fact that the expressions "not all" and "there does not exist" have a doubtful meaning, and one will perhaps no longer be surprised at the paradoxes of the most extreme intuitionists. Even Hilbert recognizes that these phrases are devoid of a clear and immediate meaning. *The intuitionists refuse to make an alternative of the affirmation of a universal affirmative or of a singular negative*, when an infinite class is in question; of saying, for example, *either all the integers of a class are factorable or else there exists a determinate one which is prime*.

Here are two examples illustrative of Brouwer's attitude:

1. Let $m = \phi(n)$ and $m' = \phi'(n)$ be two laws of correspondence between a positive integer n and two integers m and m'. Let us say that the two functions ϕ and ϕ' are identical if the numbers m and m' are equal for all values of n, and that the two functions are different if there exists a value of n giving two unequal numbers m and m'. To demonstrate the identity of the two functions, we should have to be able to reduce the one to the other algebraically or analytically; to demonstrate their difference we should have to discover a number n giving rise to two distinct numbers m and m'. Considering what such discovery entails, it perhaps will not seem surprising that the functions are not *a priori* identical or different.

2. Fermat's theorem that the sum of two nth powers of two positive integers is never equal to the nth power of another integer as soon as n is greater than 2 has no known demonstration. One is tempted to say: if the proposition is false, I can assure myself of it by a finite number of trials on the integers. For then, there exist three integers and a power larger than 2 giving rise to the equality, and I can order my experiences in one series in such a way as to be certain of finding the numbers in question within a finite range

in the series. Brouwer absolutely refuses to argue this. For him, even the demonstration that Fermat's theorem led to a contradiction would not imply the existence of four numbers invalidating it.

The crux of the intuitionist thesis is the meaning to attribute to the existential judgment and the general judgment. For Weyl, a true judgment is the attribution of a predicate to a singular subject. Where the formalist is content to affirm some sort of ideal existence of an object possessing such an attribute (e.g., there exists an even number), the intuitionist requires the discovery of such an object as will enable him to replace the existential judgment by a true judgment (the number 4 is even).

As Lebesgue has already said, we can only prove the existence of a mathematical entity by constructing it. The "there exists" would be only a check, without value in itself, so long as we cannot find the bank. And perhaps we shall never find it to convert its nominal value into its effective one. The "there exists" of the idealist is only an incitation to formulate a true judgment; ideal existence is worthless so long as it is not converted into actual existence. It is also to be noted that general judgments have meaning only through the fact that they imply an indefinite number of singular judgments; they are only true because they are constantly verifiable.

At this point of his article, Wavre goes on to tell why he, Brouwer, Weyl, and other intuitionists reject the Cantor-Dedekind continuum (a concept explained and repeatedly applied in previous chapters of this book). Thus, most infinite sets become taboo in the intuitionist philosophy. There is, however, no ban on infinite *sequences,* that is, countably infinite aggregates, for, it is argued, our primitive intuition enables us to conceive of a single object, then another, then another, etc., indefinitely. In addition, there is a constructive process for building a sequence—a formula for its general term or a "recursion formula" by which every term after the first can be obtained from the one preceding. In this way, intuitionist procedures are "finitistic" rather than exclusively finite. But Brouwer's school claims that the Cantorian continuum must be renounced because we cannot make that entire ensemble an intuitive construction. What we can conceive is the sequence of intervals of diminishing length, one within the other, whose limit is classically defined to be a real number (Chapter 2). But we never, in intuition, make the actual passage to the limit. Hence Weyl introduced the notion of "becoming" to correspond to our intuitive recognition of how a sequence of intervals gradually "becomes" a real number, and claimed that only in that way do we arrive at an intuitive conception of the number.

Brouwer proclaimed his logically restrictive doctrine in 1907 and elaborated it until his death in 1967, even though he made other important contributions to mathematics, notably to topology; Wavre's article appeared in 1934; but other members of the intuitionist cult are *still* vigorously working at the unfinished task of reformulating classical mathematics so as to avoid the law of the excluded middle and the Cantorian continuum. To indicate a link between their problems and those considered earlier in this chapter, we remark that, although the iconoclastic intuitionist viewpoint sometimes seems difficult and obscure, the notion of *intuitive* criteria for "truth" avoids, in a sense, the frustrating formalist issue of the internal consistency of abstract systems where reasoning is carried out with "meaningless" symbols.

Because the unsettled problems of mathematical foundations are challenging issues whose solution may determine the mathematical "shape of things to come," considerable space has been given to a critical consideration of such questions. Whether or not the future will resolve the logical "crises" we have discussed is an open question. But we shall now consider what may be the possible fate of other mathematical issues and activities in the years ahead.

Chapter 30

Retrospect and Prospect

Plato said that there are three daughters of necessity, not only Lachesis singing of the past and Clotho of the present, but Atropos of the *future*. Mathematicians and scientists of all periods have held similar views and hence have always been fond of predicting the nature of things to come and envisioning, as all mortals are prone to do, one of two extremes—a more perfect world or an *"après moi, le déluge"* affair.

According to Byron, the best of prophets of the future is the *past*; according to Montaigne, it is the *present*. If one accepts either of these viewpoints, he must believe that all we can hope to know concerning the future of mathematics is implicit in those developments already discussed in the previous chapters of this book. People in general are interested in specific predictions, however. They are ever attentive to meteorological or economic forecasts; they take pleasure in prophecies about "the next hundred years" or science-fiction fantasies about the future where characters are robots or creatures from other planets.

To cater both to mathematical tradition and to popular taste, it seems fitting therefore to close our story with some thoughts concerning the possible progress of mathematics in the eighth decade of our century and thereafter. If, as Byron, Montaigne, and others have held, history repeats itself, one can obtain guidance by recapitulating what has gone before. Let us then prepare for predictions by summarizing very briefly our story of mathematics as a living, growing endeavor, holding a strong place in human culture and maintaining a vital, stimulating relationship with all the sciences.

After primitive beginnings, there were the Babylonians, as we have seen. Their remarkable contributions remained undiscovered and undeciphered until recently, but in all likelihood had some influence on mathematics in India, where arithmetic and algebra were developed by four great leaders, the latest being Bhaskara in the twelfth century. Even before that time, the Moslems had become intermediaries for bringing Hindu mathematics and science to the western world. The outstanding character of the early Mesopotamian arithmetic, algebra, and astronomy has been described, but we must recall that the most significant mathematics of antiquity was the product of Hellenic thought in the "golden age." The deductive method, which is the pattern of all mathematics, reached such a standard of excellence in Euclid's *Elements* that it sufficed up to the nineteenth century, when the highly critical spirit of the era indicated inadequacies in classical logic and in mathematical foundations in general. While Euclid's name was attached to the work that gave mathematics its *method*, it was Archimedes who was the greatest applied mathematician of antiquity. In addition to giving birth to postulational thinking and handing down the work of Archimedes, the Hellenic golden age launched two major streams of mathematics—the discrete and the continuous, as exemplified respectively in Pythagorean number theory and in Eudoxus' resolution of problems associated with incommensurable magnitudes.

After the dark ages in Europe, the first important mathematical work was that of the Italian school. It contributed to arithmetic and produced the ultimate in classical algebra. Symbolic algebra *per se* first appeared at the very end of the sixteenth century, however, in the ideas of Vieta, who preceded by a short time interval the men whom we have called the forefathers of modern mathematics, namely, Descartes and Fermat. The era of Newton and Leibniz was the "age of genius," and their immediate successors were occupied with clarifying and extending the ideas of the masters. Next, in the hands of the Bernoullis and the sequence of giants—Euler, Lagrange, and Laplace—mathematics reached a stage of advanced development by the opening of the nineteenth century.

The contributions of the ensuing period were so numerous, so original, and so critical that they dwarfed all previous mathematical discoveries. During the nineteenth century the manifold creativeness of Gauss manifested itself. Cauchy, Weierstrass, Cantor, and Dedekind made analysis rigorous by "arithmetizing" it; Cantor's *Mengenlehre*, in particular, contained provocative notions that reached far beyond the domain of analysis; Hamilton and Galois were trail-blazers in the new abstract algebra, Riemann in the new geometry. Researches of the universalists, Poincaré and Hilbert, brought the century to a triumphant close, and provided the inspiration that launched the era to which the work of Borel, Lebesgue, Emmy Noether, Hermann Weyl, and von Neumann belongs.

Throughout mathematical history, astronomy, mechanics, various branches of mathematical physics, mathematical statistics, and other subjects classified under the heading of applied mathematics have played an important role. As we have explained, such sciences are less general than the pure mathematical systems which they interpret. At the other extreme there are subjects described as "math for math's sake"—for example, the higher arithmetic, which is as yet almost completely devoid of practical applications. We have seen what challenges this field provided for men like Tchebycheff, De la Vallée Poussin, Hadamard, Hardy, and Ramanujan. Still further in the direction of abstractness and generality are the "metamathematical" considerations arising from logical issues. Symbolic logic, which stems from ideas of Leibniz, enjoyed a renaissance in the nineteenth century after Boole proclaimed his *Laws of Thought*, and is an essential tool at the present time. Nevertheless many logical problems are still unresolved, and constitute a sort of "crisis," in which opposing schools of thought see different ways of handling some of the difficulties. Recent figures in both pure and applied mathematics, as well as in logic and foundations, have been numerous, and the lives and accomplishments of some of the most prominent of these mathematicians have formed the subject matter of previous discussion.

To supplement the above thumbnail summary of the history of mathematics, one should consider a topical outline of the content of leading discoveries. To provide this type of brief survey, and to indicate the wide territory covered in preceding chapters of this book, a sort of check list might be offered. Categories which could be cited are some of the major headings employed at the present time in *Mathematical Reviews*, the "bible" of current mathematical research. A monthly publication of the American Mathematical Society, this journal provides digests, by leading mathematicians, of recent mathematical research papers appearing in the numerous scholarly scientific journals (in various languages) all over the world. It also contains critical reviews of the most important of the recently released books, monographs, and treatises on advanced mathematical topics.

The reader might ask himself, then, what meaning he attaches to the following listings, and, if he feels so inclined, should reinforce his opinions by referring to those previous chapters or pages in our book where particular topics have been mentioned or treated in some detail: History and Biography; Logic and Foundations; Set Theory; Combinatorial Analysis; Order, Lattices; Theory of Numbers; Fields; Linear Algebra; Associative Rings and Algebras; Groups and Generalizations; Functions of Real Variables; Measure and Integration; Functions of a Complex Variable; Ordinary Differential Equations; Partial Differential Equations; Sequences, Series; Integral Transforms; Integral Equations; Functional Analysis; Calculus of Variations; Geometry; General Topology; Algebraic Topology; Differential Geometry; Probability; Statistics; Mechanics of Particles and Systems; Thermodynamics; Statistical Physics; Relativity; Games.

Can, then, the nature of past and present developments lead to any rational conjectures concerning the mathematics of the immediate future? Obviously, one is treading on dangerous ground in all forms of extrapolation, and forecasts must be probabilistic, not deterministic in nature. Therefore it would seem best to frame as open questions all issues to be considered, lest more affirmative treatment appear to be dogmatic, or else be colored by hopes, fears, and personal preferences. Nevertheless, the author will attempt to give partial answers to some of the questions she will now raise. Wherever any prophecy is made, it will be based on the most recent trends and it will be understood that all forecasts are short-range ones applicable, say, to the next decade or so. To begin the sequence of queries, let us ask:

Will the present vogue for axiomatics and pure mathematics continue or grow even stronger?

"Yes" appears to be the correct answer to this question. The mathematical world is aware of the all embracing quality of abstract theories and the construction of such theories, rather than a search for specific applications, is the goal of many leaders who, in addition, are influencing their disciples and the newer generations of mathematicians to advocate the same point of view. One example will now be given of how the mathematicians themselves are setting up schools of thought which stress and hence tend to perpetuate axiomatics, rigor, and abstraction as the essence of mathematics.

A current best seller among the longest of mathematical long-hairs, and one for which no royalties are being paid, is a treatise consisting of many individual volumes, written by Nicolas Bourbaki, and bearing the unpretentious title, *Éléments de Mathématique*. In 1949, a brief biographical note stated that Professor Bourbaki, formerly of the Royal Poldavian Academy, was residing in Nancy, France. Somewhat later, around 1953–1954, he appears to have made some affiliation with the Mathematics Institute of the University of Nancago.

In actuality, Bourbaki is just a pseudonym for a group of ten to twenty French mathematicians, and Nancago is a fusion of Nancy and Chicago, two universities where members of the group have served. The purpose of the *Éléments* series of monographs is to study the fundamental "structures" of mathematics and to present in *abstract* fashion the concepts and problems with which any one who calls himself a mathematician in mid-twentieth century must be acquainted. Throughout the twenty Bourbaki volumes that have appeared thus far, axiomatics and the Hilbertian spirit prevail. The facts presented are not new discoveries, but the method of presentation is highly original. The work purports to be a textbook, on a very high level, of course.

The Bourbaki group was organized shortly before World War II and its first volume (now revised in a new edition) appeared in 1939. Among the members at that time were Henri Cartan, son of Élie Cartan (Chapter 20), Jean Dieudonné, Charles Ehresmann, C. G. Chabauty, Pierre Samuel, Jean-Louis Koszul, and Roger Godemont; Samuel Eilenberg of Columbia University is a present member; André Weil, now at our Institute for Advanced Study, and M. E. Brelot have been semi-affiliated. All of these are leading names in the world of mathematics today. Concerning André Weil, for example, we have the following statement made by Professor Paul R. Halmos of the University of Chicago: "Although André Weil is not known to the general public, many of his colleagues are prepared to argue that he is the world's greatest living mathematician."

No one seems to know the origin of the name Bourbaki. Perhaps the general, Charles Denis Sauter (*not* Nicolas) Bourbaki (1816–1897) is a legendary figure for French schoolboys, much as Davy Crockett, say, is for boys in the United States. Charles Bourbaki was the son of a Greek colonel and in 1862 was actually offered the Greek throne, an honor he refused. After graduation from St. Cyr, the French West Point, he joined the Zouaves, and became a lieutenant in the French Foreign Legion. He commanded Algerian troops in the Crimean War and became famous in connection with the battles of Alma, Inkerman, and Sevastopol. He continued his military career in heroic fashion, but ultimately the German tactics in the Franco-Prussian War were his undoing. To avoid surrender to the Germans he attempted suicide in 1871, but he used a faulty pistol and the bullet he fired flattened against his skull. His life was thereby saved for another quarter of a century.

Professor Laurent Schwartz of the University of Paris has this to say about the general attitude and the mode of work of the Bourbaki group:*

Scientific minds are essentially of two types, neither of which is to be considered superior to the other. There are those who like fine detail, and those who are only interested in grand generalities. . . . Each of the two categories contains great names. . . . In the development of a mathematical theory, the ground is generally broken by scientists of the "detailed" school, who treat problems by new methods, formulate the important issues that must be settled, and tenaciously seek solutions, however great the difficulty. Once their task is accomplished, the ideas of the scientists with a penchant for generality come into play. They sort and sift, retaining only material vital for the future of mathematics. Their work is pedagogic rather than creative but nevertheless as essential and difficult as that of thinkers in the alternative category. . . . Bourbaki belongs to the "general" school of thought.

The preparation of one of its volumes is carried on somewhat as follows. There are meetings of the group lasting a week or two about three or four times a year, when work is carried on intensively all day long. The outline and first draft of a tract are

* Laurent Schwartz, "Les Mathématiques en France Pendant et Après la Guerre," *Proceedings of the Second Mathematical Congress,* University of Toronto Press, 1951, pp. 62–65.

presented to a general *Congrès* where it is subjected to the severest of criticism. Revision is made and then the whole process is repeated, possibly as many as half a dozen times before a particular monograph is sent to press.

The profits, most of which come from sales in the United States, are used to defray the expenses involved in assembling members and holding a *Congrès*. One meeting a year is held in some vacation area in France, and the Bourbaki members use some "royalty" funds for indulging in the best French wines and in specialties of the famous French cuisine. This is indeed a slight reward to members for devoting themselves so selflessly to setting down our mathematical heritage in what they consider to be the best possible form. Because the Bourbaki purpose is so serious, it is not surprising to learn that members must relax in some way, and, according to Professor Laurent Schwartz, there is a spirit of *canular* (practical joking) at even the most important meetings.

There has been some repercussion of this sort of fun-making even three thousand miles away. When Bourbaki calls itself a *société anonyme* (corporation), it means *anonymous* in the literal sense, and no one is supposed to mention individual names as we have done above. However, we shall place the blame on Professor André Delachet who, in his *L'Analyse Mathématique*, boldly lists the names furnished above. When Professor Ralph P. Boas of Northwestern University wrote a short account of the Bourbaki group for one of the Encyclopaedia Britannica "books of the year," the editors received a letter from Nicolas Bourbaki stating that he was hurt by Boas' claim that there was no such person. In addition, the group spread the rumor that if there was any pseudonym, it was *Boas*, and that there was no individual mathematics professor by that name. The Encyclopaedia editors were embarrassed and confused, and it required action on the part of the American Mathematical Society to settle the matter.

Not every mathematician approves of this kind of horse-play, nor do all mathematicians see completely eye to eye with the point of view of the Bourbaki school. Opponents refer to Bourbakism as "scholasticism," "hyperaxiomatics," and "hypergeneralization," tendencies which ignore the value of intuition and the aesthetic beauty of a less formal approach to mathematics. Nevertheless, all mathematicians today adhere to some form of axiomatics, and proclaim the superiority of *pure* research. For this reason it is almost certain that the same attitude will prevail in the near future.

The above provides an answer to the first question raised concerning the future of mathematics. The issue was a matter of mathematical *method*. But what about the mathematicians themselves, the men who will carry out this method? What will be the nationalities and mathematical specialties of the mathematical leaders of the future, that is, just how will mathematicians as a group be distributed with regard to country and field of interest?

We have seen that Felix Klein, carrying on the tradition of Gauss, made Göttingen the hub of the mathematical world in the early years of the present century. In the hands of Richard Courant, Klein's successor, the status of Göttingen became even more glorious. Then Hitler and Fascism brought about a complete change of venue for mathematical activity. The migration of mathematicians which started in 1933 is the reason we now raise the question:

Will the history of intolerance repeat itself at any time in the future, thereby producing further changes in locale for the great mathematical researchers of future eras?

Everyone must hope that the answer to this question is no. But as has been stated previously, such matters must remain open issues whose solution is dependent on the non-mathematical factors of civilization. In 1942 grounds for both optimism and pessimism could be found in an article by Arnold Dresden (1882–1954), entitled "The Migration of Mathematicians" and published in the August–September issue of the *American Mathematical Monthly*. In that paper Dresden revealed how and why, starting in 1933, a large proportion of the outstanding European mathematicians gradually came to American shores. He listed names of the distinguished emigrants year by year. His roll call of greats included many of the mathematicians featured in the present book—for example, Albert Einstein, Emmy Noether, Hermann Weyl, Richard Brauer, Richard Courant, Emil Artin, Stanislaw Ulam, Otto Neugebauer, Abraham Wald, Jerzy Neymann, John von Neumann, Samuel Eilenberg.

Dresden's account ceased with the year 1940, but the migration to the United States of the greatest mathematical minds went on and on. In more recent years, those foreign mathematical leaders who have not come to the United States to become citizens have come to these shores from time to time as visiting professors in our universities, or on research grants from the Institute for Advanced Study.

This state of affairs, combined with Dresden's facts and figures, might well furnish the grounds for predicting that the United States will be the locale of a considerable part of the world's creative mathematical research in the immediate future. The basis for this prophecy leads naturally to the next question:

If the situation of major mathematical activity shifts as a result of political and economic circumstances, will these likewise affect the *dramatis personae* who play the leading roles?

In response to this query, it is our contention that the future is likely to witness one particular change refuting the maxim "History repeats itself." It is our belief that, in the years ahead, the roster of mathematicians will contain a much greater proportion of feminine names than has been the case in the past. It was pointed out by the geometer and historian Julian L. Coolidge* that during all the centuries prior to 1900 A.D. there were only half a dozen women who carried on mathematical work of any real distinction, namely, Hypatia, the Marquise du Châtelet, Maria Gaetana Agnesi, Mary Somerville, Sophie Germain, and Sonya Kovalevsky. Hence, to support the prognostication that the distaff side of mathematics will be much enlarged in the future, evidence will be drawn from present facts or those of the immediate past.†

If we were to start with Emmy Noether, who received her Ph.D. from Göttingen in 1900, and if we were to record the names and accomplishments of all the women who have subsequently attained real eminence in the mathematical field, we would have a considerable task of cataloguing. Many of the women involved would be American, but a large percentage of these would have been born in Europe and have initiated their mathematical careers there, coming to the United States as part of the migration of mathematicians described above.

We have thought it best not to include discussion of the work of any of these able American mathematicians, lest it appear that some critical judgment is being exercised as to

---

* J. L. Coolidge, "Six Female Mathematicians," *Scripta Mathematica*, March–June 1951, pp. 20 ff.

† Edna E. Kramer, "Six More Female Mathematicians," *Scripta Mathematica*, Vol. 23, Memorial Issue, 1957, pp. 83 ff. (revised).

the relative merit of their work. Current history is delicate ground and the recorder must try to achieve by remoteness in space what he cannot accomplish by separation in time. Therefore in selecting a sample of seven women presently engaged in advanced mathematical research, the author has chosen outstanding representatives from England, France, Switzerland, and Italy.

Very little is known with certainty of the mathematical contributions of Hypatia, the earliest of the female mathematicians, but she is reputed to have been an algebraist (Chapter 4). Let us then talk first of a modern algebraist. Fifteen hundred years separate Hypatia's *Diophantine Analysis* from Hanna Neumann's research studies of "group amalgams," "generalized free products," "nearrings," "varieties of groups." The last topic listed is Hanna Neumann's most recent subject of investigation, in fact, one to which she has devoted an entire treatise* and which her husband chose as the topic of his address at an annual meeting of the American Mathematical Society.† Husband and wife carry on research on somewhat different aspects of abstract algebra, but their major interest is in *groups*. They have collaborated on many group-theoretical papers. Even when they write individually, one is likely to refer to the work of the other.

Hypatia, the Neoplatonist, suffered martyrdom at the hands of Christian fanatics in 415 A.D. Twentieth-century intolerance made it necessary for Hanna von Caemmerer to leave her native Germany for England in 1938. Since her fiancé, Dr. Bernhard H. Neumann was of Jewish extraction, he had found it expedient to emigrate to Great Britain a few years earlier. The Nazi race theories were already prevalent in Germany. Miss von Caemmerer was classified as an Aryan, Dr. Neumann as a Semite. Under any circumstances, the Nuremberg laws of 1935 made it illegal for couples to marry if they belonged to different "races."

For Hypatia there was no refuge from fifth century Alexandria, but the young Neumanns were able to find a haven in England. In spite of the adjustment to a new land and all the vicissitudes of the war, they were able to continue research in their specialized mathematical fields. Hanna

---

* Hanna Neumann, "Varieties of Groups," *Ergebnisse der Mathematik und ihrer Grenzgebiete*, Band 37, Springer-Verlag, New York, 1967.

† Bernhard H. Neumann, "Varieties of Groups," *Bulletin of the American Mathematical Society*, Vol. 73, No. 5 (September 1967), pp. 603 ff.

Neumann was given university credit for the mathematical studies she had completed at Berlin and Göttingen, and her subsequent research led to the Ph.D. at Oxford. She then held academic positions at the University of Hull, England, and at the Manchester College of Science and Technology, while her husband was a mathematics professor at the University of Manchester.

In 1964 Hanna Neumann was the first woman to be appointed to a Professorship in Pure Mathematics at the Australian National University School of General Studies. In 1968 she also became Dean of Students. Her husband, a Fellow of the Royal Society, is Professor and Head of the Department of Pure Mathematics at the Australian National University Institute of Advanced Studies.

The personal lives of the mathematical couple directing Australia's pure mathematics have been enriched by five wonderful children, four of whom are devoted to mathematics. The eldest, Mrs. Irene Dhall, holds a master's degree in literature from Manchester and is married to a distinguished surgeon. The second daughter, Mrs. Barbara Cullingworth, teaches mathematics and is married to a physical scientist. The oldest son, Dr. Peter M. Neumann (an Oxford Ph.D.), is a professor of mathematics at Queen's College, Oxford. He and his wife, Sylvia, were both recipients of first-class degrees in mathematics at Oxford. It should be remarked in passing, that an Oxford "first" is said to be an ineradicable distinction in the United Kingdom. Like his parents, Peter Neumann is a group-theorist, and the mathematical world is becoming accustomed to reading group-theoretic papers by Neumann, Neumann, and Neumann. Walter, the next son in chronological order, was graduated (with a first-class degree in mathematics) from an Australian university, and has received his Ph.D. from the University of Bonn, where he is a faculty member at its Mathematical Institute. Daniel, the youngest son, born in 1951, is also talented in mathematics. The Neumanns may be founding a successor to the historic Bernoulli family. Unfortunately, Hanna Neumann died suddenly on November 14, 1971 while she was on a mathematical lecture tour in Canada.

The knowledge of Hypatia's sad fate may have been one deterrent to women subsequently contemplating mathematical careers. At any rate, there was a lapse of 1300 years between the date of the talented Alexandrian's death and the appearance of other female names in the history of mathematics. Chronologically the Marquise du Châtelet and Maria Gaetana Agnesi are next on the list. By a coincidence there are a number of links between Agnesi's activities and those of Maria Pastori, at present professor at the Istituto Matematico of the University of Milan, research worker in the fields of tensor analysis and relativity. In the first place, both were natives of Milan. Secondly, the "magisterial" school attended by Maria Pastori was called the Maria Agnesi School. Also we recall that Agnesi's life was bound up with that of a younger sister, Maria Teresa, who is known in the history of music as a composer and pianist, that is, virtuoso on the clavicembalo. Maria Pastori has an older sister, Giuseppina Pastori, distinguished in the field of biology, and the lives of the twentieth-century sisters have been as closely associated as those of the Agnesis. When, in 1930, Guiseppina Pastori was nominated for a professorship at the Catholic University of Milan (Universita Cattolica del Sacro Cuore) the Pope referred to the precedent set by Pope Benedict XIV in appointing Maria Agnesi to the chair of mathematics and natural philosophy at Bologna in 1750. Giuseppina Pastori is a physician as well as a professor of biology, and we note that she is responsible for the naming of a nurses' training school in Milan after Agnesi, in memory of the illustrious mathematician's services as directress at the Pio Istituto Trivulzio, a Milanese home for the aged sick and poor.

While the Pastori sisters resembled the two Agnesis in the fact that they worked together in early youth in intellectual pursuits of common interest to both, there is a vast difference in other biographical details. The eighteenth-century sisters were born into a wealthy home. Their father, a patron of culture, established a salon where Maria would read a series of theses on abstruse scientific or philosophical questions and then defend them in academic disputations with learned men. The guests at a particular soirée would serve as audience, and during the intermission between two debates the younger of the Agnesi girls would play some of her original compositions on the clavicembalo. Foreign noblemen traveling in Italy (Count de Brosses or the Crown Prince of Saxony, for example) were curious to meet the talented sisters and would have no difficulty in securing an invitation to one of Signor Agnesi's assemblies.

By contrast, the Pastori sisters were two of eight children

in a Milanese family of very modest means, with no academic tradition whatsoever. Elementary education, ending at age thirteen, was all the family could manage to give the children. Giuseppina went to work in an office as soon as this early education was completed. Maria Pastori's early mathematical talent impressed her teachers and a visiting superintendent of schools marveled at her responses to his mathematical questions. Maria's mathematics teacher was aware that the Pastori family could afford no further schooling for the remarkable child. This teacher, according to Professor Pastori's personal statement, was an inspiring and conscientious pedagogue. She assisted Maria in obtaining a small scholarship for a magisterial school, the equivalent of an American teacher-training institution, and convinced her parents that she must have this minimum of additional education. Thus it was that at age seventeen the potential mathematician became an elementary school teacher in a small town near Milan.

By this time both sisters decided that their education must continue, whatever the odds. They studied together, unassisted by anyone else—at the crack of dawn before Maria took her commuter's train to the suburbs, and then again in the evenings and into all hours of the night. Three years later, when the younger of the sisters was twenty, both girls took the state examinations for the baccalaureate and, of course, passed with highest honors. In Italy, and in France, attendance at a lycée or special school is not required in order to obtain the bachelor's degree. Success in the examination is the sole criterion.

From this point on both young ladies continued to climb the academic ladder to the very top. Maria passed the difficult entrance examinations for the Scuola Normale Superiore of Pisa, and received a small scholarship. (The higher normal schools in Italy and France are really special universities for a small, carefully selected group of very exceptional students.) Tutoring and the scholarship stipend sustained the young mathematician during the four years of study for the doctorate in mathematics. Her sponsor for the degree was the great geometer, Luigi Bianchi. Now she taught in the secondary schools and was simultaneously an assistant at the University of Milan. Since Italian universities and those in other European countries are state schools, advancement in rank is decided on the basis of competitive examinations. We have seen that no tests could faze Maria

Pastori and she rose from assistant to *libera docente* (assistant professor) to the full professorship, her chair being one in rational mechanics.

College teachers of mathematics and physics in the United States know the excellence of the 1949 text, *Calcolo tensoriale e applicazione,* which she wrote in collaboration with Bruno Finzi.* Her research reports and special monographs are too numerous to list, but some readers may recall her paper at the 1953 International Symposium on Differential Geometry. In it she discussed the space of Einstein's unified field theory.† The style of her textbook and her expository memoirs is lucid, and full of simple specific applications of abstract tensor concepts and procedures. Her students at Milan are solving significant research problems under her direction. For example, a paper by Laura Martuscelli suggests a modification of Einstein's unified field theory,‡ and F. Graiff wrote a monograph on tensor integration in Riemann spaces of constant curvature.§

In placing Maria Pastori's mathematical work, we might say that her specialty makes her a true daughter of Italy and a twentieth-century disciple of Agnesi. Geometry underwent powerful development and remarkable mutations in Italy in the two centuries following Agnesi. Algebraic geometry reached such heights in the work of Cremona, Severi, and others that, in the words of E. T. Bell, it became "almost a national pastime." Differential geometry also flourished on Italian soil. Perhaps the finest flower of all was the *absolute differential calculus* of Ricci and his pupil, Levi-Civita. Without this pure mathematical instrument Einstein could not have forged his concept of the physical universe into the "greatest achievement of the human intellect." But the tensor calculus is of importance in the theoretical treatment of classical physics as well—in dynamics, hydrodynamics, elasticity. It is proving useful today in the pure mathematical investigation of generalized spaces which, so far, are abstractions without physical application. Maria Pastori's research and writings are concerned with sharpen-

---

* B. Finzi e M. Pastori, *Calcolo tensoriale e applicazioni,* Bologna, 1949.

† M. Pastori, "Sullo spazio della recente teoria unitaria di Einstein," *Convegno di Geom. Diff.,* 1953, pp. 107–113.

‡ L. Martuscelli, "Sopra una possibile modificazione della teoria unitaria di Einstein," *Ist. Lomb. Rend. Cl. Sci. Mat. Nat.,* 1955, pp. 607–615.

§ F. Graiff, "Sull'integrazione tensoriale negli spazi di Riemann a curvatura costante," *Rend. Ist. Lomb.,* 1951.

ing the Ricci tool in order to cast it into an ever more perfect mold and extend its usefulness.

In spite of the Agnesi tradition, there are very few women at the present time who occupy full professorships at the leading universities in Italy. At Milan, in addition to Maria Pastori, there is Giuseppina Masotti-Biggiogero, who occupies a chair in geometry. At Pavia, the Italian university second in venerability only to Bologna, Maria Cinquini-Cibrario is *professoressa ordinaria* (full professor) in mathematics.

Although there were no mathematicians in her ancestry, the family background of Maria Cibrario was a distinguished one. Her father was a general in the Italian army. One great-grandfather, Count Giovanni Antonio Luigi Cibrario (1802–1870), descendant of a noble Piedmontese family, was a historian of note and a prominent political figure of his day. In 1852 he was minister of finance in D'Azeglio's cabinet. Under Cavour he was at first minister of education, then minister of foreign affairs. In 1861, in recognition of Luigi Cibrario's long public service as well as this nobleman's prolific historic research dealing with the House of Savoy, Victor Emmanuel bestowed on him the title of count.

Most of Maria Cibrario's ancestors on both sides lived in the province of Turin. She spent her early years in Genoa where her father was stationed at the time. Later she studied at the University of Turin, majoring in mathematics. Preliminary to her graduation in 1927, she was required to write a thesis in mathematics. In this work, as well as other early research, she was advised by Guido Fubini, who influenced her to select *analysis* as her mathematical specialty. She was appointed assistant to the aging Giuseppe Peano, and on his death in 1932, transferred to Francesco Tricomi; but before that year was over she was named *libera docenza* in infinitesimal analysis.

Not long thereafter she made the acquaintance of Silvio Cinquini at a meeting of the Italian Mathematical Society, and in July 1938 the two young mathematicians were married. Then the war years arrived and with them the curtailment of academic activities. No national examinations for professorships were held. Madame Cinquini entered the first of these gruelling competitions held after the war. Having succeeded in the contest of intellects she was assigned by the National Board to a professorship at Cagliari, Sardinia, where she served during 1947 and 1948. Next she was appointed to the chair of mathematical analysis at Modena, and from 1950 on has held the corresponding chair at Pavia, where her husband is also full professor of mathematics.

One aspect of the numerous duties inherent in her academic position has been her tireless research on the theory of partial differential equations and related fields. Her original papers are numerous and range over a period of more than twenty-five years. She can be credited with the classification of linear partial differential equations of the second order of mixed type, with existence and uniqueness theorems for many of these, with considerable research on nonlinear hyperbolic equations and systems of such equations. She has solved the Goursat problem for the hyperbolic nonlinear equation of the second order. For quasilinear and nonlinear hyperbolic systems she has solved the Cauchy* problem, and in some cases, the problem of Goursat. She has also studied the nonlinear hyperbolic equation of the nth order.

Recently she collaborated with her husband, Silvio Cinquini, in establishing existence and uniqueness theorems for first order partial differential equations by generalizing a technique Carathéodory had found useful with ordinary differential equations. This joint effort of husband and wife was exceptional. In general they work independently and in different branches of analysis. Silvio Cinquini's early investigations were concerned with analytic functions, but later he became a devotee of Leonida Tonelli's school of thought and specialized in the calculus of variations. He has also carried out research on ordinary differential equations and quasi-periodic functions, with a special monograph on the latter subject.

The lives of husband and wife, both analysts, are completely dedicated to their scientific work and to the upbringing of their children, Giuseppe, Vittoria, and Carlo, born in 1944, 1947, and 1949 respectively.

Agnesi had as her French contemporary the brilliant Marquise du Châtelet. The French women mathematicians today appear to be more original in their research and less

---

* This basic problem of partial differential equations is usually given Cauchy's name, but we point out that it would be proper to speak of the Cauchy-Kovalevsky problem since Sonya Kovalevsky shares with Cauchy the honors of establishing rigorously the first existence theorem associated with the question. (See Chapter 22.)

frivolous in their behavior than the famous expositor of Newton's *Principia*. As a first example of French women mathematicians there is Jacqueline Lelong-Ferrand, professor of mathematics at the University of Paris. In 1956 she and her husband, Pierre Lelong, also professor at the University of Paris, were in residence at the Institute for Advanced Study, carrying on research on Riemann manifolds and functions of several complex variables, respectively. In visiting the United States, the Lelongs did not interrupt their family life, for they brought to Princeton with them their three children, Jean, Henri, and Françoise, aged seven, five, and four at the time. (Another daughter, Martine, was born to the Lelongs in January 1958.)

Jacqueline Ferrand was born in the little town of Alès, in the province of Gard in south-central France. She attended the lycée in Nîmes, a city known to the Romans. Her father was, appropriately, a teacher of Latin and Greek. While his daughter excelled in all subjects, she received the first prize in a national competition in mathematics, and was encouraged to compete again—this time for the privilege of admission to the Paris École Normale Supérieure of the rue d'Ulm. Prior to 1936, girls were not admitted to this renowned school, whose graduates include many of the leading mathematicians in France today, in particular, a quorum of the Bourbaki group. Jacqueline Ferrand was among the first group of girls permitted to take the entrance examinations and, needless to say, was admitted to the course in mathematics and science. There are about twenty such admissions out of approximately 250 applicants each year.

It is not the purpose of this discussion to search for reasons why there have been so few women mathematicians in the past, or to explain the present rapid rate of increase in female mathematicians. But it seems difficult at this point not to comment briefly on educational opportunity as a possible factor. Although girls were permitted to attend the École Normale Supérieure de Jeunes Filles at Sèvres, just outside of Paris, where the mathematics instruction was of the very highest caliber, it seems that those who had the privilege of attendance at the rue d'Ulm are researchers today, while most of the graduates of the Sèvres school are teachers in lycées. Mme. Lelong-Ferrand and others explained to the present writer that the greatest advantage of the rue d'Ulm is the coeducational one, which gives girls the chance to witness, imitate, and compete with the masculine critical, creative, courageous attitudes in approaching problems.

At any rate, Jacqueline Ferrand ranked first in the 1939 *Agrégation masculine* in mathematical sciences. (These examinations for the degree of Agrégé are as difficult as the comprehensives for the Ph.D. in mathematics at leading universities of the United States.) Mlle. Ferrand's first position was at the Sèvres normal school for girls, where from 1939 to 1943 she had the task of coaching the students for the Agrégation. Then she became *chargée de cours* (assistant professor), first at the University of Bordeaux, then at Caen. She was married in 1947, and in 1948 became full professor at Caen. From 1948 to 1956 she held the chair of calculus and higher geometry at Lille. On her return from Princeton in 1957 she was transferred to Paris. She was, at the time, the only one of the newer generation of French women mathematicians to have a full professorship in pure mathematics at the University of Paris.

Simultaneously with her teaching she has carried on continuous research in analysis and geometry. Her major specialties have been conformal representation (1942–1947), potential theory (1947–1954), Riemann manifolds and harmonic forms (1955–present). Her 1942 thesis for the Doctorat-ès-Sciences and several subsequent papers investigated the behavior of conformal transformations in the neighborhood of a boundary point. Among her next set of memoirs was one where she created the concept of *preholomorphic* functions, using these to produce a new methodology for proofs. Her research in potential theory enabled her to generalize certain classic theorems to n dimensions, namely the lemmas of Julia and Phragmen-Lindeloef. Following this work, she attacked some of the most difficult problems in the field, once again creating new concepts for the purpose. She dropped this avenue of research temporarily to write a searching, comprehensive treatise, which was published in 1955 as part of the Collections de Cahiers Scientifiques edited by Professor Gaston Julia and entitled *Représentation conforme et transformations à intégrale de Dirichlet bornée*. Then, having explored the field of conformal representation so completely, she felt that it was time to enlarge the scope of her research, an objective realized in the many original papers which she contributes year after year. There have been new books too—a work on the fundamental concepts of mathematics with emphasis on analysis, and an advanced text on differential geometry.

The present concern with missiles and satellites tends to emphasize the progress in applied mathematics, and may possibly obscure the fact that we are living in an age of most prolific creation of pure mathematical ideas. French mathematicians have made substantial contributions to this development, and some of their most significant research has been done in the field of algebraic topology. Just how the newest topological concepts can lead to powerful generalizations of related subjects is illustrated in the work of Professor Paulette Libermann of the University of Rennes. The initial approach to the problems in question was due to Élie Cartan, under whose direction Mlle. Libermann did her first research, while she was a student at the École Normale Supérieure de Jeunes Filles de Sèvres.

Using concepts from the theory of fiber spaces, Charles Ehresmann, a member of the Bourbaki group, generalized ideas of Cartan by reformulating the definitions to give them *global* meaning. Paulette Libermann attended Ehresmann's seminars at the University of Strasbourg and wrote her thesis for the degree of Doctorat-ès-Sciences Mathématiques under his direction. She is an active member of Ehresmann's research school on differentiable fiber spaces, almost complex manifolds and their generalizations. In a 1955 paper, for example, she summarized all the recent results, including her own, on "regular infinitesimal structures —almost complex, almost paracomplex, almost hermitian, almost parahermitian, etc."[*] Again, in two 1958 notes in the *Comptes Rendus*, she discusses infinitesimal pseudogroups in general, and in particular the infinitesimal pseudogroups of Lie.[†]

Lest Paulette Libermann's progress from the 1941 days with Cartan to her 1958 production of advanced memoirs and participation in Bourbaki seminars seem an uninterrupted success story, let us return to some biographical details. She was born in Paris and received her early education there. Although the greatest living geometer had accepted

---

[*] Paulette Libermann, "Structures presque complexes et autres structures infinitésimales," *Bull. de la Soc. Math. de France,* 1955, pp. 195–224.

[†] Paulette Libermann, "Pseudogroupes infinitésimaux, Faisceaux d'algèbre de Lie associés," *Comptes Rendus,* January 6, 1958. A continuation of this note, "Pseudogroupes infinitésimaux de Lie," *Comptes Rendus,* January 27, 1958.

her as a protégée, the Vichy laws excluded her from the 1941 Agrégation, and her entire professional career had to be postponed until after the Liberation. From 1945 to 1947 she studied at Oxford with J. H. C. Whitehead (Chapter 20), a leading disciple of Cartan. From 1947 to 1951 she taught at the Lycée de Jeunes Filles de Strasbourg, while preparing her thesis with Ehresmann. It was not until 1954 that she became *Maître des Conférences* at Rennes.

All writers on women mathematicians give major mention to Sophie Kovalevsky, who was Russian by birth, western European in her advanced mathematical training and professional career. As a parallel, we now discuss Sophie Piccard, Russian by birth, western European in her ancestry, advanced mathematical training, and professional career. She was born in St. Petersburg and educated at the University of Smolensk where her father was professor of natural sciences.

Just as Kovalevsky was conditioned by a cultured circle of family acquaintances Sophie Piccard was headed toward intellectual pursuits by both parents. Scientific talent came to her through ancestors who were surgeons, physicians, chemists. Her mother's ability, however, was literary. Eulalie Güee Piccard's studies of Pushkin and Lermontov earned for their author the Prix de la Fondation Schiller, the highest literary award in Switzerland. Mme. Piccard also wrote *La Grande Tragédie*, a series of five books on the Bolshevik revolution. In 1956, in spite of a siege of poor health involving radical surgery, she completed a novel *Galia*, and at the time of her death in August 1957 had almost finished a biographical and critical study of Simone Weil.[*]

As a young woman, Eulalie Piccard was a professor of languages at the Russian lycée attended by her daughter, whose teachers told the mother about the girl's exceptional aptitude for mathematics. Although young Sophie wished to become a physicist, her mother pointed out the greater importance of pure science and, in a sense, coerced her into specializing in theoretical mathematics.

During the troublous twenties in Russia the Piccard family left the country. Since the ancestors on the father's side had been Swiss, and on the mother's French Huguenot, it was natural for the family to emigrate to Switzerland. Mlle.

---

[*] We note in passing, Simone Weil's link with mathematics. Her brother André Weil, is one of the foremost living mathematicians, as already mentioned in this chapter.

Piccard entered the University of Lausanne where she obtained the degrees of Licence-ès-Sciences and Doctorat-ès-Sciences in 1927 and 1928 respectively. Her doctoral thesis, in the field of probability, was written under Professor Mirimanoff's direction.

The personal troubles of the Piccards did not come to an end in the new land. The young mathematician's father died and the financial problems of his widow and daughter became acute. Eulalie Piccard had to earn a living as a dressmaker, while Sophie, her advanced degrees notwithstanding, was unable to obtain a teaching position. She worked first as an actuary, then from 1932 to 1938 served as administrative secretary for the newspaper, *Feuille d'avis de Neuchâtel*. She used all her leisure time for study and research, but many years elapsed before she was able to attain an academic post of any real distinction. In 1936 she became assistant in geometry to Professor Gaberel of the University of Neuchâtel, and on his death in 1938 she succeeded to his position, and became *professeur extraordinaire* (associate professor). Since 1943 she has been full professor of mathematics at the University of Neuchâtel, where she holds the chair of higher geometry and probability theory. In 1965 she held a visiting professorship in Hanna Neumann's department at the Australian National University.

In spite of the obstacles to her mathematical career, she has carried on prolific research. For many years she worked on the theory of sets, and more recently has specialized in group theory. She has also written papers in a number of other fields—function theory, the theory of relations, probability theory, actuarial science. An outgrowth of her set-theoretic investigations was the publication of two comprehensive treatises entitled *Sur les ensembles de distances des ensembles de points d'un espace Euclidien* (1939) and *Sur les ensembles parfaits* (1942). Both books are original, tremendously systematic and detailed. Attention is given to certain perfect sets on the real line. These sets arise from a closed interval by a process generalized from the construction of the Cantor ternary set. Henri Lebesgue, one of the leading analysts of all time, was interested in all such set-theoretic questions since they were fundamental to his revolutionary theory of integration. In a review in the Swiss *Enseignement Mathématique* he voiced his approval of Professor Piccard's book on perfect sets.

Once again Élie Cartan comes into our story, for he gave

a laudatory review, in the French *Bulletin des Sciences Mathématiques*, to Sophie Piccard's next book, *Sur les bases du groupe symétrique* (1946). In an earlier issue of the same periodical, it was his son, Henri Cartan, whose name is well known to the mathematical world of today, who had written an analysis of the treatise on perfect sets. Another French mathematician, Professor Arnaud Denjoy of the University of Paris, has written the introduction to Professor Piccard's most recent book, the 1957 *Sur les bases des groupes d'ordre fini*. In 1957, also, the University of Paris printed, in booklet form, the text of Professor Piccard's public lecture on Lobachevsky. A part of that lecture was presented in Chapter 3.

To complete our full circle of female mathematicians, we now return to England where we started. It is not a mere question of geography that influenced our decision to discuss the work of Florence Nightingale David. It is because she is the author of the article on probability from which the historical material of Chapter 13 is drawn. The paper in question is just one of her many research memoirs in the field of probability and statistics. The half-dozen contemporary women mathematicians whose activities have been presented up to this point are devoting themselves in the main to pure rather than applied mathematics. This is not the case with Florence Nightingale David, Reader in Statistics, University College, London. Her research papers, more than sixty in number, are either directly concerned with concrete, practical questions or else are potentially capable of application to such problems.

Dr. David's given names would seem to have predestined her to become a "passionate statistician," an appellation given to the heroine of the Crimean War, on account of her keen interest in the statistical work of the Belgian L. A. J. Quételet (1796–1874), and his mathematics of human welfare. Florence Nightingale David is a collateral descendant of the most famous of all nurses.

But it takes much more than a name to provide success in a mathematical career. Dr. David was born in Hereford, received her early education in Devonshire, where her father was a schoolmaster, and had her university training in London. Even her first academic position was an important one, for she became research assistant to Karl Pearson. While she continued her association with London's university, she also carried on ordnance work during World War II, served the Ministry of Home Security, and became a member of the scientific advisory council of the Land Mines Committee. Her statistical research for this group and for the Civil Defense Research Committee comprised thirty-three papers. Because the results are still classified, we may not discuss their nature here.

In 1946 and again in 1964 Dr. David visited the United States, and lectured at the University of California at Berkeley. Teachers and students of statistics are acquainted with the excellence of her books, *Probability Theory for Statistical Methods, Elementary Statistical Exercises,* and *A Statistical Primer.* The *Biometrika* article to which allusion was made in Chapter 13 is a fascinating account of the origins and early history of probability; therefore it was good to learn, in the course of a personal interview, that Florence N. David plans "some day in the future" to write a complete history of probability.

In addition to the sample of seven careers outlined in detail above, one could furnish other examples of distinguished accomplishment in mathematics, pure or applied, on the part of women today. Their activity is the basis of a prediction of the present chapter, namely the strong likelihood that in the near future feminine participation in mathematical research will be greater than ever before.

After raising the issue of the probable nature of mathematical method and personnel in the years ahead, one might ask other questions concerning the future of mathematics. Although pure mathematics embraces its applications, scientists and laymen alike would certainly hope that applied mathematics will have many future devotees, so that the usefulness and practicality of mathematics will continue. Hence we inquire:

Will the future witness a continuance of the intimate relationship that mathematics bears to so many other fields of thought? Will applied mathematics flourish? More specifically, what will be the future results of the present age of cybernetics, feedback, mechanical brains? Will a second industrial revolution completely replace men by machines? Will thinking machines lead to a more rational conduct of human affairs? Will the new communication devices be adaptable to aiding the physically disabled? Or is automation a Frankenstein whose power will ultimately destroy the human race that created it?

"The Aztecs said this world . . . would blow up. Then what will come, in the other dimension, when we are superseded?" wrote D. H. Lawrence. Were the early inhabitants of Mexico prophetic? The story of energy and its relation to matter has been touched on in our chapters on statistics, statistical mechanics, and relativity, but now we must ask: Will the future stress the peaceful uses of the incredibly huge energy sources revealed by the A-bomb, the H-bomb, the potential cobalt bomb, or will all these discoveries result in the fate postulated by the Aztecs?

How soon will man land on Mars or Venus? Will man be able to stand the strain? Will the astronauts succeed in finding a method of navigation in space that will make interplanetary travel a reality? In this set of questions, only certain ones refer to mathematics, and these are actually concerned with applications of the subject. The queries do not refer to the future of *pure* mathematics, since most of the pure mathematics of missiles and satellites was handled long ago. For example, Kepler's laws on which planetary motion is based were formulated in the seventeenth century, and all the modifications and improvements contributed by Laplace, Gauss, Poincaré, and others were accomplished before our day. The basic principle of rocket action is just an application of Newton's third law of motion. And so it goes; no matter what pure mathematical tools are required in this area of research, they are already at hand.

Will the "crash" programs of the present and the immediate future produce a great number of mathematicians, physical scientists, engineers, etc., and thus enlarge greatly the population of the mathematical world and indirectly influence the quality and quantity of future mathematical research?

Not everyone would answer this question with a categorical affirmative. There are those who believe that positive prognosis is not possible because there is a weakness in the lucidity of mathematical exposition today as well as a general lack in communicating new mathematical research as it develops. For the well-being of mathematics in the future, "the teacher and the scholar of mathematics . . . must wear the same skin." This was the opinion of Professor E. J. McShane as expressed in his 1956 presidential address before the Mathematical Association of America.*

* E. J. McShane, "Maintaining Communication," *American Mathematical Monthly*, Vol. 64, No. 5 (May 1957), pp. 309 ff.

In that speech, Professor McShane expressed concern with the lack of communication between pure and applied mathematicians, between research mathematicians whose specialties are different, between mathematicians and teachers of mathematics, between mathematicians and nonspecialists. He made certain Cassandra-like predictions about the possible future consequences of such separation "into small groups of specialists with little intercommunication." He suggested certain palliatives, but placed before the mathematical world the problem of seeking a complete solution (if there is such a solution). In alluding to the recent rapid growth of mathematics, he made the following analogy:

About sixteen years ago I bought a house which had been unoccupied for five years. Summer after summer we fought a losing battle against honeysuckle; it grew faster than we could dig it out. Then came the discovery of the weed-killing properties of 2-4-D, and the battle was won. As I understand it, a broad-leaved plant sprayed with 2-4-D does not die at once; it begins to proliferate rapidly, growing quickly and without organization. As a result, it dies. I cannot look on the proliferation of mathematics as being in all circumstances an unqualified good. . . .

Every one of us is touched in some way or other by the problems of mathematical communication. Every one of us can make some contribution, great or small, within his own proper sphere of activity. And every contribution is needed if mathematics is to grow healthily and usefully and beautifully.

McShane emphasized the same point of view in subsequent articles and in his activities as president of the American Mathematical Society (1960). If, as a result of his influence and that of others who agree with him, communication of mathematical ideas does improve in days to come, one might ask:

Will the better comprehension of the new mathematics make the subject all-pervading in the future? In particular, will the fine arts feel its impact? While pure mathematics is expanding and almost certain to grow at an ever-increasing rate, its spheres of influence are also becoming more numerous. Everyone is aware that mathematics is important in the physical and biological sciences, and in business, industry, engineering, technology, economics, and psychology, in short, in every area that can profit from abstract analysis and formulation. But a work like Birkhoff's *Aesthetic Measure* (1933), which subjects the arts to mathematical analysis, is practically unique. Will leading mathematicians of the future continue where Birkhoff left off?

Although no one can predict the future of mathematics, the above queries should suggest that mathematics, both pure and applied, is wide open for further progress, contrary to the fears that mathematicians have sustained at various times in mathematical history. For example, toward the end of the eighteenth century, Lagrange, the leading figure of the era, wrote in a letter to D'Alembert: "Doesn't it seem to you as if our lofty mathematics is beginning to decline?" Again, Hilbert's program of 1900, in which he outlined a course for future research, was specifically designed to cure the *fin de siècle* jitters of his fellow mathematicians.

A few years ago André Weil wrote a paper bearing the title "The Future of Mathematics."* Placing himself *in loco Hilberti* he specified important unsolved problems and incompletely developed subjects of pure mathematical research. The type of prophecy practiced by Hilbert and Weil is one of the truly rational species of prediction.

For if a man is a leading mathematician of his era, and one with many disciples, he can control the future of his subject through his personal influence. His word is law, and the younger generations of mathematicians will do their best to solve the problems he has set. In the few brief years since the publication of Weil's article, a formidable attack has been made on some of the issues to which he pointed, but complete or elegant resolution must still, in the main, be left for the future. It is probable, however, as Weil said,† that the "great mathematicians of the future . . . will solve the great problems which we shall bequeath to them, through unexpected connections, which our imagination will not have succeeded in discovering, and by looking at them in a new light." And finally "the mathematician . . . believes that he will be able to slake his thirst at the very sources of knowledge, convinced as he is that they will always continue to pour forth, pure and abundant. . . . If he be asked why he persists on the perilous heights whither no one but his own kind can follow him, he will answer: . . . For the honor of the human spirit."

* André Weil, "The Future of Mathematics," *American Mathematical Monthly*, Vol. 57, No. 5 (May 1950), pp. 295 ff.
† André Weil, *loc. cit.*

Suggestions for Further Reading

Adler, I. *A New Look at Geometry.* New York: The John Day Company, Inc., 1966.

——. *The New Mathematics.* New York: The John Day Company, Inc., 1960.

——. *Thinking Machines.* New York: The John Day Company, Inc., 1961.

Aleksandrov, A. D., Kolmogorov, A. N., and Lavrent'ev, M. A. *Mathematics—Its Content, Methods, and Meaning.* 3 vols. Translated from the Russian by S. H. Gould and T. Bartha. Cambridge: M.I.T. Press, 1964.

Allendoerfer, C. B., and Oakley, C. O. *Principles of Mathematics.* 2nd ed. New York: McGraw-Hill, Inc., 1963.

Andree, R. V. *Selections from Modern Abstract Algebra.* New York: Holt, Rinehart and Winston, Inc., 1958.

Beiler, A. H. *Recreations in the Theory of Numbers.* New York: Dover Publications, Inc., 1964.

Bell, E. T. *The Development of Mathematics.* 2nd ed. New York: McGraw-Hill, Inc., 1945.

——. *Men of Mathematics.* New York: Simon and Schuster, Inc., 1937.

Birkhoff, G., and MacLane, S. *A Survey of Modern Algebra.* 3rd ed. New York: The Macmillan Company, 1965.

Born, M. *Einstein's Theory of Relativity.* Rev. ed. New York: Dover Publications, Inc., 1965.

——. *Physics in My Generation.* London: Pergamon Press, 1956.

Bowker, A. H., and Lieberman, C. J. *Engineering Statistics.* Englewood Cliffs, N.J.: Prentice-Hall, Inc., 1959.

Boyer, C. B. *The Concepts of the Calculus.* New York: Hafner Publishing Company, Inc., 1949.

——. *History of Mathematics.* New York: John Wiley & Sons, Inc., 1968.

Brennan, J. G. *A Handbook of Logic.* 2nd ed. New York: Harper & Row Publishers, Inc., 1961.

Chernoff, H., and Moses, L. E. *Elementary Decision Theory.* New York: John Wiley & Sons, Inc., 1959.

Cohen, P. J. *Set Theory and the Continuum Hypothesis.* New York: W. A. Benjamin, Inc., 1966.

Courant, R. *Differential and Integral Calculus.* 2 vols. Rev. ed. Translated from the German by E. J. McShane. New York: Nordemann Publishing Co., 1940.

———, and Robbins, H. *What Is Mathematics?* New York: Oxford University Press, 1941.

Coxeter, H. S. M. *Twelve Geometric Essays.* London: Feffer and Simons, 1968.

———, and Greitzer, S. L. *Geometry Revisited.* New York: Random House, Inc., 1967.

David, F. N. *Games, Gods, and Gambling.* New York: Hafner Publishing Company, Inc., 1962.

———. *Statistical Primer.* London: Griffin, 1953.

Davis, M., ed. *The Undecidable.* Hewlett, N. Y.: Raven Press, 1965.

Derman, C., and Klein, M. *Probability and Statistical Inference for Engineers.* New York: Oxford University Press, 1959.

Eddington, A. S. *Space, Time, and Gravitation.* New York: Cambridge University Press, 1921.

Eves, H. *An Introduction to the History of Mathematics.* Rev. ed. New York: Holt, Rinehart and Winston, Inc., 1964.

———, and Newsom, C. V. *An Introduction to the Foundations and Fundamental Concepts of Mathematics.* Rev. ed. New York: Holt, Rinehart and Winston, Inc., 1965.

Feller, W. *An Introduction to Probability Theory and Its Applications.* 2 vols. New York: John Wiley & Sons, Inc., Vol. 1, 3rd ed., 1968; Vol. 2, 1966.

Goodstein, R. L. *Fundamental Concepts of Mathematics.* New York: The Macmillan Company, 1962.

Griffin, H. *Elementary Theory of Numbers.* New York: McGraw-Hill, Inc., 1954.

Grossman, I., and Magnus, W. *Groups and Their Graphs.* New York: Random House, Inc., 1964.

Kemeny, J. G., Snell, J. L., and Thompson, G. L. *Introduction to Finite Mathematics.* 2nd ed. Englewood Cliffs, N.J.: Prentice-Hall, Inc., 1966.

Kramer, E. E. *The Main Stream of Mathematics.* New York: Oxford University Press, 1951.

Kurosh, A. G. *Lectures on General Algebra.* New York: Chelsea Publishing Company, 1965.

Ledermann, W. *Introduction to the Theory of Finite Groups.* Edinburgh: Oliver and Boyd, 1953.

Lelong-Ferrand, J. *Géométrie Différentielle.* Paris: Masson, 1963.

Lieber, L. *Galois and the Theory of Groups*. Lancaster, Pa.: Science Press, 1932.

———, and Lieber, H. G. *Infinity*. New York: Holt, Rinehart and Winston, Inc., 1953.

Luce, R. D., and Raiffa, H. *Games and Decisions*. New York: John Wiley & Sons, Inc., 1957.

McKinsey, J. C. C. *Introduction to the Theory of Games*. New York: McGraw-Hill, Inc., 1952.

MacLane, S., and Birkhoff, G. *Algebra*. New York: The Macmillan Company, 1967.

May, K. O. *Elements of Modern Mathematics*. Reading, Mass.: Addison-Wesley Publishing Company, Inc., 1959.

Mood, A. M., and Graybill, F. A. *Introduction to the Theory of Statistics*. 2nd. ed. New York: McGraw-Hill, Inc., 1963.

Nagel, E., and Newman, J. R. *Gödel's Proof*. New York: New York University Press, 1958.

Neugebauer, O. *The Exact Sciences in Antiquity*. 2nd ed. Providence, R. I.: Brown University Press, 1957.

———, and Sachs, A. J., eds. *Mathematical Cuneiform Texts*. American Oriental Series, Vol. 29. New Haven: American Oriental Society, 1946.

Neumann, B. H. *Special Topics in Algebra: Order Techniques in Algebra*. New York: N.Y.U. Courant Institute of Mathematical Sciences, 1962.

———. *Special Topics in Algebra: Universal Algebra*. New York: N.Y.U. Courant Institute of Mathematical Sciences, 1962.

Ore, O. *Graphs and Their Uses*. New York: Random House, Inc., 1963.

———. *Number Theory and Its History*. New York: McGraw-Hill, Inc., 1948.

Patterson, E. M. *Topology*. Edinburgh: Oliver and Boyd, 1956.

Quine, W. V. *Methods of Logic*. Rev. ed. New York: Holt, Rinehart and Winston, Inc., 1959.

Russell, B. *Introduction to Mathematical Philosophy*. 2nd ed. New York: The Macmillan Company, 1924.

Sainte-Laguë, A. *La Topologie*. Paris: Librairie du Palais de la Découverte, 1949.

Sanford, V. *A Short History of Mathematics*. Boston: Houghton Mifflin Company, 1930.

Selby, S., and Sweet, L. *Sets, Relations, Functions*. New York: McGraw-Hill, Inc., 1963.

Stabler, E. R. *An Introduction to Mathematical Thought*. Reading, Mass.: Addison-Wesley Publishing Company, Inc., 1953.

Struik, D. J. *A Concise History of Mathematics*. 2 vols. New York: Dover Publications, Inc., 1948.

———. *Lectures on Classical Differential Geometry*. Reading, Mass.: Addison-Wesley Publishing Company, Inc., 1961.

Swenson, J. A. *Integrated Mathematics*. 4 vols. Ann Arbor, Mich.: Edwards Brothers, 1937.

Thomas, N. L. *Modern Logic*. New York: Barnes & Noble, Inc., 1966.

Thomas, T. Y. *Concepts from Tensor Analysis and Differential Geometry*. 2nd. ed. New York: Academic Press, Inc., 1965.

Ulam, S. M. *A Collection of Mathematical Problems*. New York: Interscience Publications, 1960.

——. "What Is Measure?" *American Mathematical Monthly*, Vol. 50 (1943), 597–602.

Wallis, W. A., and Roberts, H. V. *Statistics, A New Approach*. Glencoe, Illinois: Free Press, 1956.

INDEX

(Continued)